INTERNATIONAL SERIES OF MONOGRAPHS ON

PURE AND APPLIED MATHEMATICS

GENERAL EDITOR: I. N. SNEDDON

VOLUME 5

PROBLEMS IN EUCLIDEAN SPACE: APPLICATION OF CONVEXITY

OTHER TITLES IN THE SERIES
ON PURE AND APPLIED MATHEMATICS

PROBLEMS IN EUCLIDEAN SPACE:
APPLICATION OF CONVEXITY

*The Adams Prize Essay of
the University of Cambridge
1955–6*

by

H. G. EGGLESTON

*Department of Mathematics
University of Cambridge*

PERGAMON PRESS
NEW YORK · LONDON
PARIS · LOS ANGELES
1957

PERGAMON PRESS INC.
122 East 55th Street, New York 22, N.Y.
10638 South Wilton Place, Los Angeles 47, California.

PERGAMON PRESS LTD.
4 & 5 Fitzroy Square, London W.1.

PERGAMON PRESS S.A.R.L
24 Rue des Écoles, Paris Vᵉ.

Library of Congress Card Number 57–14863

CONTENTS

PREFACE

THE CONCEPT of convexity is of considerable importance in a wide variety of mathematical disciplines and the problems in which it is used are of an equally diverse nature. We shall consider here only those problems which concern convex sets in real Euclidean space of two or three dimensions, R^2 or R^3, and our aim is to illustrate the different ways in which convexity can enter into the formulation or the solution of different problems in these spaces.

Even inside this comparatively narrow field we can consider convexity from several distinct points of view.

(a) Since any convex set which is closed is an intersection of closed half-spaces, we should expect convex sets to possess properties that reflect this characteristic.

(b) Since any two points of a convex set are connected by a segment lying inside the convex set we should expect convex sets to behave as if they were particular types of connected sets, and conversely we might expect connected sets to possess in some measure properties similar to those of convex sets. An example of this point of view is given in the first problem.

(c) Spheres, circles, triangles and most of the solids and plane figures considered by the Greek geometers are convex. There are two ways in which we make use of this fact. We can try to prove that some property of the common bodies is true for all convex sets, or we try to show that some property is extremal with regard to some particular simple figure in the class of convex sets.

(d) We can regard the relationship between simple geometrical figures and general convex sets as a direct approximation, and either study this approximation itself (as in Problem 5) or seek to establish a property generally by establishing it for simple figures, usually polygons or polyhedra, and then obtaining the general result by an approximation argument.

(e) Finally, in one-dimensional real Euclidean space R^1 the only bounded convex sets are points and intervals and thus we should expect that in R^2 and R^3 there would be problems in which convex sets are the appropriate generalisation of intervals in R^1.

In what follows we shall make use of all these points of view.

The monograph is divided into four chapters such that in each the influence of convexity is more dominating than in the preceding one. In the first chapter convexity plays a minor role. Either a result concerning convex sets suggests an analogous result for more general sets, or convexity is used in subsidiary arguments. In the second chapter we consider problems which are originally stated in a wider context but which can be reduced to problems concerning convex sets. In the third chapter the problems are defined for convex sets only and not for more general sets. Whilst in the fourth chapter we consider properties of subclasses of the class of convex sets.

Of course, this division into chapters is somewhat ephemeral. No one can confidently assert that a problem can be defined only for convex sets and not more generally, and new solutions of these problems will be found which may depend less upon convexity (or more!). But although the particular problems cannot be assigned permanently to one or other of the chapters yet the classification itself is a valid and natural one for a working mathematician to adopt.

It will be seen that there is a substantial difference between the problems of the first chapter and those of the last. In the first chapter we consider problems of a general nature whilst in the last chapter they are specific and particular. Again, the difficulties which have to be overcome are quite different. In the first chapter a major difficulty is that of conjecturing the correct result. In the last chapter one can nearly always guess the truth without much difficulty. The difficulty with these problems lies in establishing the truth of the conjecture.

H. G. EGGLESTON

NOTATION AND DEFINITIONS

WE SHALL use two Euclidean spaces, the real Euclidean plane R^2, whose points are ordered pairs of real numbers (x_1, x_2) and three-dimensional real Euclidean space R^3 whose points are ordered triads of real numbers (x_1, x_2, x_3). We define the distance between (x_1, x_2) and (y_1, y_2) in R^2 to be

$$\rho[(x_1, x_2), (y_1, y_2)] = |(x_1, x_2) - (y_1, y_2)| = \{(x_1 - y_1)^2 + (x_2 - y_2)^2\}^{\frac{1}{2}}$$

and the distance between (x_1, x_2, x_3) and (y_1, y_2, y_3) in R^3 to be

$$\rho[(x_1, x_2, x_3), (y_1, y_2, y_3)] = |(x_1, x_2, x_3) - (y_1, y_2, y_3)|$$
$$= \{(x_1 - y_1)^2 + (x_2 - y_2)^2 + (x_3 - y_3)^2\}^{\frac{1}{2}}$$

If the set X is defined by a property 'P' we write

$$X = \{x \mid x \text{ has property } P\}.$$

The void set is denoted by $\emptyset$. Unions and intersections of sets are denoted by $\bigcup X_i, \bigcap X_i$ respectively and we write

$$Y - Z = \{x \mid x \in Y, x \notin Z\}.$$

The closure, interior and frontier of the set Y are denoted respectively by $\bar{Y}$, Y^0 and $\mathrm{Fr}\,Y$.

If x and y are two points then we use the symbol xy in three senses

(a) as the segment joining x to y,

(b) as the line joining x to y,

(c) as the length of the segment joining x to y.

It will be clear from the context which meaning is intended. In R^2 by the circle centre x and radius δ we mean the set of points distant δ from x. It is denoted by $c(x, \delta)$. The set of points distant not more than δ from x is referred to as a disk.

Elementary properties of convexity

We shall give these properties for subsets of R^3, the corresponding results for R^2 can be obtained by appropriate verbal changes, for example if we refer to "support planes" in R^3 then naturally in R^2 we should use instead "support lines."

DEFINITION: *A subset X of R^2 or R^3 is **convex** if it is such that $x_1 \in X$, $x_2 \in X$ imply that the segment joining x_1 to x_2 is contained in X.*

1

The convex cover of a set Y is the intersection of all the convex sets which contain Y. It is denoted by $H(Y)$. We also use the notation $H(X_1, X_2, \ldots, X_k)$ for the convex cover of the union of the sets $X_1, \ldots, X_k$.

A support plane of a set X is a plane P such that $P \cap \bar{X} \neq \emptyset$ and X is contained in the closure of one of the two open half spaces into which P cuts R^3. Every point on the frontier of a convex set X lies on a support plane of X. Let X be a closed bounded convex set for which $X^0 \neq \emptyset$. There are exactly two support planes to X perpendicular to a given direction. For this reason we can define the mapping by parallel support planes as follows. Let S be a closed sphere, i.e.

$$S = \{x \mid x = (x_1, x_2, x_3), \qquad x_1{}^2 + x_2{}^2 + x_3{}^2 \leqslant R^2\}$$

and we shall suppose that the origin $(0, 0, 0)$ belongs to X^0. Let P be a support plane of X and Q a support plane of S parallel to P and such that $(0, 0, 0)$ does not lie between Q and P. If

$$x \in P \cap \mathrm{Fr}X; \qquad s \in Q \cap \mathrm{Fr}S$$

then we regard the process as establishing a correspondence between x and s. If, for each support plane P, $P \cap \mathrm{Fr}X$ is a single point then the mapping

$$s \to x$$

defined by this correspondence is continuous and maps $\mathrm{Fr}S$ on $\mathrm{Fr}X$.

A convex set is said to be *central* if there is some point p such that the reflection of the set in p is the set itself. p is called the *centre* of the set.

In R^2 the frontier of a convex set which is neither a segment nor a point nor void is called a *convex curve*.

If X_1, X_2 are two convex sets then the *vector sum* of X_1, X_2 is $X_1 + X_2$ defined by

$$X_1 + X_2 = \{x \mid x = x_1 + x_2, x_1 \in X_1, x_2 \in X_2\}.$$

Similarly if λ is a real positive number then λX_1 is defined by

$$\lambda X_1 = \{x \mid x = \lambda x_1, x_1 \in X_1\}.$$

The *width* of a convex set in a particular direction is the distance apart of the support planes perpendicular to that direction. The least of these widths is the minimal width of the set and if they are all equal the set is said to be of constant width.

A *Reuleaux triangle* is a plane convex set of diameter D bounded by three equal circular arcs all of radius D. It is of constant width.

Every set of diameter D is contained in a set of constant width D.

Every plane set of constant width D is contained in a regular hexagon of minimal width D.

Hausdorff measure

The Hausdorff α dimensional measure of the set X is defined as follows. Let $K(X, \delta)$ be any aggregate containing enumerably many convex sets each of diameter less than δ and whose point set union contains X. Let $F(K(X, \delta))$ be the sum of the α-powers of the diameter of the members of $K(X, \delta)$. Let K_δ be the class of all $K(X, \delta)$. Then

$$\liminf_{\substack{\delta \to 0 \\ K_\delta}} F(K(X, \delta))$$

exists and is defined to be the α-dimensional Hausdorff measure of X, denoted by $\Lambda_\alpha (X)$, (or $\Lambda (X)$ when $\alpha = 1$). Questions of measurability will not occur in our considerations.

CHAPTER 1

PROBLEMS IN WHICH CONVEXITY IS USED EITHER BY ANALOGY OR FOR SUBSIDIARY ARGUMENTS

1ST PROBLEM. THE INTERSECTION OF CONNECTED OPEN SETS

Introduction

A simple but striking property of convexity is that the intersection of any number of convex sets is a convex set. This property can be roughly phrased as "linear connectedness is preserved under intersections." A natural problem which is suggested when we use connected sets in place of convex sets is the following. Are there any distinctive features of those sets which are intersections of connected sets? As it stands this question is too wide to be answered satisfactorily. A more practical question is "Are all open sets the intersection of a sequence of open connected sets?" The answer which would be expected is in the negative. By analogy with the convex case one would expect something of the connectedness of the sets in the sequence to persist in their intersection, and we shall see that this is the case.

This problem originally arose in a different connection. Suppose that the complex valued function $f(z)$ of the complex variable z is meromorphic in $|z| < 1$ and that its range set $\mathscr{R}(f)$ is defined to be the set of points w for each of which the equation $w = f(z)$ has infinitely many solutions in z with $|z| < 1$. In other words if $A(n)$ denotes the annulus $1 - 1/n < |z| < 1$ and $f(A(n))$ the image of this annulus under the mapping f then $\mathscr{R}(f) = \bigcap_{n=1}^{\infty} f(A(n))$.

Since f, regarded as a mapping of R^2 onto itself †, maps open sets onto open sets, $\mathscr{R}(f)$ is a G_δ set, but it is also more than this because it is the intersection of a decreasing sequence of open connected sets. It has been known for some time that every such set (i.e. the intersection of a decreasing sequence of open connected subsets of R^2) is the range set of some function meromorphic in $|z| < 1$ but the question as to whether the property that these sets be connected is necessary or not has so far been unanswered (see [1]

† Strictly f maps a subset of R^2 into the compactification of R^2.

4

and [2]).† The construction leads one to suspect (erroneously) that it can be dispensed with. We shall show that this is not the case. In fact there are G_δ sets and even open sets which are not the range set of any meromorphic function.

In what follows we shall assume, unless the contrary is explicitly stated that all sets are subsets of R^2.

§1. Definitions

DEFINITION 1. *The **nub** of a closed set.*

Let K be the given closed set and let the components of the complement of K be enumerated as C_1, C_2, C_3, ... There are either a finite number of such components or an enumerable infinity. In the first case we define the nub of K to be the void set and in the second case we define it as follows. Select a point $p_i \in C_i$; write $P = \bigcup_{i=1}^{\infty} p_i$. The set $\bar{P} - P$, which is necessarily a closed subset of $\mathrm{Fr}K$, the frontier of K, is called *the nub of K* and is written $n(K)$. Strictly speaking this notation is inadequate since the nub depends upon both K and the set P used in its definition. But this matter is immaterial.

DEFINITION 2. *The **ultimate nub** of an open set.*

We set up a succession of sets as follows. Let G_0 be the given open set and K be its complement. Define the nub of K, $n(K)$, and form the union of those components of the complement of $n(K)$ that contain points of G_0. This open set is called G_1. We now proceed by a definition in terms of transfinite induction.

Suppose that G_β has been defined for all ordinals $\beta < \alpha$. Then if α is a limit number we define G_α by $G_\alpha = \bigcup_{\beta < \alpha} G_\beta$; if α is not a limit number, write $K_{\alpha-1}$ for the complement of $G_{\alpha-1}$, $n(K_{\alpha-1})$ for the nub of $K_{\alpha-1}$ and G_α for the union of those components of the complement of $n(K_{\alpha-1})$ which contain points of $G_{\alpha-1}$. The set G_α is not necessarily uniquely defined in this second case, but, if possible, we choose such a G_α that $G_{\alpha-1}$ is strictly contained in G_α. Since the equality $G_{\beta+1} = G_\beta$ implies $G_\alpha = G_\beta$, $\alpha > \beta$, there is a first ordinal ζ such that $G_\alpha = G_\zeta$ if $\alpha > \zeta$. Since the sets G_α are open and strictly increasing for $\alpha \leqslant \zeta$, we have $\zeta < \Omega$ where Ω is the first ordinal corresponding to the cardinal $\aleph_1$.

We denote the complement of G_ζ by $\mathrm{N}(G_0)$ and call it the *ultimate nub of G_0*. The justification for this notation is given in the next theorem.

THEOREM 1.1. *The ultimate nub of an open set G_0 is uniquely determined by G_0.*

† The references for this section are listed on p. 18.

Proof: Suppose that we set up two transfinite sequences of sets as described above,

$$G_0, G_1, \ldots, G_\omega, G_{\omega+1}, \ldots, G_\zeta$$

and

$$G_0, G_1', \ldots, G_\omega', G_{\omega+1}', \ldots, G_\zeta',$$

and suppose that the complement of G_ζ, say $\mathrm{N}(G_0)$, contains a point p not belonging to the complement of G_ζ', (denoted by $\mathrm{N}'(G_0)$). Since $p \in G_\zeta'$ there must be a first ordinal $\alpha(p)$ such that $p \in G_{\alpha(p)}'$. Amongst all the points p of $\mathrm{N}(G_0) \cap G_\zeta'$, there is one, say p_0, such that $\alpha(p_0)$ is the first of all the ordinals $\alpha(p)$. Since $G_0 \cap \mathrm{N}(G_0) = \emptyset$ it follows that $\alpha(p_0) \geqslant 1$. Thus

$$p_0 \in \mathrm{N}(G_0) \cap G_{\alpha(p_0)}'.$$

and if $\beta < \alpha(p_0)$,

$$\mathrm{N}(G_0) \cap G_\beta' = \emptyset.$$

Since $p_0 \in G_{\alpha(p_0)}'$ and $p_0 \notin G_\beta'$, $\beta < \alpha(p_0)$, $\alpha(p_0)$ is not a limit ordinal and $\alpha(p_0)$ has an immediate predecessor $\alpha(p_0) - 1$.

Since $p_0 \in \mathrm{N}(G_0)$, either (a) there exists a sequence of components of G_ζ that converge to p_0, or (b) p_0 is an interior point of $\mathrm{N}(G_0)$. For otherwise p_0 would be a frontier point of $\mathrm{N}(G_0)$ such that for some $\delta > 0$ the disk $c(p_0, \delta)$ whose centre is p_0 and radius δ, contains points of at most a finite number of components of G_ζ. But then we can find a positive number δ_1, $\delta_1 < \delta$, such that every component of G_ζ has points outside the circle $c(p_0, \delta_1)$. Let the components of G_ζ be $C_1, C_2, C_3, \ldots$ and let $q_i \in C_i$ be chosen to lie outside $c(p_0, \delta_i)$ then if $Q = \bigcup_{i=1}^{\infty} q_i$, $\overline{Q} - Q$ is contained in $\mathrm{N}(G_0)$ and its complement is a possible $G_{\zeta+1}$. But $\mathrm{G}_{\zeta+1}$ contains p_0 and thus $G_{\zeta+1}$ is strictly greater than G_ζ. This is impossible by the definition of ζ.

Consider case (a). Every component of G_ζ contains one or more components of G_0 and therefore contains points that do not belong to the complement of G_β' for any β and in particular for $\beta = \alpha(p_0) - 1$. Now $\mathrm{N}(G_0) \cap G_{\alpha(p_0)-1}'$ is void and thus every component of $G_{\alpha(p_0)-1}'$ is contained in a component of G_ζ. Since there is a sequence of components of G_ζ that converges to p_0 and each of these components contains the whole of a component of $G_{\alpha(p_0)-1}'$ it follows that there is a sequence of components of $G_{\alpha(p_0)-1}'$ that converges to p_0. But this implies that however we define $G_{\alpha(p_0)}'$ from $G_{\alpha(p_0)-1}'$ we have $p_0 \notin G_{\alpha(p_0)}'$ a contradiction which shows that case (a) cannot arise.

Consider case (b). Let the component of $N(G_0)$ to which p_0 belongs be denoted by T. The above argument shows that $\mathrm{Fr}\,T \subset N'(G_0)$. Thus for every β, $\beta \leqslant \zeta'$, $\mathrm{Fr}\,T$ separates G'_β from p_0. Hence $p_0 \notin G'_\beta$ for any β and $p_0 \in N'(G_0)$.

It follows that $N(G_0) \subset N'(G_0)$ and, by the same argument repeated with the roles of $N(G_0)$ and $N'(G_0)$ interchanged, that $N'(G_0) \subset N(G_0)$.

Thus $N(G_0)$ is $N'(G_0)$.

§2. The main result

THEOREM 1.2. *The necessary and sufficient condition that the non-void open set G_0 be the intersection of a decreasing sequence of open connected sets T_n is that the ultimate nub of G_0 be void.*

(a) *Necessity.* Suppose that G_0 is an open set for which $N(G_0) \neq \emptyset$. Then the set $\mathrm{Fr}(N(G_0)) \neq \emptyset$; denote this frontier set by H. H is a closed subset of $N(G_0)$ and every point of H is a limit point of a convergent sequence of components of the complement of $N(G_0)$. Since each of these components contains one or more components of G_0 and since the complement of G_0 contains $N(G_0)$ it follows that every point of H is the limit of a convergent sequence of components of G_0.

Considered as a space in itself, H is of second category. Any open set D that is connected and contains G_0 is dense in H, by the remark made above. The set $D \cap H$ is an open dense subset of H. Thus if $\{D_n\}$ is a sequence of open sets containing G_0, the set $\bigcap_n D_n \cap H$ contains all of H except at most a set of first category in H. Thus $\bigcap_n D_n \cap H$ is non-void and since $H \cap G_0 = \emptyset$ it follows that $G_0 \neq \bigcap_n D_n$.

Thus G_0 is not the intersection of any sequence of open connected sets, whether the sequence is decreasing or not.

(b) *Sufficiency.* We require the following lemma.

LEMMA. *D is an open connected set which contains an open set L whose components L_1, L_2, L_3, ... have the property that it is possible to select a point p_i of L_i such that if $P = \bigcup_i p_i$ then $\bar{P} - P \subset \mathrm{Fr}\,D$. In these circumstances we can construct a sequence of open connected sets $\{G_n\}$ such that $D \supset G_n \supset G_{n+1}$ and $\bigcap_{n=1}^{\infty} G_n = L$.*

Each of the sets L_i is a component of an open set and is therefore open; thus each point p_i is the centre of a disk which is contained in L_i. This disk cannot contain any point $p_j, j \neq i$ hence each p_i is an isolated point of the set P. Thus any subset of D which is compact in the whole plane contains at most a finite number of the points p_i, for if it contained infinitely many it would also contain a cluster point, say q. Then q would belong to $\bar{P}$, and as it is not isolated in P, q would not belong to P. Thus $q \in \bar{P} - P$ and by hypothesis $q \in \mathrm{Fr}\,D$. But $q \in D$ and D is open so that $D \cap \mathrm{Fr}\,D = \emptyset$. This is a contradiction and there is no such point as q. Thus any compact set contained in D meets P in at most a finite number of points.

Join p_1 to p_2 by an arc α_1 in D. Since α_1 is compact it is at a positive distance, say η_1, from $\mathrm{Fr}\,D$. Let $A_1 = U(\alpha_1, \tfrac{1}{2}\eta_1)$ be the set of points whose distance from α_1 is less than $\tfrac{1}{2}\eta_1$. Since

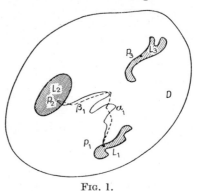

FIG. 1.

$\bar{A}_1$ is a compact set contained in D, it follows that A_1 meets a finite subset of P, say P_1. Then $(A_1 - P_1) \cup p_1 \cup p_2$ is an open connected set containing p_1 and p_2. Let β_1 be a polygonal arc in $(A_1 - P_1) \cup p_1 \cup p_2$ joining p_1 to p_2. β_1 is at a positive distance, say ρ_1, from $\mathrm{Fr}\,\{(A_1 - P_1) \cup p_1 \cup p_2\}$. Put $B_1 = U(\beta_1, \tfrac{1}{2}\rho_1)$. Then B_1 is an open connnected set joining p_1 to p_2 in D and each point of B_1 is at a distance greater than or equal to $\tfrac{1}{2}\rho_1$ from $\mathrm{Fr}\,D$ and from $P - (p_1 \cup p_2)$.

Since β_1 is an arc in D that does not meet $\mathrm{Fr}\,D$ the set $D - \beta_1$ is connected and contains $P - (p_1 \cup p_2)$. But β_1 is a polygonal arc. Let δ_1 be the lower bound of the distances between any two points of β_1 that do not belong to the same or to adjacent segments of β_1: if β_1 is composed of one or two segments, let δ_1 be the largest length of a segment of β_1. Let ε be a positive number less than $\min\,(\tfrac{1}{2}\rho_1, \tfrac{1}{3}\delta_1)$ and write $C(\varepsilon) = U(\beta_1, \varepsilon)$. We show next that $D - \overline{C(\varepsilon)}$ is connected. Let k be the number of segments of β_1. The result is trivial if β_1 is composed of one or two segments. Suppose, inductively, that the result has been proved for all polygonal arcs with $k - 1$ segments. Denote the segments of β_1 by

$\mu_1, \mu_2, \ldots, \mu_{k-1}, \mu_k, k \geqslant 3$. Consider the subarc of β_1 formed by the segments $\mu_1, \mu_2, \ldots, \mu_{k-1}$ say β_1'. Then, as $\beta_1' \subset \beta_1$ the number δ_1' defined with respect to β_1' as δ_1 was with respect to β_1 satisfies $\delta_1' \geqslant \delta_1$. Thus by the inductive hypothesis any two points of $D - \overline{C(\varepsilon)}$ can be joined in $D - \overline{U(\beta_1', \varepsilon)}$ and further they can be joined in $D - \overline{U(\mu_k, \varepsilon)}$ by the simple case $k = 1$. Moreover, the set

$$\overline{U(\mu_k, \varepsilon)} \cap \overline{U(\beta_1', \varepsilon)} = \overline{U(\mu_k, \varepsilon)} \cap \overline{U(\mu_{k-1}, \varepsilon)}$$

is connected, and thus, by Alexander's lemma, any two points of $D - \overline{C(\epsilon)}$ can be joined in $D - \overline{C(\epsilon)}$. Thus, by induction on the number of segments of β_1, $D - \overline{C(\epsilon)}$ is connected.

Denote the upper bound of the distances of points of L_2 from β_1 by $d(L_2)$ and write

$$2k_1 = \min \{\tfrac{1}{2}\rho_1, \tfrac{1}{3}\delta_1, \tfrac{1}{2}d(L_2)\}.$$

Write $E_1 = U(\beta_1, k_1)$ and let q_2 be a point of $L_2 - \overline{U(\beta_1, 2k_1)}$. Thus we have a polygonal arc β_1 joining p_1 to p_2 in D, a positive number k_1, and a set E_1, such that E_1 is an open set which contains β_1, every point of E_1 is at a distance of at least k_1 from $P - (p_1 \cup p_2)$, q_2 and from $\mathrm{Fr}D$, and such that $D - \bar{E}_1$ is an open connected set that contains q_2 and $P - (p_1 \cup p_2)$.

We now consider the set $D - \bar{E}_1$ in place of D and the sequence of points $q_2, p_3, p_4, \ldots$ in place of $p_1, p_2, p_3 \ldots$. It is easy to see that the same conditions as before are fulfilled. Thus by exactly the same argument as above we can find a polygonal arc β_2 a positive number k_2 and a point q_3 with the following properties. β_2 is contained in $D - \bar{E}_1$ and its end points are q_2 and p_3. If we write $E_2 = U(\beta_2, k_2)$ the set $D - \bar{E}_1 - \bar{E}_2$ is connected and contains $P - (p_1 \cup p_2 \cup p_3)$. Every point of $\mathrm{Fr}(D - \bar{E}_1)$ and of $P - (p_1 \cup p_2 \cup p_3)$ is at a distance from $\bar{E}_2$ of at least k_2. The point q_3 belongs to $L_3 - \bar{E}_1 - \bar{E}_2$ and is also at a distance from $\bar{E}_2 \cup \bar{E}_1$ of at least k_2.

Proceeding in this manner we obtain a sequence of points q_2, $q_3, \ldots$; of arcs $\beta_1, \beta_2, \ldots$; of positive numbers $k_1, k_2, \ldots$ for which the following properties hold.

(i) β_i is a polygonal arc whose end points are $q_i p_{i+1}$ if $i > 1$ or $p_1 p_2$ if $i = 1$; $\beta_i \subset D - \bigcup_{j=1}^{i-1} \bar{E}_j$ where $E_i = U(\beta_i, k_i)$

(ii) $D - \bigcup_{j=1}^{i} \bar{E}_j$ is connected and contains $P - \bigcup_{j=1}^{i+1} p_j$.

(iii) Every point of $\mathrm{Fr}(D - \bigcup_{j=1}^{i-1} \bar{E}_j)$ and of $P - \bigcup_{j=1}^{i+1} p_j$ is at a distance from $\bar{E}_i$ of at least k_i.

2

(iv) There is a point q_{i+1} belonging to $L_{i+1} - \bigcup\limits_{j=1}^{i} \bar{E}_j$ whose distance from $\bigcup\limits_{j=1}^{i} \bar{E}_j$ is at least k_i.

Write

$$E_i(n) = U(\beta_i, k_i/n),$$

$$T_n = \bigcup_{j=1}^{\infty} L_j \cup \{\bigcup_{j=1}^{\infty} E_j(n) - \bigcup_{j=1}^{\infty} \beta_j\}.$$

We shall show that the sequence of sets $\{T_n\}$ has the required properties.

(a) T_n *is open.* Each set L_j is open and so we need only show that the set

$$X_1 = \bigcup_{j=1}^{\infty} E_j(n) - \bigcup_{j=1}^{\infty} \beta_j.$$

is open. But this set is identical with the set

$$X_2 = \bigcup_{j=1}^{\infty} (E_j(n) - \beta_j).$$

for it is trivial that $X_1 \subset X_2$ and to show that $X_2 \subset X_1$ we observe that if p is a point of $E_j(n) - \beta_j$ then p also belongs to $E_j(n) - \bigcup\limits_{r=1}^{\infty} \beta_r$ because by the construction $\beta_r \cap E_j(n) = \emptyset, r \neq j$. Hence $X_2 \subset X_1$ and in fact X_2 is X_1.

But by construction $E_j(n) - \beta_j$ is open and thus X_2, and hence T_n is open.

(b) T_n *is connected.* For $T_n = \bigcup\limits_{i=1}^{\infty} Y_i$ where

$$Y_i = \bigcup_{j=1}^{i} L_j \cup \bigcup_{j=1}^{i} (E_j(n) - \beta_j)).$$

Each set Y_i is connected, $Y_{i+1} \supset Y_i$, thus T_n is connected.

(c) $T_n \supset T_{n+1}$ *and* $\bigcap\limits_{n=1}^{\infty} T_n = L$. The statement $T_n \supset T_{n+1}$ is trivially true as is also the inclusion $\bigcap\limits_{n=1}^{\infty} T_n \supset L$. We have to show that $\bigcap\limits_{n=1}^{\infty} T_n \subset L$. Suppose that this is false and that there is a point p, $p \in \bigcap\limits_{n=1}^{\infty} T_n$ and $p \notin L$. Then for every n there exists an integer i such that $p \in E_i(n) - \beta_i$. But $E_i \cap E_j = \emptyset$ if $i \neq j$ and $E_i \supset E_i(n)$, $E_j \supset E_j(m)$ for all n, m. Thus the integer i is independent of n and $p \in \bigcap\limits_{n=1}^{\infty} (E_i(n) - \beta_i)$. But $\bigcap\limits_{n=1}^{\infty} E_i(n) \subset \beta_i$ and

$\bigcap\limits_{n=1}^{\infty} (E_i(n) - \beta_i)$ is void. Thus we have a contradiction. Hence there is no such point as p and $\bigcap\limits_{n=1}^{\infty} T_n \subset L$.

Then

$$\bigcap_{n=1}^{\infty} T_n = L.$$

The sequence $\{T_n\}$ has all the properties required of the sequence $\{G_n\}$ and the lemma is proved.

We can now complete the proof of the theorem. Suppose that G_0 is an open set for which $\mathrm{N}(G_0) = \emptyset$ and that the sequence of open sets

$$G_0, G_1, \ldots, G_\omega, G_{\omega+1}, \ldots, G_\zeta$$

is one which is defined as explained in the definition of the ultimate nub.

Denote the components of G_α by

$$G_\alpha(1), G_\alpha(2), \ldots, G_\alpha(k), \ldots$$

Since G_α is open there are at most an enumerable infinity of components $G_\alpha(k)$ and each is open. Each component of $G_{\alpha+1}$ say $G_{\alpha+1}(j)$ contains a subset of the components of G_α which we denote by

$$G_\alpha(j, 1), G_\alpha(j, 2), G_\alpha(j, 3), \ldots$$

Since $G_{\alpha+1}(j)$ contains no point of the nub of the complement of G_α, it follows that we can select a point $p_i \in G_\alpha(j, i)$ such that, if $P = \bigcup\limits_{i \geqslant 1} p_i$ then

$$\bar{P} - P \subset \mathrm{Fr} G_{\alpha+1}(j)$$

By the lemma there exists a decreasing sequence of open connected sets contained in $G_{\alpha+1}(j)$ say $T(\alpha+1, j, n)$, $n = 1, 2, \ldots$, such that $\bigcap\limits_{n=1}^{\infty} T(\alpha+1, j, n) = \bigcup\limits_{i \geqslant 1} G_\alpha(j, i)$. Write $G_\alpha(j, i, n)$ for the set of those points of $G_\alpha(j, i)$ which are at a distance not less than $1/n$ from $\mathrm{Fr} G_\alpha(j, i)$.

Write

$$T(\alpha+1, j, n) - \bigcup_{i \geqslant 1} G_\alpha(j, i, n) = H(\alpha+1, j, n).$$

This equation defines the set $H(\beta, j, n)$ for every non-limit ordinal β, $1 \leqslant \beta < \zeta$, for every positive integer n and every appropriate positive integer j. For other ordinals β, define $H(\beta, j, n)$ to be the void set for all j, n. Finally write

$$J(n) = G_0 \cup \bigcup_{\beta, j} H(\beta, j, n),$$

where the sum is over all ordinals $\beta < \zeta$ and over all appropriate integers j. We show that the sequence $J(1)$, $J(2)$, ... has the required properties.

(i) $J(n)$ *is open.* The set $H(\beta, j, n)$ is either void or equal to $T(\beta, j, n) - \bigcup_{i \geqslant 1} G_{\beta-1}(j, i, n)$. If the second of these two possibilities holds, let p be a point of this set. Since $T(\beta, j, n)$ is open, there is a positive number ε such that the open disk centre p and radius ε, $U(p, \varepsilon)$ is contained in $T(\beta, j, n)$. Now β is a non-limit ordinal and there exists the ordinal $\beta - 1$. If $p \notin G_{\beta-1}(j, i)$ for any integer i, then $U(p, 1/n)$ does not meet $G_{\beta-1}(j, i, n)$ for any integer i and if

$$\varepsilon' = \min (\varepsilon, 1/n)$$

we have

$$U(p, \varepsilon') \subset T(\beta, j, n) - \bigcup_{i \geqslant 1} G_{\beta-1}(j, i, n).$$

On the other hand, if, for some integer i, $p \in G_{\beta-1}(j, i)$ then there is only one such integer i for the sets $G_{\beta-1}(j, i)$, $i = 1, 2, \ldots$ are disjoint. Suppose $p \in G_{\beta-1}(j, 1)$, then since, by the definition of $H(\beta, j, n)$, $p \notin G_{\beta-1}(j, 1, n)$, the set $G_{\beta-1}(j, 1) - G_{\beta-1}(j, 1, n)$, which is open, is such that $p \in G_{\beta-1}(j, 1) - G_{\beta-1}(j, 1, n) \subset H(\beta, j, n)$. Thus in any case the set $H(B, j, n)$ is open and we conclude that $J(n)$ is open.

(ii) $J(n)$ *is connected.* We shall show that, given any two points p_1, p_2 of $J(n)$, there exists an arc in $J(n)$ that joins them. Since the ultimate nub of G_0 is void there is a least ordinal α such that p_1 and p_2 belong to the same component of G_α. The argument is by transfinite induction.

If $\alpha = 0$, p_1 and p_2 belong to the same component of G_0 and as $G_0 \subset J(n)$ the result is trivially true.

Suppose then that any two points of $J(n)$ which belong to the same component of some G_β, $\beta < \alpha$, can be joined by an arc in $J(n)$, and that the two points p_1 and p_2 belong to the same component of G_α but not to the same component of any G_β, $\beta < \alpha$.

We observe first that α is not a limit ordinal. For if it were, there would be an enumerable sequence of strictly increasing ordinals β_1, β_2, ... which tend to α in the limit. Since p_1 and p_2 belong to the same component of G_α, there is a polygonal line joining p_1 to p_2 in G_α, say L. Denote the subset of L exterior to G_{β_i} by M_i. The sequence of sets $\{M_i\}$ is decreasing and each member is compact and non-void. Thus their intersection has a common point q. Thus we have

$$q \in G_\alpha, \quad q \notin G_\beta \quad \beta < \alpha.$$

But by definition $G_\alpha = \bigcup\limits_{\beta < \alpha} G_\beta$ and this contradiction shows that α is not a limit ordinal.

Next we may suppose that the notation is such that

$$p_1, p_2, \in G_\alpha(1); \quad p_1 \in G_{\alpha-1}(1, 1); \quad p_2 \in G_{\alpha-1}(1, 2).$$

Let q_1, q_2 be two points such that

$$q_1 \in G_{\alpha-1}(1, 1) - G_{\alpha-1}(1, 1, n); q_2 \in G_{\alpha-1}(1, 2) - G_{\alpha-1}(1, 2, n)$$

Since the points p_1 and q_1 belong to $J(n)$ and to the same component of $G_{\alpha-1}$, it follows by the induction hypothesis that p_1 and q_1 can be joined by an arc in $J(n)$. The same is true of p_2, q_2; thus it is sufficient to show that q_1 and q_2 can be joined by an arc in $J(n)$. Let K be a polygonal line of finite length joining q_1 to q_2 in $T(\alpha, 1, n)$. Such a line exists because both q_1 and q_2 belong to $T(\alpha, 1, n)$ and this set is open and connected. The line K may meet some of the sets $G_{\alpha-1}(1, i, n)$. If K meets $G_{\alpha-1}(1, i_1 n)$ and $G_{\alpha-1}(1, i_2, n)$ in, say, t_1 and t_2, then the distance apart of t_1 and t_2 is at least $2/n$, and the length of arc of K between t_1 and t_2 is at least $2/n$. Suppose that K meets, in order, the sets

$$G_{\alpha-1}(1, i_1, n), \quad G_{\alpha-1}(1, i_2, n), \dots, \quad G_{\alpha-1}(1, i_k, n);$$

the order here is from q_1 to q_2 and consecutive integers in the sequence $i_1, i_2, \dots, i_k$ are distinct although there may be repetitions in this sequence. By the remark made above there are only a finite number of these integers $i_1, i_2, \dots, i_k$. If there are none of these integers, then

$$K \subset T(\alpha, 1, n) - \bigcap_{i \geqslant 1} G_{\alpha-1}(1, i, n) \subset J(n),$$

and we have the required result. Suppose then that there exist such integers.

Write S_l for a point of $G_{\alpha-1}(1, i_l, n) \cap K$ where $S_1, S_2, \dots, S_k$ are in the order from q_1 to q_2, and then, denote by Q_l an arc of K such that $Q_l \subset G_{\alpha-1}(1, i_l)$, $K - \bigcup Q_l \subset T(\alpha, 1, n) - \bigcup G_{\alpha-1}(1, i, n)$, and the end points of Q_l belong to $G_{\alpha-1}(1, i_l) - G_{\alpha-1}(1, i_l, n)$. Denote the end points of Q_l in order on K from q_1 to q_2 by r_l and s_l and so choose Q_1 and Q_k (if necessary) that $r_1 \neq q_1$ and $s_k \neq q_2$.

Now r_l and s_l belong to $G_{\alpha-1}(1, i_l)$ and to $J(n)$ hence by the induction hypothesis there is an arc Θ_l in $J(n)$ which joins them. The arc $s_l r_{l+1}$ of K lies inside $T(\alpha, 1, n) - \bigcup\limits_{i \geqslant 1} G_{\alpha-1}(1, i, n)$ and thus in $J(n)$.

We construct an arcwise-connected set joining q_1 to q_2 in $J(n)$ as follows: arc $q_1 r_1$ of K, arc Θ_1, arc $s_1 r_2$ of K, arc $\Theta_2, \dots$, arc Θ_k, arc $s_k q_2$ of K.

This set contains an arc joining q_1 to q_2 in $J(n)$, and so the proof of the next stage of the induction is complete. Thus $J(n)$ is connected.

(iii) $\bigcap\limits_{n=1}^{\infty} J(n) = G_0$. Clearly $\bigcap\limits_{n=1}^{\infty} J(n) \supset G_0$ and it is sufficient to show that

$$\bigcap_{n=1}^{\infty} \left\{ \bigcup_{\beta, j} H(\beta, j, n) \right\} \subset G_0.$$

Suppose that on the contrary there is a point p such that $p \notin G_0$ and $p \in H(\beta, j, n)$ for every n and some appropriate β, j depending on n. There is a first ordinal α such that $p \in G_\alpha$. Suppose that $p \in G_\alpha$ (1).

For $\beta < \alpha$, $H(\beta, j, n) \subset T(\beta, j, n) \subset G_\beta$; hence $p \notin H(\beta, j, n)$ for $\beta < \alpha$.

For $\beta > \alpha$, denote by $G_\beta(1)$ the component of G_β which contains p. Let δ be the distance of p from $\mathrm{Fr} G_\alpha(1)$. Since $G_\beta(1) \supset G_\alpha(1)$, the distance of p from $\mathrm{Fr} G_\beta(1)$ is greater than or equal to δ. Thus if n is so large that $1/n < \delta$ then $p \notin H(\beta, j, n)$.

Thus we have $p \in H(\alpha, j, n)$ all $n \geqslant n_0$ where α is a fixed non-limit ordinal. But the sets $H(\alpha, j, n)$, $j = 1, 2, \ldots$ are disjoint; thus j is fixed, say $j = 1$. Now

$$H(\alpha, 1, n) \subset T(\alpha, 1, n); \quad \bigcap_{n=1}^{\infty} T(\alpha, 1, n) = \bigcup_{i \geqslant 1} G_{\alpha-1}(1, i) \subset G_{\alpha-1}.$$

But $p \notin G_{\alpha-1}$ and the sequence $T(\alpha, 1, n)$ decreases as n increases; thus for some n_1, $p \notin H(\alpha, 1, n)$ all $n \geqslant n_1$. Hence, if $p \notin G_0$, there is an n such that $p \notin \bigcup\limits_{\beta, j} H(\alpha, j, n)$.

This implies that $\bigcap\limits_{n=1}^{\infty} J(n) = G_0$.

(iv) $J(n) \supset J(n+1)$. This result is trivial.

We next give an example of an open set whose ultimate nub is not void. Let C_1 denote a circle of unit radius and let A_1 be an enumerable dense subset of points of C_1. Suppose that A_1 is the sequence $a_1, a_2, \ldots$. Let $C_{1,j}$ be a circle which touches C internally at a_j, has radius less than one-third that of C_1, and is such that $C_{1,j} \cap C_{1,i} = \emptyset$ if $i \neq j$. Let $A_{i,j}$ be an enumerable dense subset of points of $C_{1,j}$, say $a_{j,1}, a_{j,2}, \ldots$. Generally, when circles $C_{1,j_1,j_2\cdots,j_k}$ have been defined let $A_{1,j_1,j_2\cdots,j_k}$ be an enumerable dense subset of points of $C_{1,j_1,j_2\cdots,j_k}$, say $a_{j_1,j_2,\ldots,j_k,i}$, $i = 1, 2, \ldots$, and let $C_{1,j_1,\ldots,j_k,j_{k+1}}$ be a circle that touches $C_{1,j_1,j_2,\ldots,j_k}$ internally at $a_{j_1,j_2,\ldots,j_k,j_{k+1}}$, has radius less than one-third that of $C_{1,j_1,j_2,\ldots,j_k}$, and is such that $C_{1,j_1,j_2,\ldots,j_k,j} \cap C_{1,j_1j_2,\ldots,j_k,i} = \emptyset$ if $i \neq j$.

Denote the closure of the union of all these circles by K and the complement of K by G. To show that G has a non-void ultimate nub it is sufficient to show that if P is any enumerable set of points, one in each component of G, then $\bar{P} - P \supset K$.

Suppose then that t is any point of K. K is a non-dense set. Let δ be a positive number and let n be a positive integer such that $1/3^n < \delta$. If, for some $m > n$, t is one of the points $a_{j_1, \ldots, j_m}$, then the circle $C_{1, j_1, \ldots, j_m}$ contains points of G and is contained in the circle centre t and radius δ. Thus this latter circle contains the whole of at least one component of G and thus contains a point of P. If t is not one of these points, $a_{j_1, \ldots, j_m}$, then since for any integer r the circles $C_{1, j_1, \ldots, j_k}$, $k \geqslant r$ are dense in K and the set $A_{1, j_1, \ldots, j_k}$ is dense in $C_{1, j_1, \ldots, j_k}$, the totality of all the sets $A_{1, j_1, \ldots, j_k}$ $k \geqslant r$ is dense in K. Thus we can find a sequence of points b_1, b_2, b_3, $\ldots$ such that $b_i \rightarrow t$ as $i \rightarrow \infty$ and each b_i is of the form $a_{j_1, \ldots, j_m}$ with $m > n$. We again conclude that there is a point of P inside the circle with centre t and radius δ. Since this is true for all $\delta > 0$, $t \in \bar{P}$. As $P \subset G$, $t \in K$ and $G \cap K = \emptyset$, we have $t \notin P$. Hence $t \in \bar{P} - P$ and thus $K \subset \bar{P} - P$, and the ultimate nub of G is K.

§3. G_δ sets with void ultimate nub

DEFINITION 3. *A G_δ set K is said to have a **void ultimate nub** if every open set G that contains K and is such that every component of G contains some point of K, is itself of void ultimate nub.*

THEOREM 1.3. *The necessary and sufficient condition that a G_δ set K should be of void ultimate nub is that K should be the intersection of a decreasing sequence of open connected sets.*

Proof: For suppose that K is a G_δ set of void ultimate nub. Then $K = \bigcap_{j=1}^{\infty} L_j$ where each L_j is an open set each component of which contains a point of K, and $L_j \supset L_{j+1} \supset K$. By definition L_j is of void ultimate nub; thus by Theorem 1.2 there exists a sequence of open connected sets $T_{i,j}$, $i = 1$, 2, $\ldots$ such that $T_{i,j} \supset T_{i+1,j}$ $\bigcap_{i=1}^{\infty} T_{i,j} = L_j$. Now $T_{i,j}$ is an open connected set and $T_{i,j} \supset L_j \supset L_{j+1}$. It is clear from the argument of Theorem 1.2 that we may choose $T_{1,j+1}$, $T_{2,j+1}$, $\ldots$ so that $T_{i,j} \supset T_{k,j+1}$ $i = 1$, 2, $\ldots$ $k = 1$, 2, $\ldots$ $k \geqslant i$†.

Consider the sequence $T_{1,1}$, $T_{2,2}$, $T_{3,3}$, $\ldots$. This is a decreasing sequence of open connected sets and we have

$$\bigcap_{i=1}^{\infty} T_{i,i} \supset \bigcap_{i=1}^{\infty} L_i = K$$

† The argument of Theorem 1.2 proves more than is stated in the enunciation of that theorem.

and
$$\bigcap_{i=1}^{\infty} T_{i,i} \subset \bigcap_{i \geqslant j} T_{i,i} \subset \bigcap_{i \geqslant j} T_{i,j} = L_j.$$

Thus finally $\bigcap_{i=1}^{\infty} T_{i,i} = K$ and this is the required result.

On the other hand, if K is the intersection of a decreasing sequence of open connected sets $\{L_j\}$, and G is any open set that contains K and is such that every component of G contains a point of K, then

$$G = \bigcap_{j=1}^{\infty} (L_j \cup G),$$

and since the sequence $L_j \cup G$ is a decreasing sequence of open connected sets then, by Theorem 1.2, G is of void ultimate nub.

In what follows we omit the word ultimate and refer simply to sets of void nub.

THEOREM 1.4. *If K_1 and K_2 are two G_δ sets of void nub, then so are* (i) $K_1 \cup K_2$ *and* (ii) $K_1 \cap K_2$.

(i) We have $K_1 = \bigcap_{i=1}^{\infty} L_i^{(1)}$, $K_2 = \bigcap_{i=1}^{\infty} L_i^{(2)}$ where $L_i^{(1)}$, $L_i^{(2)}$ are decreasing sequences of open connected sets. Select a point $p_1 \in K_1$ and a point $p_2 \in K_2$ and let S be the segment $p_1 p_2$. Denote by J_i the open connected set of points whose distance from S is less than $1/i$, $i = 1, 2, \ldots$ and which do not lie on S. Write

$$H_i = J_i \cup L_i^{(1)} \cup L_i^{(2)}.$$

Clearly the sequence $\{H_i\}$ is a decreasing sequence of open connected sets and $\bigcap_{i=1}^{\infty} H_i \supset K_1 \cup K_2$. To show that $K_1 \cup K_2 \supset \bigcap_{i=1}^{\infty} H_i$ we have only to observe that for any point p there is an integer $i_0 = i_0(p)$ such that $p \notin J_i$ for $i \geqslant i_0(p)$. Thus $K_1 \cup K_2 = \bigcap_{i=1}^{\infty} H_i$ is of void nub.

(ii) With the same notation as in (i) $K_1 \cap K_2 = \bigcap_{i=1}^{\infty} (L_i^{(1)} \cap L_i^{(2)})$. Let G be open, each component containing a point of its subset $K_1 \cap K_2$. Then $G = \bigcap_{i=1}^{\infty} (L_i^{(1)} \cup G) \cap \bigcap_{i=1}^{\infty} (L_i^{(2)} \cup G)$; thus G is the intersection of a sequence of open connected sets, but this sequence need not be decreasing. By the necessary part of Theorem 1.2 this is sufficient to ensure that the nub of G is void. Since this is true for every open set that contains $K_1 \cap K_2$, we conclude that $K_1 \cap K_2$ is of void nub.

Remarks. 1. Theorem 1.4 cannot be extended to cover enumerable sums or enumerable intersections.

2. Since the properties of openness, connectedness, and inclusion are preserved under interior mappings, the same is true of the property that a set K be a G_δ set of void nub. This is also true of mappings generated by meromorphic functions if the sets are considered to lie on the Riemann sphere instead of on the plane.

3. The analogue of open sets with void nub amongst subsets of a line are open sets whose frontiers consist of enumerable sets of points and are thus scattered (clair-semé, separierte) sets.

§4. A property of meromorphic functions

In this paragraph we establish a curious property of the class of meromorphic functions. The method used is similar to that used in §2 to construct an example of an open set with a non-void ultimate nub.

THEOREM 1.5. *There exists an F_σ set K of enumerably infinite linear measure such that if $\mathcal{R}(f)$ is dense in any open set G, then $\mathcal{R}(f)$ meets K. K is a fixed set, the same for all meromorphic functions f and all open sets G.*

Let L denote the union of all the circles whose centres are points with two rational coordinates and whose radius is a rational number. Let C be a circle of L; we shall construct a closed set $T(C)$ as follows. Amongst the points which are centres of circles of L and which lie interior to C, select a sequence $a_1, a_2, a_3, \ldots$ such that the closure of the union of this sequence regarded as a set of points, is the sequence itself together with C. Denote by C_j a circle† of L with centre a_j and radius r_j such that every two circles C_j are exterior to one another and interior to C and $\Sigma r_j < 1$.

Repeat the process with each C_j in place of C to obtain circles $C_{j,k}$ contained in C_j, mutually exterior and of radius $r_{j,k}$ where $\sum_k r_{j,k} < 2^{-j-1}$. Moreover, $\overline{\bigcup_k C_{j,k}} = C_j \cup \bigcup_k C_{j,k}$. The process is continued indefinitely.

Let $D_{j_1,\ldots,jr}$ be the closed disk bounded by $C_{j_1,\ldots,jr}$. Write

$$T(C) = D \cap \overline{\bigcup_j D_j} \cap \overline{\bigcup_{j,k} D_{j,k}} \cap \ldots .$$

$T(C)$ is closed and of enumerably infinite linear measure. Define K to be the union of the sets $T(C)$ for all C of L. K is an F_σ set of enumerably infinite linear measure. If $\mathcal{R}(f)$ is dense in the open

† A circle here means the frontier of a disc, i.e. the set of points distant r_j from a_j is the circle C_j.

set G, let C be any circle of L contained in G. As in the example constructed in §2 $\mathscr{R}(f)$ intersects $T(C)$ and thus intersects K.

§5. Remarks

The question solved here was first raised by W. Gross in 1918 [3] (see also Collingwood and Cartwright [1]), and solved simultaneously and independently by myself and W. Rudin [2] and [4]. Rudin gave an example of an open set which is not the range of a meromorphic function, but did not pursue the matter any further.

There are several problems that are suggested by this result. It is easy to see that the argument can be adapted to R^3 and indeed any Euclidean space. The question then arises of characterizing those spaces (if any) in which every G_δ set is the intersection of a sequence of connected open sets.

Again one might expect these sets to play some part in complex variable theory. One frequently requires a set to have some sort of connectedness and it may be that sets of the above type could be used.

Finally we can consider the Borel classification. Let G be any open set and H any open connected set. There are two sequences of classes of sets.

$$G, G_\delta, G_{\delta\sigma}, G_{\delta\sigma\delta}, \ldots \qquad H, H_\delta, H_{\delta\sigma}, H_{\delta\sigma\delta}, \ldots \ .$$

Any G is an H_σ and therefore is also a $H_{\delta\sigma}$ and there are G sets which are not H_δ. Similarly by considering the complement of the set K in Theorem 1.5 we see that there are G_δ sets that are not $H_{\delta\sigma}$. But of course every G_δ is an $H_{\delta\sigma\delta}$. The question then arises as to whether every $G_{\delta\sigma}$ is an $H_{\delta\sigma\delta}$ or not, and so on.

References

1. E. F. COLLINGWOOD and M. L. CARTWRIGHT; "Boundary theorems for a function meromorphic in the unit circle" *Acta Math.* **87** (1952) 83–146.
2. H. G. EGGLESTON; "The range set of a function meromorphic in the unit circle" *Proc. Lond. Math. Soc.* **5** (1955) 500–11.
3. W. GRÖSS; "Über die Singularitaten analytischen Funktionen" *Monatshefte für Math v. Phys.* **29** (1918) 1–47.
4. W. RUDIN; "On a problem of Collingwood and Cartwright" *J. London Math. Soc.* **30** (1955) 231–8.

2ND PROBLEM: APPROXIMATIONS TO HOMEOMORPHISMS OF R^2 ONTO ITSELF

Introduction

The second problem was first suggested by S. Ulam [4]†. It is as follows.

† The references are on p. 34.

In a R^2 let (x,y) denote the Cartesian coordinates of a point p, and let Θ denote the set of all homeomorphisms of R^2 onto itself which are of the form

$$(x, y) \to (x', y')$$

where

$$x' = x, \quad y' = f(x, y) \quad \text{or} \quad x' = f(x, y), \quad y' = y.$$

It is supposed that either the first alternative holds for every point (x,y) of R^2 or the second alternative holds for every point of R^2. Denote by Ξ the group formed by all finite superpositions of any of the transformations of Θ. S. Ulam raised the question as to whether it is possible to approximate to any arbitrary homeomorphism of the plane onto itself by members of Ξ.

The solution of the problem depends upon the meaning to be assigned to the word "approximate." In §1 it is shown that if the approximation is to be uniform then the answer is in the negative, that is to say, if for any two homeomorphisms $\mathcal{H}_1$, $\mathcal{H}_2$ of the plane R^2 we write

$$\delta(\mathcal{H}_1, \mathcal{H}_2) = \sup_{p \in R^2} \rho(\mathcal{H}_1(p), \mathcal{H}_2(p)),$$

where ρ denotes the Euclidean distance, then a homeomorphism $\mathcal{G}$ can be constructed such that for any member $\mathcal{H}$ of Ξ, $\delta(\mathcal{H}, \mathcal{G}) > 1$.

The example that is constructed here, depends essentially upon the fact that the plane is not compact. If we restrict ourselves to compact subsets the situation is different. In §§2 and 3 we prove that if S is a closed square with its sides parallel to the coordinate axes and if Θ' is the subclass of the members of Θ which leave each frontier point of S fixed and if Ξ' is the group generated by finite superpositions of members of Θ'; then given any plane homeomorphism $\mathcal{G}$ of S onto itself that leaves the frontier points of S fixed, there exists a sequence of homeomorphisms $\mathcal{H}_n$ belonging to Ξ' such that

$$\delta_1(\mathcal{H}_n, \mathcal{G}) = \sup_{p \in S} \rho(\mathcal{H}_n(p), \mathcal{G}(p)) \to 0 \quad \text{as} \quad n \to \infty.$$

The result proved in §3 is used in §4 to show that if we interpret $\mathcal{H}_n \to \mathcal{G}$ as $n \to \infty$ to mean that $\mathcal{H}_n(p) \to \mathcal{G}(p)$ for every point p of R^2 then to any given homeomorphism $\mathcal{G}$ corresponds a sequence of homeomorphisms $\mathcal{H}_n$, belonging to Ξ such that $\mathcal{H}_n \to \mathcal{G}$ as $n \to \infty$.

§1. Uniform approximation

Let A denote a simple arc with end-points a_1, a_2 in the plane E and let p be any point of the plane which does not belong to A. Let q denote a variable point on A. Consider the change in direction of the line pq, directed from p to q when q describes A from a_1 to a_2. If we fix on a direction through p from which to measure angles say pl, take a particular sense of rotation as positive and assign a particular appropriate value to $\angle a_1 pl$, then there will be two points (or more) of A say q' and q'' such that for all q of A,

$$\angle q'pl \leqslant \angle qpl \leqslant \angle q''pl.$$

Write

$$\angle q''pl - \angle q'pl = a(A,p), \tag{1}$$

$$\beta(A) = \underset{p \in E-A}{\text{up.bd.}}\ a(A,p). \tag{2}$$

$a(A,p)$ is independent of the sense of description of A and of the particular way in which the angles $\angle qpl$ are measured. It is always a positive or zero number. It is also finite (for if it were infinite A would wind round p infinitely often and since p is at a positive distance from A this would mean that A was not locally connected) but $\beta(A)$ may be infinite. However we shall use this function of A only when it is finite. We then have the following lemma:

LEMMA 1. *If $\beta(A)$ is finite and $\mathscr{H}$ is a homeomorphism of the class Θ then*

$$\beta(\mathscr{H}(A)) \leqslant 2\pi + \beta(A). \tag{3}$$

Proof: Suppose that $\mathscr{H}$ is $(x, y) \to (x', y')$

where $\qquad\qquad x' = x, \qquad y' = f(x, y).$

If $\mathscr{H}$ is of the alternative form the argument is similar with x and y interchanged. Since when p varies over $E - A$, $\mathscr{H}(p)$ varies over $E - \mathscr{H}(A)$ it is sufficient to show that for any p of $E - A$

$$a(\mathscr{H}(A), \mathscr{H}(p)) \leqslant 2\pi + a(A, p). \tag{4}$$

In proving (4) we assume (without loss of generality since $a(A,p)$ varies continuously with A) that A is a polygonal arc with no segments parallel to the y-axis. Let A' be a minimal subarc of A for which

$$a(\mathscr{H}(A'), \mathscr{H}(p)) = a(\mathscr{H}(A), \mathscr{H}(p)). \tag{5}$$

If A' degenerates to a single point the result is trivially true, otherwise let p be the point (x_1, y_1).

Firstly consider the case when A' does not intersect the line $x = x_1$. Then $\mathscr{H}(A')$ does not intersect the line $x = x_1$. Thus, since this line contains the point $\mathscr{H}(p)$,

$$a(\mathscr{H}(A), \mathscr{H}(p)) = a(\mathscr{H}(A'), \mathscr{H}(p)) \leqslant \pi < 2\pi + a(A, p). \tag{6}$$

Next consider the case when A' does intersect the line $x = x_1$. Let A' have end-points e, f and meet the line $x = x_1$ in points whose order on A' from e to f is $p_1, p_2, \ldots, p_n$ where e may be p_1 and f may be p_n. Since the subarc ep_1 of A' lies entirely (except for the point p_1) on one side of $x = x_1$, so does the subarc $\mathscr{H}(ep_1)$ of $\mathscr{H}(A')$.

Similarly $\mathscr{H}(fp_2)$ lies entirely on one side of $x = x_1$. Thus if the line $\mathscr{H}(p)m$ is in a fixed direction through $\mathscr{H}(p)$ we have,

$$a(\mathscr{H}(A'), \mathscr{H}(p)) \leqslant 2\pi + |\angle \mathscr{H}(p_n)\mathscr{H}(p)m - \angle \mathscr{H}(p_1)\mathscr{H}(p)m|. \quad (7)$$

Further

$$|\angle p_n pl - \angle p_1 pl| = |\angle \mathscr{H}(p_n)\mathscr{H}(p)m - \angle \mathscr{H}(p_1)\mathscr{H}(p)m| \quad (8)$$

and

$$a(A, p) \geqslant a(A', p) \geqslant |\angle p_n pl - \angle p_1 pl|. \quad (9)$$

Thus from (5), (7), (8), (9)

$$a[\mathscr{H}(A), \mathscr{H}(p)] \leqslant 2\pi + a(A, p), \quad (10)$$

and this is the required inequality (4).

We can now prove the main result which we state as a theorem.

THEOREM 2.1. *There are homeomorphisms of the plane onto itself which are not the uniform limit of any sequence of members of* Ξ.

Proof. Let K_n be the arc whose equation in polar coordinates is

$$r = (4 + e^{-\theta} - 5e^{-2n\pi})(1 - e^{-2n\pi})^{-1}, \ 0 \leqslant \theta \leqslant 2n\pi; \ n = 1, 2, \ldots \quad (11)$$

This arc is part of a spiral which starts at $r = 5$, $\theta = 0$ winds round the origin n times with r monotonically decreasing and ends at the point $r = 4$, $\theta = 2n\pi$.

Denote by M_n the arc obtained from K_n by a translation parallel to the x-axis by an amount $10n$. The arcs $M_1, M_2, \ldots, M_n, \ldots$ are disjoint. There is a homeomorphism of the plane onto itself which maps the segment $L_n = \{(x,y); \ 10n - 1 \leqslant x \leqslant 10n, y = 0\}$ onto the arc M_n, $n = 1, 2, \ldots$. Denote this homeomorphism by $\mathscr{G}$ and let $\mathscr{H}$ be a member of Ξ which we may suppose is obtained by the superposition of the members $\mathscr{H}_1, \mathscr{H}_2, \ldots, \mathscr{H}_s$ of Θ.

Then $\beta(L_n) = \pi$ and thus by Lemma 1,

$$\beta(\mathscr{H}(L_n)) \leqslant (2s + 1)\pi, n = 1, 2, \ldots \quad (12)$$

Consider the segment L_{s+1}. Let q be the point with coordinates $x = 10(s + 1)$, $y = 0$. Write $p = \mathscr{G}^{-1}(q)$. Then

$$a(\mathscr{G}(L_{s+1})\mathscr{G}(p)) = a(M_{s+1}, q) = (2s + 2)\pi. \quad (13)$$

Now if it were the case that $\delta(\mathscr{H}, \mathscr{G}) \leqslant 1$, then $\mathscr{H}(L_{s+1})$ would be an arc whose end-points would be distant at most 1 from the end-points of $\mathscr{G}(L_{s+1}) = M_{s+1}$ and which is such that when p' describes

L_{s+1} the points $\mathscr{H}(p')$ and $\mathscr{G}(p')$ are distant apart at most 1. But $\mathscr{G}(p')$ winds round the point $q\,s+1$ times keeping at a distance of at least 4 from it. Thus $\mathscr{H}(p')$ also winds round $q\,s+1$ times except that its end-points may be such that it fails to complete the $(s+1)$th rotation by an angle less than $2\sin^{-1}(1/4)$†.
Hence

$$a(\mathscr{H}(L_{s+1}),\ \mathscr{G}(p)) \geqslant (2s+2)\pi - 2\sin^{-1}(1/4) > (2s+1)\pi. \quad (14)$$

Since the inequalities (12) and (14) are in contradiction with one another, $\delta(\mathscr{H},\mathscr{G}) > 1$ and the theorem is proved.

§2. Homeomorphisms of certain subsets of a closed square onto themselves

Let S be a closed square with sides parallel to the coordinate axes. We shall consider approximations to homeomorphisms of S onto itself which leave each frontier point of S fixed. Let Θ' be the class of homeomorphisms of the form

$$x' = x, \quad y' = \phi(x, y) \quad \text{or} \quad x' = \phi(x, y), \quad y' = y \quad (15)$$

and which map S onto itself and leave each frontier point of S fixed.

In the present paragraph we consider homeomorphisms which are defined over certain polygonal arcs contained in S and we shall use these results to show that homeomorphisms of a closed square onto itself can be uniformly approximated to by means of members of Ξ', the group generated by Θ'.

We require a number of auxiliary lemmas. The following convention is used. If a segment L is such that, apart from its end-points, it belongs to the interior of a closed Jordan domain T then we shall say that L belongs to the interior of T.

LEMMA 2. *If a simple polygonal arc $aq_0q_1 \ldots q_m b$, where $m \neq 0$, together with the segment ab bounds a simple closed Jordan domain T, then at least one of the segments $aq_1, q_0q_2, \ldots, q_{i-1}q_{i+1}, \ldots, q_{m-1}b$ belongs to the interior of T.*

Proof. We consider the maximal closed star domain whose centre is a and which is contained in T. Denote this domain by T^{st}. Let the two half lines which terminate at a and which contain q_0 and b respectively be denoted by $1(q_0)$ and $1(b)$.

There are two possibilities. Either (a) all the vertices of T^{st} lie on $1(q_0)$ or $1(b)$, or (b) there is a vertex of T^{st} lying neither on $1(q_0)$ nor on $1(b)$. In the first case T^{st} is a triangle that contains q_0b in its interior. Thus $q_0b \in T^\circ$. In the second case let r be a vertex of T^{st} that lies neither on $1(b)$ nor on $1(q_0)$. r may not itself be a vertex of

† The angle $\sin^{-1}(\tfrac{1}{4})$ that is needed here lies between 0 and $\pi/2$.

T but the segment ar contains vertices of T of which that nearest to a is denoted by q_j. Then $aq_j \in T^\circ$.

In case (a) we replace $aq_0q_1 \ldots q_m ba$ by $q_0q_1 \ldots q_m bq_0$ and in the second case we replace $aq_0q_1 \ldots q_m ba$ by $aq_0q_1 \ldots q_{j-1}q_j a$. In the first case q_0b and in the second case aq_j is a cross-cut of T. In either case we obtain a polygonal curve which bounds a domain T_1 with the following properties.

(a) T_1 is contained in T and does not contain both a and b.

(b) The polygonal curve bounding T_1 is formed from a smaller number of segments than that bounding T.

(c) The segments of the curve bounding T_1 are all, except one, segments of the curve bounding T.

(d) The exceptional segment in (c) is contained in T°.

Either T_1 is a triangle or by (b) we can repeat the process a finite number of times until we reach a triangle say T^*. By (c) two sides of T^* belong to the frontier of T and by (d) the third side is contained in T°. That is to say, one of the segments $aq_1, q_1q_2, \ldots, q_{m-1}b$, or aq_m or bq_0 belongs to T°.

If $m = 1$ the proof of the lemma is complete. If $m > 1$ then we wish to exclude aq_m and bq_0 as possibilities. Now if T_1 is obtained from T by the first alternative process then T_1 does not contain a and neither does T^* contain aq_m as a side. Further T_1 is not T^* since T_1 contains at least four vertices, and when the process is repeated the next polygonal line omits one of b and q_0. Thus T^* does not contain bq_0. Next if T_1 is obtained from T by the second alternative, T_1 does not contain b and thus T^* does not contain bq_0. If T_1 does not contain q_m then T^* does not contain aq_m. On the other hand if T_1 does contain q_m then T_1 is not T^* and at the second repetition of the process we omit either a or q_m and hence T^* does not contain aq_m.

Thus in fact the third side of T^* is one of the segments $aq_1, q_1q_2, \ldots, q_{m-1}b$ and the proof of the lemma is complete.

LEMMA 3. *Two polygonal arcs* $ap_0p_1 \ldots p_kb$ *and* $aq_0q_1 \ldots q_mb$, $m \geqslant 0$, *together form the boundary of a simple closed Jordan domain* T. *The arc* $ap_0p_1 \ldots p_kb$ *together with* ab *bounds a convex set* U *and those of the vertices* $q_0, q_1, \ldots, q_m$ *which lie on the same side of* ab *as does* U *lie either on the segment* ab *or interior to* U *(it is assumed that* U *has interior points). Also all the points* p_j, q_i *lie in the strip bounded by the two lines that are perpendicular to* ab *and pass through* a *and* b *respectively. Then either*

(i) *the arc* $aq_0q_1 \ldots q_mb$ *together with the segment* ab *bounds a convex set* V *that is exterior to* T, *or*

(ii) *one of the segments* $aq_1, q_0q_2, \ldots, q_{i-1}q_{i+1}, \ldots, q_{m-1}b$ *is contained in* T°.

Proof. Let B denote the arc $ap_0p_1 \ldots p_kb$ and let K denote the convex cover of the arc $aq_0q_1 \ldots q_mb$. Since all the points q_i lie inside the strip bounded by the two lines through a and b perpendicular to ab both a and b are frontier points of K. Thus $\mathrm{Fr}K$ consists of two arcs that join a to b. (See Fig. 2.) (The set K will have

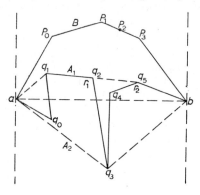

FIG. 2.

interior points because the arc $aq_0q_1 \ldots q_mb$ has at least three vertices where by a vertex is meant a point which is either an end-point or a point that lies on two segments that lie on distinct lines. We take the notation to imply that the segments aq_0, q_0q_1, for example, are not collinear.) Let these two arcs be A_1 and A_2. Now no points of B are interior points of K and, of all the vertices of K (which are some of the points a, b, q_0, q_1, $\ldots$, q_m), only a and b belong to B. Thus K meets B either in the whole segment ab or in just the two points a and b. The first case can arise only when B is precisely the segment ab. In this case U would have no interior points which is contrary to the hypotheses of the lemma. We suppose then that B meets K in the two points a and b.

The two arcs A_1 and B bound a domain say W_1. Similarly we define W_2 to be the domain bounded by A_2 and B. Either every segment of A_1 belongs to W_2^0 or every segment of A_2 belongs to W_1^0. We choose the notation so that the first of these alternatives holds. If the whole of A_1 belongs to the arc $aq_0q_1 \ldots q_mb$ then it coincides with the whole of this arc and the lemma is proved since (i) is true. If however there is a segment of A_1 that does not belong to $aq_0q_1 \ldots q_mb$ then we can find two points of the set a, q_0, q_1, $\ldots$, q_mb, say r_1 and r_2 such that these points belong to A_1 and there are no other points of the arc $aq_0q_1 \ldots q_mb$ that belong to the segment r_1r_2. The points r_1 and r_2 are not necessarily vertices of K but they are vertices of the arc $aq_0q_1 \ldots q_mb$.

The points r_1 and r_2 are not consecutive vertices of $aq_0q_1 \ldots q_m b$ for if they were the whole of the segment r_1r_2 would belong to the arc $aq_0q_1 \ldots q_m b$. If they are separated in this sequence by only one other vertex then the segment r_1r_2 itself is of the form required in (ii). If however r_1 and r_2 are separated by more than one vertex in the order $aq_0q_1 \ldots q_m b$ then the subarc of $aq_0q_1 \ldots q_m b$ whose end-points are r_1 and r_2, bounds with the segment r_1r_2 a domain contained in T. We can apply Lemma 2 to it and deduce the existence of a segment as required in (ii).

The lemma is proved.

We now prove a result that will be needed in the next paragraph. Suppose that the square S is cut by a number of segments parallel to the x-axis. Let these segments which join the two sides of S that are parallel to the y-axis, be denoted by $A_1, A_2, \ldots, A_n$. We also suppose that the segments A_1 and A_n are sides of S and that the notation is such that the ordinate of the line containing A_i is greater than or less than that containing A_j according as i is less than or greater than j. Denote the totality of these segments by K.

THEOREM 2.2. *If $\mathscr{G}^{-1}$ is a homeomorphism defined over $K \cup \mathrm{Fr}S$ which leaves every point of the frontier of S fixed and maps each of the segments A_i onto a polygonal line contained in S, then there is a homeomorphism $\mathscr{H}$ of the group Ξ' such that for any point p of K $\mathscr{H}(\mathscr{G}^{-1}(p)) = p$.*

Write a_i, b_i for the two end points of A_i and use the symbols A_i' for $\mathscr{G}^{-1}(A_i)$. By the given conditions $\mathscr{G}^{-1}(a_i) = a_i$, and $\mathscr{G}^{-1}(b_i) = b_i$.

We need the following lemmas.

LEMMA 4. *If A_2' is a polygonal line with t segments, $t > 1$, then either* (a) *it bounds with the segment a_2b_2 a convex set that is exterior to the set bounded by A_1, A_2, segment a_1a_2 and segment b_1b_2, or* (b) *there is a member $\mathscr{H}$ of Ξ' such that $\mathscr{H}(A_2')$ is a polygonal line of at most $t - 1$ segments and every point of each $A_j', j \neq 2$ is a fixed point under $\mathscr{H}$.*

We apply Lemma 3 with a_2 for a and b_2 for b, with $a_2a_1b_1b_2$ for $ap_0p_1 \ldots p_kb$ and A_2' for $aq_0q_1 \ldots q_mb$. By that lemma if (a) is not true then there are two consecutive segments of A_2' say cd and de such that the segment ce is contained in T°, where T is the domain bounded by $A_1', A_2', a_1a_2, b_1b_2$, i.e. ce is, apart from its end-points, contained in the interior of T. The segment ce does not meet any A_j' with $j \neq 2$. We next select two points d' and d'' on opposite sides of the line ce such that the closed quadrilateral $cd'ed''$ is convex, contains d as an interior point, does not meet $A_j', j \neq 2$, and meets A_2' only in the segments cd, de†. (See Fig. 3.) This last

---

† The quadrilateral $cd'ed''$ is contained in S° unless $c = a_2$ or $c = b_2$ in which case it meets $\mathrm{Fr}S$ at these points only.

requirement can be satisfied because only the end-points of the segment ce belong to A_2' and thus the triangle cde meets A_2' only in the segments cd and de. Join d to a point of ce other than c or e, by a polygonal line lying in the interior of $cd'ed''$, such that each segment of this line is parallel either to the x-axis or to the y-axis. Let this polygonal line be $dr_1r_2 \ldots r_s$, where r_s is the point of ce.

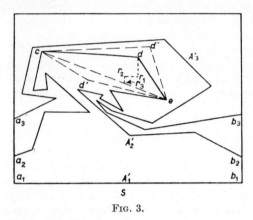

FIG. 3.

We shall now show that there is a member of Ξ' say $\mathscr{I}_1$ such that

$$\mathscr{I}_1(d) = r_1; \quad \mathscr{I}_1(cd) = cr_1; \quad \mathscr{I}_1(de) = r_1e, \tag{16}$$

and such that every point on the frontier of or exterior to the quadrilateral $cd'ed''$ is fixed under $\mathscr{I}_1$.

Suppose for the moment that such a homeomorphism exists, then the lemma follows. For just as we have defined $\mathscr{I}_1$ so we can define $\mathscr{I}_i$ such that

$$\mathscr{I}_i(r_{i-1}) = r_i, \quad \mathscr{I}_i(cr_{i-1}) = cr_i, \quad \mathscr{I}_i(r_{i-1}e) = r_ie, \quad i = 2, \ldots, s$$

and every point on the frontier of or exterior to the quadrilateral $cd'ed''$ is fixed under $\mathscr{I}_i$. Then the homeomorphism $\mathscr{I}_s\mathscr{I}_{s-1} \ldots \mathscr{I}_1$ maps cd onto cr_s and de onto r_se. Since all the other points of A_2' are fixed it reduces the number of segments of A_2' by at least one. Also every point of every $A_j', j \neq 2$ is fixed and the lemma established.

Thus we have only to construct the homeomorphism $\mathscr{I}_1$. Suppose that dr_1 is parallel to the y-axis. In the other case we use the same argument with x and y interchanged. On a particular line $x = x'$, $\mathscr{I}_1$ is defined as follows. All points exterior to or on the frontier of $cd'ed''$ are fixed. If the line $x = x'$ meets the pair of segments cd, de in one point say p, then it also meets the pair of segments cr_1, r_1e in one point q. Define $\mathscr{I}_1(p)$ to be q and complete the definition of

$\mathscr{I}_1$ on $x = x'$ by linearity. If the line $x = x'$ meets cd, de in two points say p' and p'' and the ordinate of p' is greater than that of p'', then the line also meets the segments cr_1, r_1e in two points which we may call q' and q'' where the ordinate of q' is greater than that of q''. Define $\mathscr{I}_1(p')$ to be q' and $\mathscr{I}_1(p'')$ to be q'' and complete the definition of $\mathscr{I}_2$ on the line by linearity. If the line $x = x'$ contains the whole of the segment cd or de then it also contains the point r_1. Define $\mathscr{I}_1(d)$ to be r_1 and complete as before by linearity. If the abscissae of the two points d' and d'' are equal to one of or lie between the abscissae of c and e then the definition of $\mathscr{I}_1$ is complete. Otherwise we still have to define it for those lines $x = x'$ that meet the quadrilateral $cd'ed''$ but do not meet the pair of segments cd, de. In this case there is a line $x = x''$ on which $\mathscr{I}_1$ has been defined, and which passes through one or more of the points c, d, e, and which is such that the segment of the line $x = x''$ that is interior to the quadrilateral $cd'ed''$, say tu, forms with either d' or d'', say d'', a triangle that contains that part of the line $x = x'$ that is interior to the quadrilateral $cd'ed''$. Let the part of $x = x'$ that is contained in $cd'ed''$ be the segment vw. To define $\mathscr{I}_1$ on vw, join d'' to a point say z on vw, produce to meet tu in z'. Let $\mathscr{I}_1(z')$, which has been defined to be a point of tu, be the point z_1'. Join z_1' to d'' cutting vw in z_1. Define $\mathscr{I}_1(z)$ to be z_1.

Then $\mathscr{I}_1$ has been completely defined, it is of the form $(x,y) \rightarrow (x',y')$ where $x' = x$, $y' = \phi(x,y)$, and has the properties stated in (16).

The proof of the lemma is complete.

LEMMA 5. *A rectangle T is given with its sides parallel to the coordinate axes. A homeomorphism $\mathscr{K}$ defined over the frontier of T is of the form*

$$(x, y) \rightarrow (x', y) \quad where \quad x' = \phi(x, y). \tag{17}$$

Further, $\mathscr{K}$ leaves fixed the points of the sides of T that are parallel to the y-axis. Then there is a homeomorphism which is of the form (17), maps the whole of T onto itself and coincides with $\mathscr{K}$ on $\mathrm{Fr}\,T$.

Suppose that T is a rectangle $a_1 \leqslant x \leqslant a_2$; $b_1 \leqslant y \leqslant b_2$. Consider the two rectangles

$$T_1 \colon a_1 \leqslant x \leqslant a_2, \quad \tfrac{1}{2}(b_1+b_2) \leqslant y \leqslant b_2,$$
$$T_2 \colon a_1 \leqslant x \leqslant a_2, \quad b_1 \leqslant y \leqslant \tfrac{1}{2}(b_1+b_2).$$

In T_1 define the homeomorphism $\mathscr{K}$ by $(x, y) \rightarrow (x', y)$ where

$$x' = x + (\phi(x, b_2) - x)(y - \tfrac{1}{2}(b_1 + b_2))/\tfrac{1}{2}(b_2 - b_1).$$

In T_2 define $\mathscr{K}$ by $(x, y) \rightarrow (x', y)$ where

$$x' = x + (\phi(x, b_1) - x)(\tfrac{1}{2}(b_1 + b_2) - y)/\tfrac{1}{2}(b_2 - b_1).$$

It may be verified that $\mathscr{H}$ is a homeomorphism with the properties stated in the lemma.

LEMMA 6. *There is a member $\mathscr{H}$ of Ξ' such that $\mathscr{H}(A_j') = A_j$, $j = 1, \dots, n$.*

Consider A_2'. By Lemma 4, either A_2' is an arc convex with respect to $a_2 b_2$ and A_2' lies on the same side of $a_2 b_2$ as A_1', or we can find $\mathscr{I}_1$ of Ξ' which reduces the number of segments of A_2' and leaves every point of every A_j', $j \neq 2$, fixed. By successive repetitions of this argument it follows that we can find a member of Ξ' say $\mathscr{F}_1$ such that either $\mathscr{F}_1(A_2')$ is the straight line segment $a_2 b_2$ or it is convex with respect to $a_2 b_2$ and lies on the same side of $a_2 b_2$ as does A_1'. In either case $\mathscr{F}_1(A_2')$ together with the segments $a_2 a_3$, $a_3 b_3$, $b_3 b_2$, bounds a convex set. We may now apply Lemma 3 to A_3' exactly as we applied it to A_2' in the proof of Lemma 4. We obtain $\mathscr{F}_2$ of Ξ' such that every point of every A_j', $j > 3$, and of A_1 and $\mathscr{F}_1(A_2')$ is fixed, and such that $\mathscr{F}_2(A_3')$ is convex with respect to the segment $a_3 b_3$ and lies on the same side of $a_3 b_3$ as does A_1', or alternatively $\mathscr{F}_2(A_3')$ is a straight line segment. Proceeding in this fashion we eventually arrive at a member $\mathscr{F}$ of Ξ' such that each $\mathscr{F}(A_j')$ is either the segment $a_j b_j$ or bounds with $a_j b_j$ a convex set.

Now every line parallel to the y-axis that meets $\mathscr{F}(A_j')$ at all does so in exactly one point and also meets A_j in exactly one point. Suppose that such a line meets $\mathscr{F}(A_j')$ in x_j and A_j in y_j. Then the points $x_1 x_2 \dots x_n$ occur on this line in the same order as $y_1 y_2 \dots y_n$. We define a homeomorphism on this line by mapping x_j onto y_j and making the mapping linear between x_j and x_{j+1}. Such a mapping is defined for all the points of S. For points outside S we define each point to be its own image. Denote this mapping by $\mathscr{L}$. Then $\mathscr{L}\mathscr{F}$ is a member of Ξ' with the property stated in the enunciation of the lemma.

We can now complete the proof of Theorem 2.2. This theorem is nearly contained in Lemma 6, but although that Lemma provides a homeomorphism that maps A_j' onto A_j we do not know that it coincides with $\mathscr{G}$ for each point p of K. To secure this result we proceed as follows.

The homeomorphism $\mathscr{L}\mathscr{F}\mathscr{G}^{-1}$ maps each segment A_j onto itself and leaves each point of the frontier of S fixed. If Lemma 5 is applied to the rectangle that is bounded by A_j, A_{j+1}, and the two segments $a_j a_{j+1}$, $b_j b_{j+1}$ then there is a homeomorphism of the form (17) say $\mathscr{M}_j$ that maps this rectangle onto itself and coincides with $\mathscr{L}\mathscr{F}\mathscr{G}^{-1}$ on the frontier of this rectangle. Denote by $\mathscr{M}$ the homeomorphism of the whole plane onto itself that coincides with $\mathscr{M}_j$ in the rectangle in which it is defined and leaves every point exterior to S fixed. Then for any point p of K $\mathscr{M}(p)$ is the point $\mathscr{L}\mathscr{F}\mathscr{G}^{-1}(p)$. Thus $p = \mathscr{M}^{-1}\mathscr{L}\mathscr{F}\mathscr{G}^{-1}(p)$, that is to say the homeomorphism $\mathscr{M}^{-1}\mathscr{L}\mathscr{F}$ which is a member of the group Ξ' has the property required in the theorem.

§3. Homeomorphisms of a closed square onto itself

As before let S denote a closed square with sides parallel to the axes. In this paragraph all the homeomorphisms concerned map S onto itself and leave the frontier points of S fixed. This class of homeomorphisms is denoted by Γ. Again we write Θ' for the class of homeomorphisms that belong both to Γ and to Θ, and we write Ξ' for the group generated by finite superpositions of members of Θ'.

THEOREM 2.3. *If $\mathscr{G}$ is a homeomorphism belonging to the class Γ, then, given a positive number ε there exists a homeomorphism $\mathscr{H}$ of Ξ' such that*

$$\delta(\mathscr{H}, \mathscr{G}) = \sup_{p \in S} \rho(\mathscr{H}(p), \mathscr{G}(p)) < \varepsilon.$$

Let l be the side length of S and choose a positive integer n so large that

$$4 \cdot 2^{1/2} l < n\varepsilon.$$

Divide S into n^2 equal squares each of side length l/n and let the vertices of these squares be a_{ij}, $i = 1, 2, \ldots, n + 1, j = 1, 2, \ldots, n + 1$, where the vertices of S itself are a_{11}, $a_{1,n+1}$, $a_{n+1,n+1}$, $a_{n+1,1}$. Denote the segment $a_{i1}a_{i,n+1}$ by A_i and the segment $a_{1j}a_{n+1,j}$ by B_j. Also write $\mathscr{G}^{-1}(A_i) = A_i'$, $\mathscr{G}^{-1}(a_{ij}) = a_{ij}'$, $\mathscr{G}^{-1}(B_j) = B_j'$; and let E_{ij} be the subarcs of A_i' with end points a_{ij}', $a_{i,j+1}'$ and F_{ij} be the subarcs of B_j' with end points a_{ij}', $a_{i+1,j}'$. (See Fig. 4.) Let the axes be such that the x-axis is parallel to each A_i and the y-axis is parallel to each B_j.

Define η to be a positive number, less than the least distance apart of any pair of nonintersecting arcs E_{ij} or F_{ij}.

Let C_{ij} be the closed disc whose centre is a_{ij}' and whose radius is $\eta/3$. No two of the discs C_{ij} intersect; let C denote their point-set union. The arc A_j' contains a subarc that is minimal with respect to the property of joining C_{ji} to $C_{j,i+1}$, and which we denote by L_{ji}, $j = 1, 2, \ldots, n + 1$, $i = 1, 2, \ldots, n$. Similarly there is a minimal subarc of B_i' that joins C_{ji} to $C_{j+1,i}$, say M_{ji}, $j = 1, 2, \ldots, n$, $i = 1, 2, \ldots, n + 1$.

Any two segments of the form A_j or B_i either do not meet or do so in one of the points a_{ji}. Thus any two of the arcs A_j', B_i' either do not meet at all or if they do meet their point of intersection belongs to the set C°. Thus all the arcs of the form L_{ij} and M_{kr} are disjoint from one another. Also of all the circles $\mathrm{Fr}C_{ij}$ the arc L_{pq}

meets only two namely the two circles $\mathrm{Fr}C_{pq}$ and $\mathrm{Fr}C_{p,q+1}$, similarly M_{rs} meets only the two circles $\mathrm{Fr}C_{rs}$ and $\mathrm{Fr}C_{r+1,s}$. For suppose that the arc L_{pq} met a circle other than the two stated above, say it met $\mathrm{Fr}C_{tu}$, then on the one hand L_{pq} is a subset of E_{pq} and is thus at a distance of at least η from any of the arcs E_{ij} or F_{ij}

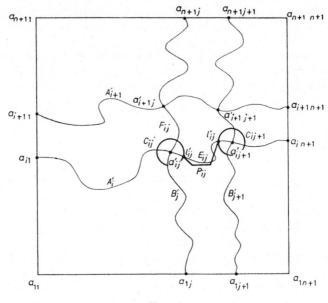

·FIG. 4.

which do not actually meet E_{pq} and on the other hand a'^{t}_{u} lies on two arcs of the form E_{ij} and on two arcs of the form F_{ij}.† It follows that a'_{tu} lies on an arc of one of these two types that does not meet E_{pq}. Thus the point a'_{tu} is distant at least η from L_{pq} and L_{pq} does not meet C_{tu}. In fact L_{pq} is distant at least $2\eta/3$ from C_{tu}.

Let η_1 be a positive number less than the distance apart of any two arcs L_{ij} or M_{rs} and let η_0 be the smaller of the two numbers η and η_1. Let P_{ij} be a polygonal line $1 < i, j < n$ joining the end-points of L_{ij} and lying both inside S and within a distance of $\eta_0/3$ of L_{ij} and outside C°_{ij} and $C^{\circ}_{i,j+1}$, $i = 2, 3, \ldots n, j = 1, 2, \ldots, n$. Let the point of intersection of the arc L_{ij} with the circle C_{ij} be l'_{ij} and the point of intersection of L_{ij} with $C_{i,j+1}$ be l''_{ij}. Let P'_{ij} be the polygonal line consisting of segment $a'_{ij}l'_{ij}$, polygonal line P_{ij}, and segment $l''_{ij}a'_{i,j+1}$. We also suppose that P'_{1j} is the

† Provided $1 < t, u < n + 1$. The other cases are simpler and omitted.

segment $a_{1j}a_{1,j+1}$ and that $P'_{n+1,j}$ is the segment $a_{n+1,j}\ a_{n+1,j+1}$. Finally let P_i denote the union $\bigcup\limits_{j=1}^{n} P'_{ij}$, $i = 1, 2, \ldots, n + 1$.

Next define polygonal lines Q_j in the same way as P_j has been defined but using the minimal arcs M_{rs} in place of the minimal arcs L_{ij}.†

The polygonal lines P_i, Q_j approximate to A'_i and B'_j respectively and have the following properties:

(i) P_i intersects Q_j in exactly one point namely a'_{ij}.

(ii) Of the points a'_{ij}; P_i contains in order the points $a'_{i1}, a'_{i2}, \ldots,$ $a'_{i,n+1}$.

(iii) Of the points a'_{ij}; Q_j contains in order the points $a'_{1j},$ $a'_{2j}, \ldots, a'_{n+1,j}$.

(iv) The four sides of the square S are P_1, P_{n+1}, Q_1, Q_{n+1}.

Next let $\mathscr{K}$ be any homeomorphism of the class Γ such that

$$\mathscr{K}(P_j) = A_j, \qquad \mathscr{K}(Q_j) = B_j.$$

It is clear that such a homeomorphism exists. If z is a point of S then it belongs to a domain bounded by four arcs of which two are of the form E_{ij} and two are of the form F_{rs}. z may belong to more than one such domain. (We take these domains to be closed.) Suppose that z belongs to the domain bounded by E_{ij}, $F_{i,j+1}$, $E_{i+1,j}$, F_{ij}. If $2 \leqslant i, j \leqslant n - 1$, then z also belongs to the domain bounded by the polygonal lines $P'_{i-1,j-1}$, $P'_{i-1,j}$, $P'_{i-1,j+1}$, $Q'_{i-1,j+1}$, $Q'_{i,j+1}$, $Q'_{i+1,j+1}$, $P'_{i+1,j+1}$, $P'_{i+1,j}$, $P'_{i+1,j-1}$, $Q'_{i+1,j-1}$, $Q'_{i,j-1}$, $Q'_{i-1,j-1}$. A similar statement is true when one or both of i or j is one of 1 or n. Thus we have

$$\rho(\mathscr{K}(z), \mathscr{G}(z)) \leqslant 2 \cdot 2^{1/2}(l/n) < \tfrac{1}{2}\varepsilon. \tag{18}$$

Hence it is sufficient to show that there is a member $\mathscr{H}$ of Ξ' such that for every point z of S

$$\rho((\mathscr{K}(z), \mathscr{H}(z)) \leqslant \tfrac{1}{2}\varepsilon. \tag{19}$$

By Theorem 2.2 there is a member $\mathscr{I}$ of Ξ' such that for any point p of any of the polygonal lines P_j, $j = 1, 2, \ldots, n + 1$, $\mathscr{I}(p) = \mathscr{K}(p)$. Consider the homeomorphism $\mathscr{K}\mathscr{I}^{-1}$. This mapping leaves fixed each point of the frontier of S and of each of the segments A_j. Denote by T_j that rectangle which has A_j and A_{j+1} as two opposite sides. T_j is contained in S and is mapped onto itself by $\mathscr{K}\mathscr{I}^{-1}$. Thus for any point p of S the ordinate of $\mathscr{K}(p)$ differs from that of $\mathscr{I}(p)$ by at most the width of one of the rectangles T_j, i.e. by at most l/n.

† Q_{rs}, Q'_{rs} are defined first with respect to M_{rs}.

Now the homeomorphism $\mathscr{K}\mathscr{I}^{-1}$ not only maps T_j onto itself but also leaves each point of the frontier of T_j fixed, and (even though T_j is a rectangle and not a square) all the preceding argument is valid with T in place of S. Thus by an argument similar to that used in Theorem 2 with x and y interchanged we can show that there is a homeomorphism $\mathscr{F}_j$ which belongs to Ξ, maps each point of the frontier of T_j onto itself and is such that for any point p of T_j the abscissae of $\mathscr{F}_j(p)$ and $\mathscr{K}\mathscr{I}^{-1}(p)$ differ by at most l/n.

Define $\mathscr{F}$ to be the homeomorphism which coincides with $\mathscr{F}_j$ in $T_j, j = 1, 2, \ldots, n+1$, and leaves every point of E exterior to S fixed. Then $\mathscr{F}$ belongs to Ξ' and for any point p of S we have:

(i) The ordinates of $\mathscr{F}(p)$ and $\mathscr{K}\mathscr{I}^{-1}(p)$ differ by at most l/n because these points both belong to the same rectangle T.

(ii) The abscissae of $\mathscr{F}(p)$ and $\mathscr{K}\mathscr{I}^{-1}(p)$ differ by at most l/n. Hence

$$\rho((\mathscr{F}(p), \mathscr{K}\mathscr{I}^{-1}(p)) \leqslant 2^{1/2}(l/n) < \tfrac{1}{2}\varepsilon.$$

Now for any point q of S there is a point p such that $p = \mathscr{I}(q)$, and thus for any point q of S

$$\rho(\mathscr{F}\mathscr{I}(q), \mathscr{K}(q)) = \rho(\mathscr{F}(p), \mathscr{K}\mathscr{I}^{-1}(p)) < \tfrac{1}{2}\varepsilon.$$

and this is the inequality (19) as required with $\mathscr{F}\mathscr{I}$ as the homeomorphism $\mathscr{H}$.

Theorem 2.3 is proved.

§4. Non-uniform approximations

In this paragraph we use Theorem 3 to establish the result stated in the introduction.

THEOREM 2.4. *If $\mathscr{G}$ is any given homeomorphism of the plane onto itself, then there exists a sequence of members of Ξ say $\mathscr{H}_n$ such that for every point q of the plane $\mathscr{H}_n(q)$ tends to $\mathscr{G}(q)$ as n tends to infinity.*

Let $C = \overline{C(p,R)}$ denote the set of points of the plane whose distance from the fixed point p is not more than R, and let $\mathscr{G}(C)$ be D. It is sufficient to show that given two positive numbers R and ε, there is a member of Ξ say $\mathscr{H}$, such that the distance apart of the points $\mathscr{H}(z)$ and $\mathscr{G}(z)$ for all points z of $C(p,R)$ is less than ε.

Let S be a square so large that it contains both C and D in its interior. We show first that there is a homeomorphism $\mathscr{J}$ of R^2 onto itself that coincides with $\mathscr{G}$ on C and leaves each point of the frontier of S fixed. Let S_1 be the set $S^\circ - C$ and let S_2 be the set $S^\circ - D$. Both S_1 and S_2 are open, connected and doubly connected sets. Thus there are conformal mappings say $\mathscr{M}_1$ and $\mathscr{M}_2$ such that $\mathscr{M}_1(S_1)$ is an annulus A_1 and $\mathscr{M}_2(S_2)$ is an annulus A_2. Since $\mathrm{Fr}S$, $\mathrm{Fr}C$, and $\mathrm{Fr}D$ are all Jordan curves we can extend $\mathscr{M}_1$ and $\mathscr{M}_2$ to be homeomorphic over the closures of S_1 and S_2. We use the same notation $\mathcal{M}_1$ and $\mathcal{M}_2$ for these two homeomorphisms of the closed sets. Let $\mathscr{C}$ be a homeomorphism of the closure of A_2 onto the closure of A_1 such that for any point p of FrS $\mathscr{C}\mathcal{M}_2(p) = \mathcal{M}_1(p)$. Let the circles bounding A_1 be K and L and suppose that L is the image under $\mathcal{M}_1$ of FrS.

We next define a homeomorphism of K onto itself say $\mathscr{K}$, as follows. For q belonging to K write

$$\mathscr{K}(q) = \mathscr{C}\mathcal{M}_2\mathscr{G}\mathcal{M}_1^{-1}(q).$$

Now we can extend $\mathscr{K}$ so that we obtain a homeomorphism of the closure of A_1 onto itself say $\mathscr{I}$ with the properties,
if $p \in K$ $\mathscr{I}(p) = \mathscr{K}(p)$, if $p \in L$ $\mathscr{I}(p) = p$.

Now define $\mathscr{J}$ as follows. For $p \in C$, $\mathscr{J}(p) = \mathscr{G}(p)$; for $p \in$ FrS $\mathscr{J}(p) = p$; for $p \in S^\circ - C$ $\mathscr{J}(p) = \mathcal{M}_2^{-1}\mathscr{C}^{-1}\mathscr{I}\mathcal{M}_1(p)$; for $p \notin S$ $\mathscr{J}(p) = p$. Then $\mathscr{J}$ is a homeomorphism of the required form.

By Section 3 we can find a member $\mathscr{H}$ of Ξ such that for every point z of S, $\mathscr{H}$ and $\mathscr{J}$ differ by at most ε. The homeomorphism $\mathscr{H}$ has the required property and the Theorem 2.4 is proved.

§5. Remarks

In this problem we make use of convexity. The idea behind the results is to smooth out the windings which a polygonal arc may have until it becomes convex, and the proof of Theorem 2.3 consists of two parts; firstly we have to show that the homeomorphisms at our disposal will in fact perform this smoothing operation and secondly, that we can approximate to a given homeomorphism by one in which certain segments are mapped into polygonal arcs.

There is a similar problem in n-dimensional Euclidean space. The corresponding result in R^3 can be obtained from a theorem of E. E. Moise [3] (see also W. Graeub [2]). In R^3 of course there are a number of problems according as to whether the homeomorphisms which generate the group concerned leave all lines parallel to an axis fixed or all planes perpendicular to an axis fixed. The first of these where there are three types of homeomorphism is analogous to the situation in R^2. In this case also approximations uniformly over the whole of R^3 is impossible.

There is also of course the general problem: given two connected topological spaces X_1 and X_2 and their Cartesian product $X_1 \times X_2$ under what conditions can a homeomorphism of $X_1 \times X_2$ onto itself be approximated to by members of a group generated by homeomorphisms of $X_1 \times X_2$ onto itself which are of the form

$$(x_1, x_2) \rightarrow (x_1, f(x_1, x_2))$$

or
$$(x_1,x_2) \rightarrow (f(x_1,x_2),x_2).$$
for all $x_1 \in X_1$, $x_2 \in X_2$?

References

1. H. G. EGGLESTON; "A property of plane homeomorphisms." *Fundamenta Math.* **42** (1955) 61–74.
2. W. GRAEUB; "Die semilinearen Abbildungen." *Sitz. der Heidelberger Akad. Wiss.* (1950).
3. E. E. MOISE; "Affine structures in 3-manifolds. IV Piecewise Linear Approximations of Homeomorphisms." *Annals of Math.* **55** (1952) 215–222.
4. S. ULAM; "Problème 60." *Fundamenta Math.* **24** (1935) 324.

3RD PROBLEM.   ON THE PROJECTION OF A PLANE SET OF FINITE LINEAR MEASURE

Introduction

In this problem we need convexity much more thoroughly than we did in the 2nd Problem. Apart from a number of subsidiary arguments which depend upon convexity the problem itself has an intimate connection with the properties of convex sets.

For any set X we denote by $\Lambda(X)$ the linear measure of X and by $\Lambda(X_\theta)$ the linear measure of the projection of X onto a line perpendicular to the direction θ. Write $\mu(X)$ for the lower bound of $\Lambda(X_\theta)$ taken over all θ. We shall consider three classes of planar sets, namely, measurable sets, connected sets and arcs, and for each class we shall find the upper bound of the ratio $\mu(X)/\Lambda(X)$.

For the class of measurable sets the result is connected with the properties of regular and irregular sets and is a trivial consequence of properties of these sets established by Besicovitch. For the class of connected sets and for the class of arcs, $\mu(X)$ is the minimal width of the convex cover of X, and the problem can be regarded as establishing a relationship between a set and its convex cover. There are of course a large number of such properties, and further results of this type are given in §5.

An interesting feature of this problem is the difficulty of determining completely the class of extremal figures. For the class of measurable sets the upper bound of $\mu(X)/\Lambda(X)$ is never attained, but we give examples to show that the upper bound which we establish is in fact the least upper bound. On the other hand both the upper bounds for the class of connected sets and for the class of arcs are attained; in the first class by a set composed of three equal segments equally inclined to one another and in the second case by an arc composed of four linear segments and two circular arcs (which will be specified more exactly later). To simplify the proofs we shall consider in both cases the subclasses of connected sets or of arcs whose convex covers are polygons with at most n vertices. Since, in fact, one extremal figure for the class of arcs is not of this nature we have no hope, by this means, of specifying all the extremal figures. But even for the case of connected sets when the only known extremal figure is of this kind I have not been able to specify completely all the extremal figures. Some further remarks about this point will be given later. (See §**6**.)

The actual results proved in the following paragraphs are

(i) for any measurable set E with $\Lambda(E) > 0$,

$$\mu(E) < \frac{2}{\pi} \Lambda(E),$$

(ii) for any connected set E

$$\mu(E) \leqslant \tfrac{1}{2} \Lambda(E),$$

(iii) for any simple arc E

$$\mu(E) \leqslant \Lambda(E) / (\sec \alpha + 2 \tan \alpha + \pi - 4\beta - 2\alpha)$$

where α and β are defined by

$$\tfrac{1}{2} + \sin \alpha = 4 \cos^2 \alpha / (1 + 4 \cos^2 \alpha)$$

and

$$\tan \beta = \tfrac{1}{2} \sec \alpha.$$

The results proved in §**5** are stated in that paragraph.

§1. E any measurable plane set of finite positive linear measure.

We can write $E = E_1 \cup E_2$ where E_1 is a regular and E_2 an irregular set (see [1] p. 304).† Further $E_1 = E_1' \cup E_1''$ where $\Lambda(E_1'') = 0$ and E_1' is a measurable subset of the union of an enumerable infinity of rectifiable arcs (see [1] pp. 324 and 304). The only other property that we require is that the projection of an irregular set is of zero measure in almost all directions (see [2] p. 357). Since we do not require many other properties of regular and irregular sets I shall not give their definitions nor the derivation of the properties stated above. They can be found in the papers [1] and [2].

Write $P(X, \theta)$ for the set which is the projection of X in the direction θ. The following lemmas are needed.

LEMMA 1. $\Lambda[P(E_1', \theta)]$ *depends continuously on* θ.

Proof. Let A_i be a sequence of arcs each of finite linear measure such that $\bigcup\limits_{i=1}^{\infty} A_i \supset E_1'$ and let ε_i be a sequence of positive numbers

† References will be found on p. 76.

decreasing to zero. For each integer i there exists a closed subset F_i of E_1' and a positive integer N_i such that

$$\Lambda(F_i) > \Lambda(E_1') - \varepsilon_i \qquad \Lambda(F_i \cap \bigcup_{j=1}^{N_i} A_j) > \Lambda(F_i) - \varepsilon_i.$$

The set $A_j \cap F_i$ is a closed subset of the arc A_j and its complement in A_j is an at most enumerable infinity of open subintervals of A_j say $B_{j,1}, B_{j,2}, \ldots$ These subintervals of A_j are open relative to A_j and there may of course be only a finite number of them. We can choose an integer M_{ij} such that

$$\Lambda(\bigcup_{k \geqslant M_{ij}} B_{jk}) < \frac{1}{N_i} \varepsilon_i.$$

The complement of $\bigcup_{1 \leqslant k < M_{ij}} B_{jk}$ in A_j consists of a finite number of arcs or points, say $A_{j,1}, \ldots, A_{j,h}$ where h depends on both i and j. We omit the points in this set and rename the set of all these arcs for all j from 1 to N_i as $C_1, C_2, \ldots, C_{L_i}$. Write C for $\bigcup_{j=1}^{L_i} C_j$, then if H denotes the set of points omitted in renaming the $A_{j,k}$ as C_e, we have

$$C \cup H \supset F_i \cap \bigcup_{1 \leqslant j \leqslant N_i} A_j, \tag{1}$$

$$C - F_i \subset \bigcup_{1 \leqslant j \leqslant N_i} \bigcup_{k \geqslant M_{ij}} B_{jk}. \tag{2}$$

From (2) it follows that

$$\Lambda(C - F_i) < \varepsilon_i. \tag{3}$$

Hence

$$\Lambda(C - E_1') + \Lambda(E_1' - C) < 3\varepsilon_i$$

Thus

$$\left| \Lambda[P(E_1', \theta)] - \Lambda[P(C, \theta)] \right| < 3\varepsilon_i. \tag{4}$$

But $\Lambda[P(C, \theta)]$ depends continuously on θ, and (4) shows that $\Lambda[P(E_1', \theta)]$ is the uniform limit of a sequence of continuous functions. Thus $\Lambda[P(E_1', \theta)]$ is continuous and the lemma is proved.

LEMMA 2. $\displaystyle\int_0^{2\pi} \Lambda[P(E_1', \theta)] \, d\theta \leqslant 4\Lambda(E_1').$

Proof. As in Lemma 1 there is a sequence of sets $\{C_i\}$ each of which is a union of a finite number of rectifiable arcs and such that $\Lambda[P(C_i, \theta)]$ tends to $\Lambda[P(E_1', \theta]$ uniformly in θ and $\Lambda(C_i)$ tends to $\Lambda(E_1')$. Thus we need only prove Lemma 2 when E_1' is a union of a finite number of rectifiable arcs. Clearly this case will follow if we can establish the inequality of one arc. But we can approximate to an arc A by a polygonal line R such that, given $\varepsilon > 0$ every point of A is within a distance $\frac{1}{2}\varepsilon$ of some point of R and $\Lambda(R) \leqslant \Lambda(A)$.

Then $\Lambda[P(R,\theta)] \geqslant \Lambda[P(A,\theta)] - \varepsilon$ and it is sufficient to prove the inequality for a polygonal line. Finally, this case will follow if the inequality is true for a single segment. But the truth of the inequality in this last case is easily verified. The lemma is proved.

In the next lemma we need to consider the relationship between the set E_1' and the union of an enumerable infinity of rectifiable arcs of which E_1' is a measurable subset. There are of course many such sets of arcs. We select one, A, and call the arcs of which it is the union $A_1, A_2, \dots$. Let p be a point of E_1' lying on arc A_i of A. The densities of A_i and of $E_1' \cap A_i$ at p are defined to be

$$\lim_{r \to 0} \frac{\Lambda(A_i \cap \overline{C(p,r)})}{2r}, \quad \lim_{r \to 0} \frac{\Lambda(E_1' \cap A_i \cap \overline{C(p,r)})}{2r}$$

respectively when these limits exist where $C(p, r)$ is the closed set of points whose distance from p is less than or equal to r. It is known that at almost all† points p of A_i the first density exists and is equal to unity and at almost all points p of $E_1' \cap A_i$ the second density exists and is equal to unity. (See [1] pp. 303–4.) Further, since A_i is a rectifiable arc it is known that at almost all points of it there is a tangent to it. Thus finally at almost all points p of E_1', the densities of A_i and $E_1' \cap A_i$ are unity and the tangent to A_i exists. There is of course a certain ambiguity in this since p may belong to more than one arc A_i. But in this case we simply select one A_i corresponding to each p and consider this arc A_i associated with p throughout what follows. The tangent to p will be denoted by $t(p)$ and any point p of E_1' with the above properties will be called an R-point.

LEMMA 3.   *Either*

(a) *almost all points of E_1' lie on one straight line or*

(b) *there are two R-points of E_1' say p_1, p_2 such that p_2 does not lie on $t(p_1)$ and p_1 does not lie on $t(p_1)$.*

If (a) is false we can select an R-point of E_1', q_1 and a second R-point q_2 that does not lie on $t(q_i)$. If q_1 does not lie on $t(q_2)$ then q_1, q_2 have the properties required. If q_1 lies on $t(q_2)$ we select, if possible, a third R-point q_3 not on $t(q_1)$ nor $t(q_2)$. Now $t(q_3)$cannot contain both q_1 and q_2 since if it did q_3 would lie on q_1q_2 i.e. $t(q_2)$. Thus one of the pairs q_1q_3 or q_2q_3 has the required properties. If we cannot select a point such as q_3 then almost all of E_1' lies on $t(q_1) \cup t(q_2)$ and there are points of E_1' other than q_1 or q_2 on each of these lines. Let q_4 be an R-point of E on $t(q_1)$ distinct from q_1. Since $t(q_4)$ must coincide with $t(q_1)$ we can take the pair q_2, q_4 as the pair p_1, p_2.

The lemma is proved.

† "almost all" means "all but a set of zero linear measure."

We are now in a position to prove the main result.
If $\Lambda(E_2) = \delta > 0$, then for almost all θ

$$\Lambda[P(E_2, \theta)] = 0 \qquad (5)$$

By Lemma 2 we can choose an angle θ such that

$$\Lambda[P(E_1', \theta)] < \frac{2}{\pi}(\Lambda(E_1') + \delta) \qquad (6)$$

and since by Lemma 1 $\Lambda[P(E_1', \theta)]$ is a continuous function of θ we may suppose that both (5) and (6) hold for the same value of θ. Since $\Lambda(E_1'') = 0$ we have $\Lambda[(E_1'', \theta)] = 0$ for all θ. Thus finally

$$\Lambda[P(E, \theta)] < \frac{2}{\pi}\Lambda(E).$$

If $\Lambda(E_2) = 0$, and (a) of Lemma 3 holds for E_1', then almost all points of E lie on one straight line and projecting parallel to this line we see that $\mu(E) = 0$. This implies the required result.

If $\Lambda(E_2) = 0$ and (a) of Lemma 3 is false for E_1' let p_1 and p_2 be two R-points of E_1' for which (b) holds. We now require the property that if p, an R-point of E_1' projects onto the point q of the set $P(E_1', \theta)$ and the direction of projection is not parallel to $t(p)$, then the set $P(E_1', \theta)$ has unit density at q. We suppose A_i is the arc associated with p, $\overline{C(p, \delta)}$ is the closed disc centre p and radius δ (as above), and write $I(q, \delta)$ for the linear closed interval perpendicular to the direction of projection with q as mid-point and of length 2δ. Given a positive number ε we can find a positive number δ_0 such that

$$\Lambda(E_1' \cap A_i \cap \overline{C(p, \delta)}) > (1 - \varepsilon)\,2\delta \qquad (7)$$

$$\Lambda(A_i \cap \overline{C(p, \delta)}) \qquad < (1 + \varepsilon)\,2\delta$$

for all $\delta < \delta_0$. Now write A_i^* for $A_i \cap \overline{C(p, \delta)}$, then

$$\Lambda[P(E_1' \cap A_1^*, \theta) \cap I(q, \delta)] \geqslant \Lambda[P(A_1^*, \theta) \cap I(q, \delta)]$$
$$- \Lambda[P(A_1^* - E_1', \theta) \cap I(q, \delta)] \qquad (8)$$

and

$$\Lambda[P(A_i^* - E_1', \theta) \cap I(q, \delta)] \leqslant \Lambda[A_i^* - E_1') \cap \overline{C(p, \delta)}] < 4\varepsilon\delta \qquad (9)$$

if $\delta < \delta_0$. But if δ is sufficiently small, say $\delta < \delta_1$, then

$$P(A_i^*, \theta) \supset I(q, \delta).$$

Thus from (8) and (9)

$$\Lambda[P(E_1' \cap A_i^*, \theta) \cap I(q, \delta)] \geqslant 2\delta(1 - 2\varepsilon)$$

for $\delta < \min(\delta_0, \delta_1)$. Since obviously

$$\Lambda[P(E_1' \cap A_i^*, \theta) \cap I(q, \delta)] \leqslant 2\delta$$

it follows that q is a point of unit density of $P(E_1', \theta)$.

Now suppose that the direction of the line joining the two R-points $p_1 p_2$ of E_1' is θ_0. We divide E_1' into two sets, E_1^* formed from those points of E_1' whose distance from p_1 is less than one half the distance of p_1 from p_2 and E_1^{**} defined by $E_1^{**} = E_1' - E_1^*$. Then since $P(E_1^*, \theta_0)$ and $P(E_1^{**}, \theta_0)$ have a common density point,

$$\Lambda[P(E_1', \theta_0)] < \Lambda[P(E_1^*, \theta_0)] + \Lambda[P(E_1^{**}, \theta_0)].$$

By the continuity established in Lemma 1 and by Lemma 2 applied to E_1^* and E_1^{**} it follows that

$$\int_0^{2\pi} \Lambda[P(E_1', \theta)] \, d\theta < 4\Lambda(E_1^*) + 4\Lambda(E_1^{**}) = 4\Lambda(E_1')$$

Since we have $\Lambda(E) = \Lambda(E_1')$ we conclude that for some θ

$$\Lambda[P(E, \theta)] < \frac{2}{\pi} \Lambda(E).$$

Thus in all cases we have

$$\mu(E) < \frac{2}{\pi} \Lambda(E)$$

Example. We next construct an example to show that this result is the best possible.

Let ε be a given positive number and n a large positive integer, the actual lower bound of which will be specified later. Let M_1, M_2, ..., M_{4n} be $4n$ points with $M_i M_j$ different directions. Let L_i be a segment of length $\delta/4n$ in a direction making an angle $2\pi i/4n$ with a fixed direction, and with mid-point at M_i. Choose δ so small that if we project the segments in any direction at most two of the segments overlap. Denote $\bigcup\limits_{i=1}^{4n} Li$ by E. Then

$$\Lambda[P(E, \theta)] \geqslant \sum_{j=1}^{4n} \frac{\delta}{4n} \left| \cos\left(\frac{2\pi j}{4n} + \theta\right) \right| - \frac{\delta}{4n}, \qquad (10)$$

and since the expression on the right hand side of (10) is periodic in θ with period $\frac{\pi}{2n}$ we may assume that $0 \leqslant \theta \leqslant \pi/2n$. Substitute those values of θ which lie in this range and reduce the right hand side terms to their least values, i.e. for $0 < j < n$ and $2n \leqslant j < 3n$,

$j = 4n$, put $\theta = \pi/2n$; for $n \leqslant j < 2n$ and $3n \leqslant j < 4n$ put $\theta = 0$. Then

$$\Lambda[P(E, \theta)] \geqslant \frac{\delta}{4n} \sum_{j=0}^{4n-1} \left| \cos \frac{\pi j}{2n} \right| - \frac{3\delta}{4n} \tag{11}$$

$$= \delta \left(\int_0^{2\pi} |\cos 2\pi x| \, dx + o(1) \right)$$

as $n \to \infty$. Thus choosing first n sufficiently large, and then points $M_1 \ldots M_{4n}$, and δ we have for all θ

$$\Lambda[P(E, \theta)] > \delta(\frac{2}{\pi} - \varepsilon) \tag{12}$$

Thus

$$\frac{\mu(E)}{\Lambda(E)} \geqslant \frac{2}{\pi} - \varepsilon$$

and this shows that the result obtained is the best possible.

§2. Some preliminary results

In the following two theorems the containing space is R^2.

THEOREM 3.1.   *Let T be a closed connected set of finite linear measure and let $H(T)$ be its convex cover. Then either there is a tree T_1 contained in T such that the convex cover of T_1 coincides with that of T or there is a simple closed convex curve K contained in T such that its convex cover coincides with that of T.*

We use $H(X)$ to denote the convex cover of the set X.

There is a subset K of T which is irreducible with respect to the three properties

(i) $K \subset T$

(ii) $H(K) = H(T)$,

(iii) K is closed and connected.

There certainly exist sets with these three properties since T is one such set. If possible form a sequence of sets K_i such that each K_i has properties (i), (ii), (iii) and K_j is a proper subset of K_i if $j > i$. If it is only possible to define a finite sequence of such sets then the last member of the sequence is irreducible. If the sequence has infinitely many members it can contain at most an enumerable infinity of members† (since the sequence of sets complementary to K_i in T forms a strictly increasing sequence of sets open in T). But then $\bigcap_i K_i = K^*$ has properties (i) and (iii). We shall show that it also has property (ii). If $p \in H(T)$ then $p \in H(K_i)$ and therefore, since K_i is connected, by Bunt's refinement of Carathéodory's theorem (see [5] p. 590) there exist two points k_i, k_i' of K_i such that

† The sequence K_i may of course be transfinite but since the cardinal is less than $\aleph_1$, we can always find an enumerable sequence of ordinals as stated.

p is a point of the segment $k_i k_i'$. We can select a subsequence of ordinals n_i such that for every j of the sequence there exists an i with $n_i > j$ and such that $k_{n_i} \to k$, $k_{n_i} \to k'$. Then since $k_i \in K_j$ if $i > j$ and K_j is closed $k \cup k' \in K_j$ all j. Thus $k \in K^*$ and $k' \in K^*$. Also p is a point of the segment kk'. Hence $p \in H(K^*)$ and this means that $H(T) \subset H(K^*)$: since the reverse inclusion is trivial (ii) is proved. Clearly K^* is irreducible and the statement is proved.

If K^* is a tree we have the desired result. If K^* is not a tree, then there are two points p_1, p_2 of K such that two arcs exist α_1, α_2 both contained in K^* and having in common only their end points p_1 and p_2. K^* is of finite linear measure and therefore both locally connected and arc wise connected. If these two arcs lie in $\mathrm{Fr}(H(T))$ $= \mathrm{Fr}(H(K^*))$ then they comprise the whole of that frontier and form a closed convex curve with the properties stated in the theorem. Otherwise there is a point say p on them which is an interior point of $H(T)$. Let the distance of p from $\mathrm{Fr}H(T)$ be δ.

Now every component of $\overline{K^* - (\alpha_1 \cup \alpha_2)}$ meets $\alpha_1 \cup \alpha_2$ in a single point for if this were not the case we could join two distinct points of $\alpha_1 \cup \alpha_2$ say p and q by an arc that lies in $\overline{K^* - (\alpha_1 \cup \alpha_2)}$. This arc cannot lie in $\alpha_1 \cup \alpha_2$ since K^* is locally connected and thus this arc contains a subarc meeting $\alpha_1 \cup \alpha_2$ only at its end points p_1 and q_1. But this means that in K^* there are three distinct arcs joining p_1 to q_1 and intersecting only in their end points. Then one of these arcs lies in the bounded domain of which the other two form the frontier. Denote this open domain by D. $K^* - D$ has the same convex cover as K^*, is closed connected and is a proper subset of K^*. This is impossible by the irreducibility property of K^*.

Let β be a subset of $\alpha_1 \cup \alpha_2$ contained in $\overline{C(p, \tfrac{1}{2}\delta)}$. Since K^* is irreducible every component of $K^* - (\alpha_1 \cup \alpha_2)$ meets $\mathrm{Fr}H(K^*)$. If it also meets β such a component must have linear measure of at least $\tfrac{1}{2}\delta$. Since K^* is of finite linear measure there are at most a finite number of such components and hence a subarc β_1 of β which is disjoint from $\overline{K^* - (\alpha_1 \cup \alpha_2)}$. But then $\overline{K^* - \beta_1}$ is a closed connected set with the same convex cover as K^* (since β_1 is interior to this convex cover) and is a proper subset of K^*. This is impossible since K^* is irreducible.

Thus arcs such as α_1, α_2 do not exist and Theorem 3.1 is proved.

DEFINITION: *A **polygonal tree** is a tree formed from a finite number of linear segments. We always consider such a tree to have a simplicial decomposition into linear segments. So that if two segments meet they do so only in a common end point, and every end point of a segment is either an end point of the tree or an end point of at least one other segment of the tree.*

4

A point which belongs to more than one segment of the tree is called a ***singular point*** of the tree.

THEOREM 3.2. *Let $f(X)$ be an increasing continuous function of the convex set X, i.e. $X_1 \supset X_2$ implies $f(X_1) \geqslant f(X_2)$. Let $\mathscr{I}$ be the class of connected closed sets of finite positive linear measure. Let $\mathscr{P}(n)$ be the subclass of $\mathscr{I}$ of those polygonal trees whose convex covers are polygons with at most n sides. Then*

$$\sup_{T \in \mathscr{I}} \frac{f(H(T))}{\Lambda(T)} = \sup_{n} . \sup_{P \in \mathscr{P}(n)} \frac{f(H(P))}{\Lambda(P)} .$$

By the previous result there is a tree K contained in T such that the convex cover of K coincides with that of T, or a simple closed curve K contained in T for which the convex covers of T and K coincide.

Let $k_1, k_2, \ldots, k_n, \ldots$ be a sequence of points dense in K and consider the class of polygonal trees which contain $k_1, \ldots, k_n$. Amongst these we select one with least length and denote it by K_n. Then, whether K is a tree or a simple closed curve

$$\Lambda(K_n) \leqslant \Lambda(K) \qquad H(K) \supset \bigcup H(K_n) \supset (H(K))^{\circ}.$$

Thus given $\varepsilon > 0$ there exists an integer n such that

$$\frac{f(H(K_n))}{\Lambda(K_n)} \geqslant \frac{f(H(K))}{\Lambda(K)} - \varepsilon.$$

But $K_n \in \mathscr{P}(m)$ for some m, thus

$$\sup_{n} \sup_{P \in \mathscr{P}(n)} \frac{f(H(P))}{\Lambda(P)} \geqslant \sup_{T \in \mathscr{I}} \frac{f(H(T))}{\Lambda(T)}.$$

The inequality in the reverse direction is trivial. Thus the theorem is proved.

There is a similar result for the class of arcs.

THEOREM 3.3. *Let $f(X)$ be an increasing continuous function of the convex set X. Let $\mathscr{A}$ be the class of arcs of finite positive linear measure and $\mathsf{A}(n)$ be the subclass of those members of $\mathscr{A}$ formed from at most n segments. Then*

$$\sup_{A \in \mathscr{A}} \frac{f(H(A))}{\Lambda(A)} = \sup_{n} \sup_{A^* \in \mathsf{A}(n)} \frac{f(H(A^*))}{\Lambda(A^*)} .$$

The proof is omitted.

§3. E a closed connected plane set of finite positive linear measure

Denote by $\mathscr{L}(n)$ the class of closed connected plane sets which are of finite positive linear measure and such that their convex covers are polygons with at most n vertices.

Since the subclass of $\mathscr{L}(n)$ contained in a bounded part of the plane forms a compact space under the closed-set metric (see [1] p. 316) it follows that there is a member T of $\mathscr{L}(n)$ such that

$$\frac{\mu(T)}{\Lambda(T)} = \sup_{E \in \mathscr{L}(n)} \frac{\mu(E)}{\Lambda(E)}. \tag{13}$$

We shall show that $\dfrac{\mu(T)}{\Lambda(T)} = \tfrac{1}{2}$. This will imply that for any connected set E $\mu(E) \leqslant \tfrac{1}{2}\Lambda(E)$ for the general case when the convex cover of E is not a polygon can be dealt with by Theorem 3.2 (§2).

Our argument will be such that we can specify the extremal figures T exactly, in so far as T is a member of some $\mathscr{L}(n)$ but not when T is not a member of some $\mathscr{L}(n)$. When E is composed of three equal segments equally inclined to one another, $\mu(E) = \tfrac{1}{2}\Lambda(E)$. Thus we have

$$\mu(T) \geqslant \tfrac{1}{2}\Lambda(T). \tag{*}$$

and our aim in the rest of this paragraph is to show that $\mu(T) \leqslant \tfrac{1}{2}\Lambda(T)$. One method is to assume the contrary† namely that $\mu(T) > \tfrac{1}{2}\Lambda(T)$ and show that this leads to a contradiction. I have not followed that method here because it is not then possible to particularize the extremal figures. The method is to use (13) and (*) to establish by variational arguments a number of properties of T which will specify it more and more exactly until finally we can assert that $\mu(T) \leqslant \tfrac{1}{2}\Lambda(T)$.

Denote the polygon which is the convex cover of T by P. $\mu(T)$ is the minimal width of P. A support line of P which is at a distance $\mu(T)$ from the parallel support line will be referred to as a minimal support line. A vertex of P which lies on a minimal support line of P will be referred to as a minimal vertex. There are two properties of minimal support lines of which we shall make frequent use.

(A) A pair of minimal support lines is such that at least one of the lines meets P in a segment. For otherwise we could give each of the lines an equal rotation about the vertices of P through which they pass and reduce the distance apart of the two lines. This would contradict the fact that they are a pair of minimal support lines of P.

(B) If the lines l_1 and l_2 are a pair of minimal support lines and meet P in X_1 and X_2 respectively, then the projection of X_1 onto l_2 by means of lines perpendicular to both l_1 and l_2 is a set Y_1 which intersects X_2.

† I feel no aversion to this type of argument but I find it repugnant to have to illustrate a hypothetical argument by drawing a diagram which cannot exist!

For if this were not the case there would be a line m perpendicular to l_1 and l_2 separating X_1 from X_2. Suppose m meets l_1 in L_1 and l_2 in L_2. If we give to l_1 a rotation about L_1 and to l_2 an equal rotation about L_2 we should reduce the distance between the two parallel lines. But since X_1 and X_2 lie on opposite sides of m we can choose this rotation to be in such a sense and of such a magnitude that the rotated strip still contains P. But this contradicts the fact that the distance apart of l_1 and l_2 is the minimal width of P.

We shall later require the following lemma: it is inserted here for convenience of reference.

LEMMA. *Let ABC be a triangle every angle of which is less than $\frac{2}{3}\pi$. Let K be the unique point such that $\angle AKB = \angle BKC = \angle CKA = \frac{2}{3}\pi$. On AB erect the triangle ADB which is equilateral and such that D lies on the side of AB opposite to C, then*

(i) *of all connected sets containing A, B and C the tree formed from the three segments AK, BK, CK, has the least length.*

(ii) *the sum of the lengths $AK + BK + CK$ is equal to the length CD.*

Let $\mathscr{V}$ be a connected set joining A, B and C. If $\mathscr{V}$ has infinite linear measure we need not consider it further. If $\mathscr{V}$ has finite linear measure then it contains an arc γ_1 joining A to B and an arc γ_2 joining A to C. Let K_1 be the last point of $\gamma_1 \cap \gamma_2$ on γ_2 in the order A to C. Then arc AK_1 of γ_1 has length greater than or equal to segment AK_1: arc K_1B of γ_1 has length greater than or equal to that of segment K_1B: arc K_1C of γ_2 has length greater than or equal to that of K_1C. Thus

$$\Lambda(\mathscr{V}) \geqslant AK_1 + K_1B + K_1C$$

We next consider a variable point X and the function $XA + XB + XC = F(X)$.† There is a position of X for which $F(X)$ attains its least value. Let this position be X_0. It is easy to see that X_0 does not coincide with any of A or B or C since each angle of triangle ABC is less than $\frac{2}{3}\pi$. If we move X from X_0 in the direction perpendicular to AX_0 then $AX = AX_0 + O(XX_0)^2$ and therefore $BX + CX = BX_0 + CX_0 + O(XX_0)^2$ i.e. XX_0 is perpendicular to the internal bisector of $\angle BX_0C$. Thus $\angle AX_0C = \angle AX_0B$ and similarly both these angles are equal to $\angle BX_0C$, i.e. X_0 coincides with the point K. Thus

$$K_1A + K_1B + K_1C \geqslant KA + KB + KC$$

and (i) is proved.

To prove (ii) we have $\angle AKB + \angle ADB = \pi$ so that $ADBK$ is a cyclic quadrilateral. (See Fig. 5.) Also $\angle AKD = \angle ABD = \frac{1}{3}\pi$

† Here XA denotes the length of segment XA.

so the points C, K, D are collinear, and we need only show that $KD = AK + KB$. Take E on KD so that $\angle KEB = \angle KBE$.†
Then, since $\angle EKB = \frac{1}{3}\pi$, KEB is an equilateral triangle and $KE = KB$. Since $\angle KBE = \frac{1}{3}\pi$, $\angle KBA = \angle EBD$. Hence in triangles AKB, DEB,

$\angle KAB = \angle EDB$ since $ADBK$ is a cyclic quadrilateral,

$AB = DB$ since ABD is an equilateral triangle.

$\angle KBA = \angle EBD$ proved above.

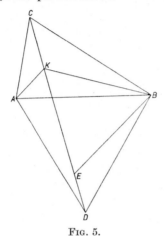

FIG. 5.

Thus triangle AKB is congruent to triangle DEB and

$$ED = AK$$

Hence $AK + KB = ED + KE = KD$ and the proof of (ii) is complete.

1. Every vertex of P belongs to T.

By Bunt's version of a theorem usually ascribed to Carathéodory [5] every point of P belongs to a segment whose end points belong to T. If the point p of P does not belong to T then it must be an interior point of such a segment. Thus it cannot be an extreme point of P, i.e. a vertex of P.

2. Of all connected sets containing the vertices of P, T has the least length.

Amongst the class of all connected sets containing the vertices of P there is one with the least length say T_1 (see [1] p. 316). If T_1

† See Fig. 5.

contained points exterior to P, there would be a line l which cuts T_1 and does not meet P. The part of T_1 on the side of l opposite to that containing P is projected onto l. This set together with $T_1 \cap l$ and the part of T_1 on the same side of l as P forms a connected set T_2 with $\Lambda(T_2) < \Lambda(T_1)$. Since T_2 also contains the vertices of P this is impossible. Thus $T_1 \subset P$. Hence $T_1 \in \mathscr{L}(n)$ and $\mu(T_1) = \mu(T)$. Since (13) holds it follows that $\Lambda(T_1) \geqslant \Lambda(T)$.

3. T is a polygonal tree formed from a finite number of linear segments.

Let the vertices of P be $p_1, p_2, \ldots, p_k$, $k \leqslant n$. There is an arc in T joining p_1 to p_2; denote it by β_2. There is an arc in T joining p_3 to p_1 say α_3. Denote the first point of $\alpha_3 \cap \beta_2$ on α_3 in the order p_3 to p_1 by q_3 and the subarc $p_3 q_3$ of α_3 by β_3. Generally, suppose that $\beta_3, \ldots, \beta_{i-1}$ have been defined. There is an arc in T joining p_i to p_1. Denote it by α_i. Let the first point of $\beta_2 \cup \beta_3 \cup \ldots \cup \beta_{i-1}$ on α_i in the order p_i to p_1 be q_i and the subarc $p_i q_i$ of α_i be β_i.

When β_i has been defined for $i = 2, \ldots, k$ and q_i for $i = 3, \ldots, k$, we construct a connected set T_1 as follows. Of the points q_i one or more belong to β_2. Form the polygonal line by joining them and the end points of β_2 by segments in the same order as that in which they lie on β_2. Make a similar construction for each arc β_i. The union of all these segments is denoted by T_1.

T_1 is a connected set containing all the vertices of P. By its method of construction $\Lambda(T_1) < \Lambda(T)$ or T_1 coincides with T. By *2* the first alternative is impossible. Thus T_1 is formed as a union of a finite number of polygonal segments. If T_1 was not a tree we could omit a subsegment to obtain a connected set T_2 that would contradict *2*. Thus $T = T_1$ is a polygonal tree.

4. Every end-point of T and every singular point of T is a vertex of P.

If an end-point t of T was not a vertex of P we could remove from T a small segment with one end point at t and obtain $T_1 \in \mathscr{L}(n)$. Since $\Lambda(T_1) < \Lambda(T)$, and (if the segment removed is sufficiently small) T_1 contains the vertices of P we have a contradiction with *2*. Thus every end point of T is a vertex of P.

Similarly if q is the end point of the two vertices of T, pq, qr and q is not a vertex of P then we can select a point q_1 on pq near to q and replace pq, qr by pq_1, $q_1 r$ to obtain T_1. Again $T_1 \in \mathscr{L}(n)$, $\Lambda(T_1) < \Lambda(T)$, and we have a contradiction with *2*.

5. Every node of T is of order 3.

If there is a node t of T whose order is greater than 3 then there are two segments of T say tt_1 and tt_2 such that if we take t_1' on tt_1 and t_2' on tt_2 with $tt_1' = tt_2'$ then every angle of triangle $tt_1' t_2'$ is less than or equal to $\frac{1}{3}\pi$. But then the connected set of least length joining $tt_1' t_2'$ is formed from three segments kt, kt_1', kt_2' inclined to each other at an angle of $\frac{2}{3}\pi$ and meeting at k inside the triangle $tt_1't_2'$. In T replace segments tt_1' and tt_2' by kt, kt_1', kt_2' to obtain T_1. Since $\Lambda(T_1) < \Lambda(T)$ we have a contradiction with 2. Thus property 5 is proved.

6. Every node of T is an interior point of P.

For otherwise, if t was a node of T on the frontier of P, there would be three segments of T say tt_1, tt_2, tt_3 and a line through t say l such that t_1, t_2, t_3 all lie either on l or on one side of l. Thus we have a situation similar to that in 5, namely two segments say tt_1 and tt_2 such that $\angle t_1 t t_2 \leqslant \frac{1}{2}\pi$. This again leads to a contradiction with 2.

7. The three segments of T which abut at a node of T are inclined to one another at an angle of $\frac{2}{3}\pi$.

Let k be the node and ka, kb, kc be the segments abutting at k. On ka, kb, kc take points a', b', c' respectively such that $ka' = kb' = kc'$. By the lemma, the connected set of least length joining $a'b'c'$ is formed from three segments $k'a'$, $k'b'$, $k'c'$ where $k'a'$, $k'b'$, $k'c'$ are all inclined to one another at an angle of $\frac{2}{3}\pi$. For this is true for any triad of points $a''b''c''$ except a triad for which one of the angles of the triangle $a''b''c''$ is greater than or equal to $\frac{2}{3}\pi$. If, for example, $\angle a''b''c'' \geqslant \frac{2}{3}\pi$ then the connected set of least length joining $a''b''c''$ is formed from the two segments $a''b''$ and $b''c''$. Now in our case k is an interior point of the triangle $a'b'c'$ (by the argument used in 6). Thus for example

$$\angle a'b'c' = \angle a'b'k + \angle c'b'k = \tfrac{1}{2}(\pi - \angle a'kb') + \tfrac{1}{2}(\pi - \angle c'kb') \leqslant \tfrac{1}{2}\pi$$

Similar inequalities hold for the other angles of the triangle $a'b'c'$.

If now k does not coincide with k' then we can replace in T the segments $a'k$, $b'k$, $c'k$, by $a'k'$, $b'k'$, $c'k'$ and actually reduce $\Lambda(T)$. By 2 this is not possible. Thus k is k' and property 7 is proved.

8. T has either 3 or 4 end-points.

Suppose that T has r end-points and that δ is a positive number less than the least length of a segment of T. Let T_1 be the subtree of T obtained from T by removing r segments each of length δ and such that each of these segments has one end point at an end point of T and each end point of T is an end point of one of these r segments. Then

$$\Lambda(T_1) = \Lambda(T) - r\delta$$

and since every point of T is distant at most δ from some point of T_1

$$\mu(T_1) \geqslant \mu(T) - 2\delta$$

(T_1 is not void because every node of T is a point of T_1, and if T has no nodes it is an arc and must contain at least two segments for otherwise $\mu(T) = 0$). If δ is small the convex cover of T_1 has the same number of vertices as P. Now if $r \geqslant 5$

$$\frac{\mu(T_1)}{\Lambda(T_1)} \geqslant \frac{\mu(T) - 2\delta}{\Lambda(T) - 5\delta} > \frac{\mu(T)}{\Lambda(T)}, \tag{14}$$

since we know that $\Lambda(T) \leqslant 2\mu(T)$. But (14) is in contradiction with (13). Thus $r = 2, 3$ or 4.

If $r = 2$ projection in the direction of the line joining the end points of T shows that

$$\mu(T) < \tfrac{1}{2}\Lambda(T)$$

in contradiction with (*). Thus $r \neq 2$, and property 8 is proved.

9. If T has four end points then P is a quadrilateral with these four points as vertices.

If P has more than four vertices then one of them say p is not an end-point of T. Let the two segments pq_1, pq_2 of T meet at p and let p' be a point on pq_1 distant δ from p. In T replace pq_1, pq_2 by $p'q_1$, $p'q_2$ giving T' and remove segments of length δ from each end-point of T' as in 8. We obtain a connected set T_1 with

$$\Lambda(T_1) < \Lambda(T) - 4\delta$$
$$\mu(T_1) \geqslant \mu(T) - 2\delta$$

and since

$$\frac{\Lambda(T_1)}{\mu(T_1)} < \frac{\Lambda(T)}{\mu(T)}$$

we again have a contradiction with (13). Thus P has at most four vertices. But by *4* P has at least four vertices and these vertices are end-points of T. Property *9* is established.

10. T has exactly three end-points.

Otherwise by *8, 9* and *2. P is a quadrilateral and T is the connected set of least length joining the vertices of P. In this case T is a polygonal tree with two third-order nodes and is formed from five segments. Let the vertices of P be a, b, c, d (in order round $\mathrm{Fr}P$) and the nodes of T be k_1k_2 with the notation chosen so that the segments of T are ak_1, bk_2, ck_2, dk_1 and k_1k_2.

The line through a perpendicular to ak_1 is a support line of P. For otherwise either $\angle bak_1 > \tfrac{1}{2}\pi$ or $\angle dak_1 > \tfrac{1}{2}\pi$. The second case cannot occur since $\angle dak_1 < \tfrac{1}{3}\pi$ see *7*. Thus we may suppose $\angle bak_1 > \tfrac{1}{2}\pi$. Let a_1 be the foot of the perpendicular from k_1 to the line ab. In T replace segment ak_1 by the segment a_1k_1 to obtain the tree T_1. The convex cover of T_1 contains P and $\Lambda(T_1) < \Lambda(T)$. Thus we have

$$\frac{\mu(T_1)}{\Lambda(T_1)} > \frac{\mu(T)}{\Lambda(T)},$$

in contradiction with (13). Thus the line through a perpendicular to ak_1 is a support line of P.

Since ck_2 is parallel to ak_1 we have a pair of parallel support lines one each through a and c. Thus, projecting the polygonal line ak_1k_2c perpendicular to ak_1 we have

$$ak_1 + \tfrac{1}{2}k_1k_2 + k_2\,c \geqslant \mu(T). \tag{15}$$

Similarly, by projecting bk_2k_1d perpendicular to bk_2,

$$dk_1 + \tfrac{1}{2}k_1k_2 + k_2b \geqslant \mu(T) \tag{16}$$

Adding, we obtain

$$\Lambda(T) \geqslant 2\mu(T). \tag{17}$$

Now strict inequality in (17) is impossible (by (*)). Thus equality must hold in (17) and therefore in each of (15) and (16). Hence the lines through a and c perpendicular to ak_1 and those through d and b perpendicular to dk_1 are all minimal support lines.

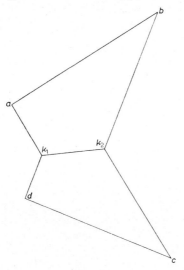

FIG. 6.

By property (A) of minimal support lines applied to the pair of minimal support lines perpendicular to ak_1, one of the segments ab, ad, bc, cd is perpendicular to ak_1. Clearly this is not true of ad

and bc since $\angle dak_1$ and $\angle bck_2$ are both less than $\frac{1}{3}\pi$. Thus either ab or cd is perpendicular to ak_1. But in an exactly similar way we see from the pair of minimal support lines perpendicular to bk_2 that either ab or cd is perpendicular to bk_2. Since ak_1 and bk_2 are not parallel we conclude that either ab is perpendicular to ak_1 and cd is perpendicular to bk_2 or ab is perpendicular to bk_2 and cd is perpendicular to ck_2. The arguments in the two cases are the same and we shall consider the first case only. (See Fig. 6.) Remove from ak_1 a segment of length δ with end point at a and similarly from dk_1 a segment of length δ with end point at d. Denote the resulting tree by T_1. Then

$$\Lambda(T_1) = \Lambda(T) - 2\delta$$
$$\mu(T_1) > \mu(T) - \delta$$

But this is impossible since it implies a contradiction with (13).

Thus T has not got four end-points and by 8 must have exactly three end-points.

Remark. T has one node and it is of order three. We shall denote it by k and the three arcs of T which terminate at k by α, β and γ. Denote the vertices of P on α, β, γ by $a_1, a_2, \ldots, a_h$; $b_1, b_2, \ldots, b_i$ and $c_1, c_2, \ldots, c_j$ where α is $a_1, \ldots, a_h$, k and this order is the order in which these points lie on α. Similarly for β and γ.

11. Every vertex of P is a minimal vertex

Suppose that the vertex p of P is not minimal. If p is an end-point of T we can remove a small segment one of whose end-points is p from T to obtain a subtree T_1, for which

$$\mu(T_1) = \mu(T), \qquad \Lambda(T_1) < \Lambda(T),$$

which leads to a contradiction with (13). Similarly if p is a point common to two segments pq, pq_2 of T we could move it into a new position p' on the internal bisector of the angle of these two segments in such a way that $\Lambda(T)$ is reduced but $\mu(T)$ remains unaltered. This again leads to a contradiction with (13).

DEFINITION: *Two vertices of P that are joined by a single segment lying in the frontier of P are said to be **P adjacent**. A point lying on two or more segments of T or an end-point of T is called a **singular point** of T. A vertex of T is a singular point that is neither an end-point nor a node. Two singular points of T that are joined by a single segment lying in T are said to be **T adjacent**.*

12. If three singular points of T, p_1, p_2, p_3, are such that p_2 is T-adjacent to both p_1 and p_3, then $\angle p_1p_2p_3 \geqslant \frac{2}{3}\pi$.

If $\angle p_1p_2p_3 < \frac{2}{3}\pi$ then either one other angle of the triangle $p_1p_2p_3$ is greater than or equal to $\frac{2}{3}\pi$, say $\angle p_2p_1p_3 \geqslant \frac{2}{3}\pi$, or there is a point l such that each segment lp_1, lp_2, lp_3 makes an angle equal to $\frac{2}{3}\pi$ with the other two segments. In the first case segment p_1p_3 has length less than that of segment p_2p_3 and if we replace segment p_2p_3 by segment p_1p_3 we obtain from T a connected set contradicting 2. In the second case we replace the segments p_1p_2 and p_2p_3 by the three segments lp_1, lp_2, lp_3 and again obtain from T a connected set which contradicts 2.

Thus $\angle p_1p_2p_3 \geqslant \frac{2}{3}\pi$ and property *12* is established.

13. To each pair of end-points of T say a_1, b_1 there corresponds a pair of parallel minimal support lines l_1 and l_2 such that l_1 contains a_1 and l_2 contains b_1.

Suppose that this is not the case. Remove length δ from the segment of T terminating at a_1 and another equal length from the segment of T terminating at b_1 to obtain the tree T_1. Let the new end-points be a_1' in place of a_1 and b_1' in place of b_1, and let the convex cover of T_1 be P_1. We shall assume that δ is a small number. Then by (13),

$$\frac{\mu(T_1)}{\Lambda(T_1)} \leqslant \frac{\mu(T)}{\Lambda(T)} \tag{18}$$

and by construction,

$$\Lambda(T_1) = \Lambda(T) - 2\delta \tag{19}$$

Since $\mu(T) \geqslant \frac{1}{2}\Lambda(T)$, (18) and (19) imply

$$\mu(T_1) \leqslant \frac{\mu(T)}{\Lambda(T)}\left(\Lambda(T) - 2\delta\right) \leqslant \mu(T) - \delta$$

Further, if $\mu(T) > \frac{1}{2}\Lambda(T)$, then

$$\mu(T_1) < \mu(T) - \delta.$$

Now by the method of construction of T_1 from T,

$$\mu(T_1) \geqslant \mu(T) - \delta$$

For of the two lines which form a pair of minimal support lines of P, one is a support line of P_1 and the other is distant at most δ from a parallel support line of P_1. By the inequality for $\mu(T_1)$ proved above it follows that

$$\mu(T_1) = \mu(T) - \delta$$

Thus

$$\mu(T) = \frac{1}{2}\Lambda(T)$$

and therefore

$$\frac{\mu(T_1)}{\Lambda(T_1)} = \frac{\mu(T) - \delta}{\Lambda(T) - 2\delta} = \frac{\mu(T)}{\Lambda(T)}$$

Thus T_1 is also an extremal connected set for which $\dfrac{\mu(T_1)}{\Lambda(T_1)}$ assumes its least upper bound.

The results proved about T apply equally well to T_1.

By *11* every vertex of P_1 is a minimal vertex and since $\mu(T_1)$ $= \mu(T) - \delta$ any pair of minimal support lines of P_1 are obtained from a pair of minimal support lines of P by keeping one line of the pair fixed and moving the other line a distance δ into a parallel portion. There are at most two support lines of P for which the parallel corresponding support line of P_1 is distant δ, and these are the two lines perpendicular respectively to a_1a_1' and to b_1b_1', further this is so only if these lines contain no points of P apart from a_1 and b_1 respectively.

Now P_1 must have at least two pairs of parallel minimal support lines. For otherwise, let the two parallel minimal support lines be l and l_1. By *11* every vertex of P_1 lies on l or on l_1 and P_1 must be either a triangle or a trapezium. If P_1 is not a rectangle it has a vertex v at which the interior angle of $\mathrm{Fr}\,P_1$ is less than $\tfrac{1}{2}\pi$.† By *12* v cannot be a vertex of T_1 and by *6* it is not a node. Thus it is an end point of T_1. Suppose it is a_1^* and let p be the T_1-adjacent singular point of T_1. Let l_1 be the minimal support line through a_1^* and let a_1^{**} be a point on l_1 near to a_1^*. Let the foot of the perpendicular from p to l_1 be q. If a_1^{**} lies between q and a_1^* and in T_1 we replace segment pa_1^* by pa_1^{**} then $\Lambda(T_1)$ is reduced and, if a_1^{**} is sufficiently close to a_1^* $\mu(T_1)$ remains unaltered. This is impossible by the extremal property of T_1. If however P_1 is a rectangle it has widths $\mu(T_1)$ and μ^* where $\mu^* > \mu(T_1)$. The vertex a_1^* is again an end point of T_1, and if p is the T_1-adjacent singular point of T_1 then pa_1^* lies in the frontier of P_1, for otherwise we can argue exactly as above. Thus p is not a node of T_1 and must be a vertex of T_1. Let q be the singular point of T_1, which is T_1-adjacent to p other than a_1^*. On segment pq take p^* near to p. Let a_1^{**} be the foot of the perpendicular from p^* to the minimal support line through a_1^*. In T_1 replace segments qp, pa_1^* by segments qp^* and $p^*a_1^{**}$. This reduces $\Lambda(T_1)$ and, if p^* is near to p, does not affect $\mu(T_1)$. This is impossible. Thus there are at least two pairs of minimal support lines of T_1.

Thus the lines through a_1 and b_1 perpendicular respectively to a_1a_1' and b_1b_1' are minimal support lines of P and contain no points of P apart from a_1 and b_1. Let the line through a_1 perpendicular to a_1a_1' be m_1 and the parallel support line of P be m_1'. Let the line through b_1 perpendicular to b_1b_1' be m_2 and the parallel support line

† And the minimal support line through v meets $\mathrm{Fr}P_1$ in a segment.

be m_2'. Since every vertex of P is a vertex of P_1 apart from a_1 and b_1 (assuming that δ is sufficiently small) it follows from *11* that every vertex of P apart from a_1 and b_1 lies on m_1' or m_2'.

Denote the rhombus bounded by $m_1 m_1' m_2 m_2'$ by R, let its vertices be $ABCD$ in order where a_1 lies on AB and b_1 on BC. (See Fig. 7.)

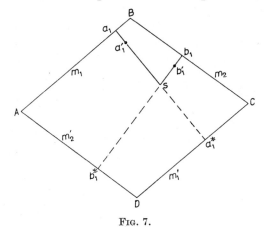

FIG. 7.

Let $a_1 a_1'$ produced meet $b_1 b_1'$ produced in s. Let $a_1 s$ produced meet DC in a_1^* and $b_1 s$ produced meet AD in b_1^*. Property (B) of minimal support lines implies that a_1^* is a point of the segment DC and b_1^* a point of the segment AD. Then $a_1 a_1^*$ and $b_1 b_1^*$ lie inside R. Thus $a_1 s$ and $b_1 s$ contain no vertices of T. If a singular point of T lay on $a_1 s$ apart from a_1 and s, it would have to be a node k. Of the segments of T terminating at k, one has points interior to the quadrilateral $a_1 B b_1 s$. This segment cannot meet $a_1 B$ or $B b_1$ since no points of P lie on these segments apart from a_1 and b_1. Nor can it terminate in the interior of this quadrilateral for such a termination would be a singular point of T, therefore a vertex of P. But there are no such vertices of P. Thus this segment must meet segment $b_1 s$ in say k_1. But then segment $b_1 s$ contains a singular point of T and this singular point must be a node of T. Since T has only one node it follows that it lies at s. In the notation which we have adopted s is k.† Let the third segment of T at $k = s$ meet the frontier of R in d. By a similar argument to that used above kd is a segment of T. Now the three segments ka_1, $kb_1 kd$ divide R into three domains one of which denoted by D_1 contains a_1^* and another, denoted by D_2 contains b_1^*. By property (B) a_1^* and b_1^* are points of P and neither a_1 nor b_1 are vertices of R (since they do not lie one each on a

† And s is not D.

pair of parallel minimal support lines of P). Thus both D_1 and D_2 contain points of T on $\mathrm{Fr}R$ other than d. Since T is a tree with one node of order three and since a_1 and b_1 are end-points of T we have a contradiction. If for example the third end point of T lay in D_1 so would the whole of the arc of T joining this point to d and would thus have no points in D_2.

Thus we are led to a contradiction. The original assumption is false and *13* is proved.

Remark. Of any two parallel support lines of P at least one passes through an end point of T. The three end points of T, a_1, b_1 and c_1, divide the frontier of P into three non-overlapping arcs which are denoted by $A(a_1, b_1)$, $A(b_1, c_1)$, $A(c_1, a_1)$ where arc $A(a_1, b_1)$ does not contain c_1 etc. Then any support line to P at a point of $A(a_1, b_1)$ is parallel to a support line of P at c_1 and there are similar relations for $A(b_1, c_1)$ and $A(c_1, a_1)$.

14. Each of the three arcs α, β, γ has length less than $\mu(T)$.

If, for example, $\Lambda(\alpha) \geqslant \mu(T)$. Then from *13* there are a pair of parallel support lines to P through the end points of $\beta \cup \gamma$. Thus

$$\Lambda(\beta \cup \gamma) > \mu(T)$$

and

$$\Lambda(T) > 2\mu(T)$$

in contradiction with (*).

15. If a_2 exists then a_1, a_2 lies in the frontier of P, i.e. if a_1 is not T-adjacent to k then a_1a_2 lies in the frontier of P.

The points a_1, a_2 belong to the frontier of P and thus if a_1a_2 does not lie in the frontier of P it divides P into two non-empty domains. Thus there is a vertex of P on each side of the line containing a_1a_2. By *1* there are points of T on each side of the line containing a_1a_2. These points are joined by an arc of T inside P. Since these points lie on opposite sides of a_1a_2 this arc meets a_1a_2. But this is not so since there is no node of T on a_1a_2. A contradiction which establishes *15*.

16. If three vertices of α, say a_s, a_{s+1}, a_{s+2}, are such that a_s, a_{s+1} and a_{s+1}, a_{s+2} are P adjacent (as well as T adjacent) then $a_s a_{s+1}$ and $a_{s+1}a_{s+2}$ are tangent to a circle whose radius is $\mu(T)$ and whose centre is b_1 or c_1.

The three points a_1, b_1, c_1 divide the frontier of P into three non-overlapping arcs which we shall denote, as before, by $A(a_1, b_1)$, $A(b_1, c_1)$ and $A(c_1, a_1)$. The three vertices $a_s a_{s+1} a_{s+2}$ cannot belong to $A(b_1c_1)$, since if they did, the support line parallel to $a_s a_{s+1}$ would pass through a_1 (by the remark after *13*) and this implies $\Lambda(\alpha)$

$\geqslant \mu(T)$ in contradiction with *14*. Thus $a_s a_{s+1}$, a_{s+2} belong entirely either to $A(a_1, b_1)$ or to $A(c_1, a_1)$. Suppose that they belong to $A(a_1, b_1)$. The argument in the alternative case is similar. The support line of P parallel to the line $a_s a_{s+1}$ passes through c_1. Thus $a_s a_{s+1}$ is either tangent to the circle whose centre is c_1 and radius $\mu(T)$, $c(c_1, \mu(T))$, or the line containing $a_s a_{s+1}$ lies outside this circle. In the second case select a point a'_{s+1} on $a_{s+1} a_{s+2}$ near to a_{s+1} such that $a_s a'_{s+1}$ lies outside the circle $c(c_1, \mu(T))$. In T replace segments $a_s a_{s+1}$, $a_{s+1} a_{s+2}$ by $a_s a'_{s+1}$, $a'_{s+1} a_{s+2}$. If a'_{s+1} is not coincident with a_{s+1} the effect is to reduce $\Lambda(T)$ without altering $\mu(T)$. This is im-possible by (13).

Property *16* is proved.

17. If the vertex a_2 exists and if p is the other vertex of P which is P-adjacent to a_1, then either the line through a_1 perpendicular to $a_1 a_2$ is a minimal support line of P or the line containing $a_1 p$ is a minimal support line of P.

We assume, without any real loss of generality that the points $a_2 a_1 p$ are in the clockwise sense round the frontier of P. Let the class of minimal support lines through a_1 be denoted by $\mathscr{I}$. Any member l of $\mathscr{I}$ together with the line $a_1 a_2$ divides the plane into four sectors of which one contains k. The angle of this sector is denoted by $\phi(l)$.

The set of values $\phi(l)$ is closed. If the line containing $a_1 p$ is not a minimal support line of P and if there is an l of $\mathscr{I}$ with $\phi(l) < \frac{1}{2}\pi$, this line l meets P in the single point a_1. For it cannot coincide with $a_1 a_2$ since $\phi(l) < \frac{1}{2}\pi$, nor with $a_1 p$ since by assumption this is not a minimal support line. By (B) the line through a_1 perpendicular to l must meet P in a segment of length $\mu(T)$. But in fact this line meets P in the single point a_1. Thus if $a_1 p$ is not a minimal support line then for every l of $\mathscr{I}$, $\phi(l) \geqslant \frac{1}{2}\pi$.

If $\phi(l) > \frac{1}{2}\pi$ for all l of $\mathscr{I}$ then there exists a small positive number ε such that $\phi(l) > \frac{1}{2}\pi + \varepsilon$ for all l of $\mathscr{I}$. Thus we can rotate $a_1 a_2$ about a_2 in the anticlockwise sense so that a_1 becomes a'_1. Replace $a_1 a_2$ by $a'_1 a_2$ to obtain the tree T'. Now if $a_1 p$ is not a minimal support line and if the rotation is sufficiently small $\mu(T') = \mu(T)$. But $\Lambda(T') = \Lambda(T)$ so that T' is an extremal figure. By *11* a'_1 is a minimal vertex of T': but by the construction a'_1 is not a minimal vertex of T'.

This contradiction shows that either the line containing $a_1 p$ is a minimal support line or the line l with $\phi(l) = \frac{1}{2}\pi$ is a minimal support line of P. Thus property *17* is established.

18. Any two vertices of P which are T-adjacent are also P-adjacent i.e. the points $a_1 a_2 \ldots a_h$ are in order round the frontier of P and so are $b_1 \ldots b_i$ and $c_1 c_2 \ldots c_j$.

By *15* a_1 and a_2 are P-adjacent. We shall show firstly that a_2 and a_3 are also P-adjacent.† The vertex a_3 is P-adjacent either to a_2 or to a_1. For otherwise the segment a_3a_2 divides P into two domains each of which contains vertices of P, say p, q such that neither p nor q is any one of a_1, a_2 or a_3. There is an arc in T joining p to q. This arc must cut a_2a_3 which therefore contains a node of T. But this is not so.

We shall assume that a_3 is P-adjacent to a_1 and show that this leads to a contradiction.

We assume for definiteness that the order $a_2a_1a_3$ round the frontier of P is clockwise. (See Fig. 8.) Consider the minimal support lines

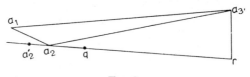

FIG. 8.

that pass through a_1. We shall show that a_1a_3 is not a minimal support line. Let q be the vertex of P that is P-adjacent and not T-adjacent to a_2. Let a_2' be a point on the line qa_2 such that a_2 lies between a_2' and q and let T' be the tree obtained from T by replacing segments a_1a_2 and a_3a_2 by a_1a_2' and a_3a_2'. Since the convex cover of T' includes P it follows from (13) that $\Lambda(T') \geqslant \Lambda(T)$. This in turn is true for any choice of a_2' as described above only if

$$\angle qa_2a_3 \leqslant \angle a_2'a_2a_1$$

But by *12* $\angle a_1a_2a_3 \geqslant \tfrac{2}{3}\pi$ and therefore

$$\angle qa_2a_3 \leqslant \tfrac{1}{6}\pi$$

Now if a_1a_3 is a minimal support line of P there is a point of P on the parallel support line inside the strip which is bounded by the lines through a_1 and a_3 perpendicular to a_1a_3. By *12* again $\angle a_2a_1a_3 \leqslant \tfrac{1}{3}\pi$ thus, if we produce a_2q to meet the line through a_3 perpendicular to a_1a_3 it will do so in a point r on the same side of a_1a_3 as a_2. Thus it follows that the lines through points of segment a_1a_3 perpendicular to a_1a_3 intersect the quadrilateral $a_1a_2ra_3$ in segments of which the largest has length greater than or equal to $\mu(T)$. The largest segment (or one of them) is either the perpendicular from a_2 to a_1a_3 or it is the segment a_3r. In the first case $\Lambda(\alpha)$ is greater than the length of the segment a_1a_2 and is therefore

† It is assumed that such vertices as a_2, a_3 etc. exist. Otherwise there is nothing to prove.

greater than $\mu(T)$. This is impossible by *14*. In the second case we consider triangle a_2ra_3. We have $\angle a_2a_3r < \frac{1}{2}\pi$ and thus $\angle a_3a_2r + \angle a_3ra_2 > \frac{1}{2}\pi$. But we have already seen that $\angle qa_2a_3 = \angle ra_2a_3 < \frac{1}{6}\pi$. Thus $\angle a_3ra_2 > \frac{1}{3}\pi$ and hence $\angle a_3ra_2 > \angle ra_2a_3$. This implies that $a_3a_2 > ra_3 \geqslant \mu(T)$. Finally we again obtain $\Lambda(\alpha) > a_3a_2 > \mu(T)$. By *14* this is impossible. Thus a_1a_3 is not a minimal support line of P.

But by *17* this implies that the line perpendicular to a_1a_2 through a_1 is a minimal support line of P. This line meets P only in the point a_1 (since $\angle a_2a_1a_3 \leqslant \frac{1}{3}\pi$, see above) and thus the line through a_1a_2 meets P in a segment of length $\mu(T)$, i.e. a_1a_2 is of length at least $\mu(T)$. By *14* this is not so since it implies that $\Lambda(\alpha) > \mu(T)$. Thus finally a_3 is not P-adjacent to a_1 and a_3 must therefore be P-adjacent to a_2.

Next we suppose that there is a first integer m such that a_m and a_{m+1} are not P-adjacent. Then $m \geqslant 3$ and by an argument similar to that used for a_3 above, it can be seen that a_1 and a_{m+1} are P-adjacent. The points $a_2, \ldots, a_m$ all belong to $A(a_1, b_1)$ or to $A(a_1, c_1)$. Suppose that they belong to $A(a_1, b_1)$ then by *16* each segment $a_1a_2, a_2a_3, \ldots, a_{m-1}a_m$ is part of a tangent to the circle centre c_1 and radius $\mu(T)$ and by (B) the segment $a_{m-1}a_m$ actually touches this circle. Thus $\angle a_{m-1}a_mc_1 < \frac{1}{2}\pi$. Since by *12* $\angle a_{m-1}a_ma_{m+1} \geqslant \frac{2}{3}\pi$ and since a_{m+1} and c_1 lie on the same side of $a_{m-1}a_m$ (they are points of P and a_ma_{m-1} is part of a support line of P), it follows that a_{m-1} and a_{m+1} lie on opposite sides of the line a_mc_1. Hence a_1 and a_{m+1} lie on opposite sides of the line a_mc_1. But a_m and c_1 are both vertices of P. Thus a_1 and a_{m+1} are not P-adjacent.

This contradiction establishes the required result.

19. If the vertex a_2 exists and if the vertices $a_2a_1b_1p$ are in order round the frontier of P (i.e. a_2a_1, a_1b_1, b_1p are P-adjacent), then the line a_1a_2 is not parallel to the line b_1p.

Remove a small segment of length δ from a_1a_2 at a_1 and from the end b_1 of the segment of T that terminates at b_1. Denote the new tree by T' with end points a_1' in place of a_1 and b_1' in place of b_1. Now if a_1a_2 is parallel to b_1p then any pair of parallel support lines of the convex cover of T' are such that at most one goes through a_1' or b_1' (except when b_1 and p are T-adjacent in which case the pair of parallel lines a_1a_2 and b_1p are support lines of the convex cover of T' and go through a_1' and b_1' respectively). But in any case

$$\Lambda(T') = \Lambda(T) - 2\delta \; \mu(T') \geqslant \mu(T) - \delta$$

As in (13) it follows that T' is an extremal figure, that $\mu(T') =$

5

$\mu(T) - \delta$ and that the line through a_1 perpendicular to a_1a_2 is a minimal support line of P meeting P in the single point a_1. By property (B) of minimal support lines the line a_1a_2 meets P in a segment of length $\mu(T)$. Thus the length of a_1a_2 is $\mu(T)$ and

$$\Lambda(\alpha) \geqslant \mu(T)$$

in contradiction with *14*.

Thus the assumption that a_1a_2 is parallel to b_1p is false and *19* is proved.

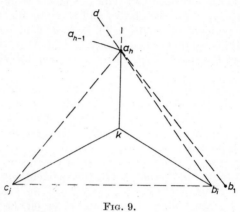

FIG. 9.

We next consider the various cases that might arise according to the different orders of $a_1, \ldots, a_h$: $b_1, \ldots, b_i$ and $c_1, \ldots, c_j$ on the frontier of P, and according as α, β, γ are formed from one segment or more than one segment.

Case I. Each arc α, β, γ is made up of more than one segment and the orders $a_1, \ldots, a_h$; $b_1, \ldots, b_i$; $c_1, \ldots, c_j$ on frontier P are all the same.

There is no real loss of generality in supposing that the vertices of P in clockwise order are $a_1, \ldots, a_h, b_1, \ldots, b_i, c_1, \ldots, c_j$. The other cases are obtained either by a change of notation or by an argument similar to the following.

Produce b_1a_h to d. Then

$$\angle ka_hb_1 \leqslant \angle da_ha_{h-1}$$

for if this was not the case we could replace a_h by a_h' on b_1a_h such that a_h lies between a_h' and b_1 and such that the new tree obtained from T by replacing ka_h and $a_{h-1}a_h$ by ka_h' and $a_{h-1}a_h'$ has less length than T (see the argument in *18*). Thus we have (see Fig. 9)

$$\cos \tfrac{1}{2}\angle ka_ha_{h-1} \geqslant \sin \angle ka_hb_1 \geqslant \sin \angle ka_hb_i$$

where we have used the fact that

$$\angle ka_h b_i < \angle ka_h b_1 < \pi - \angle ka_h b_i.$$

The second of these inequalities follows because $\angle a_{h-1}a_h k \geqslant \tfrac{2}{3}\pi$ and thus $\angle ka_h b_1 \leqslant \tfrac{1}{3}\pi$ (from 12). Similarly

$$\cos \tfrac{1}{2}\angle kb_i b_{i-1} \geqslant \sin \angle kb_i c_j.$$
$$\cos \tfrac{1}{2}\angle kc_j c_{j-1} \geqslant \sin \angle kc_j a_h.$$

Now

$$\angle ka_h b_i + \angle kb_i c_j + \angle kc_j a_h \geqslant \tfrac{1}{3}\pi, \tag{20}$$

for if (20) were false, a consideration of the angles of the triangle $a_h b_i c_j$ would lead to the inequality

$$\angle ka_h c_j + \angle kb_i a_h + \angle kc_j b_i > \tfrac{2}{3}\pi \tag{21}$$

Of the three segments ka_h, kb_i, kc_j at least one has the least length. Suppose for definiteness that it is ka_h. Then, since $ka_h \leqslant kc_j$,

$$\angle kb_i a_h + \angle kc_j b_i = \angle kb_i a_h + \tfrac{1}{3}\pi - \angle kb_i c_j \leqslant \tfrac{1}{3}\pi \tag{22}$$

Also

$$\angle ka_h c_j \leqslant \tfrac{1}{3}\pi. \tag{23}$$

(23) and (22) combine to show that (21) is false and thus that (20) is true.

From the concavity of the function of $\sin \theta$ as θ varies from 0 to $\tfrac{1}{2}\pi$, we deduce from (20) that

$$\sin \angle ka_h b_i + \sin \angle kb_i c_j + \sin \angle kc_j a_h \geqslant \tfrac{1}{2}\sqrt{3}$$

and hence, from the first inequalities which we established,

$$\cos \tfrac{1}{2}\angle ka_h a_{h-1} + \cos \tfrac{1}{2}\angle kb_i b_{i-1} + \cos \tfrac{1}{2}\angle kc_j c_{j-1} \geqslant \tfrac{1}{2}\sqrt{3} \tag{24}$$

We now obtain a new tree T_1 from T by two processes. Firstly we move a_h, b_i, c_j a distance δ along the internal bisectors of the angles $\angle ka_h a_{h-1}$, $\angle kb_i b_{i-1}$ $\angle kc_j c_{j-1}$ respectively into positions a_h', b_i', c_j', and replace segments $a_h a_{h-1}$, $b_i b_{i-1}$, $c_j c_{j-1}$, $a_h k$, $b_i k$, $c_j k$ by segments $a_h' a_{h-1}$ $b_i' b_{i-1}$, $c_j' c_{j-1}$, $a_h' k$, $b_i' k$, $c_j' k$ respectively. Secondly we remove from the ends a_1, b_1, c_1 of those segments of this new tree which terminate at these points, segments of length δ. The convex cover of T_1 has no more vertices than has P and

$$\Lambda(T_1) = \Lambda(T) - 3\delta - 2\delta \left(\cos \tfrac{1}{2}\angle ka_h a_{h-1} + \cos \tfrac{1}{2}\angle kb_i b_{i-1}\right.$$
$$\left. + \cos \tfrac{1}{2}\angle kc_j c_{j-1}\right) + O(\delta^2) < \Lambda(T) - 4\delta$$

if δ is small, from (24). But every point of T is within a distance δ of some point of T_1. Thus

$$\mu(T_1) \geqslant \mu(T) - 2\delta$$

Since this implies $\dfrac{\mu(T_1)}{\Lambda(T_1)} > \dfrac{\mu(T)}{\Lambda(T)}$ we have a contradiction with (13).

This case cannot occur.

Case II. Two arcs α, β, γ, say α and β are each formed from more than one segment and the orders $a_1, \ldots, a_h$; $b_1, \ldots, b_i$ are such that the sector of angle $\frac{2}{3}\pi$ bounded by the half lines containing ka_h, kb_i respectively and terminating at k, is void of the points $a_1, \ldots, a_{h-1}b_1, \ldots, b_{i-1}$.

The argument is of the same type as that used in Case I. We have from triangle $a_h k b_i$

$$\angle ka_h b_i + \angle kb_i a_h = \tfrac{1}{3}\pi$$

Also, as in Case I,

$$\cos \tfrac{1}{2} \angle ka_h a_{h-1} \geqslant \sin \angle ka_h b_i, \; \cos \tfrac{1}{2} \angle kb_i b_{i-1} \geqslant \sin \angle kb_i a_h.$$

Thus

$$\cos \tfrac{1}{2} \angle ka_h a_{h-1} + \cos \tfrac{1}{2} \angle kb_i b_{i-1} \geqslant \tfrac{1}{2}\sqrt{3} \qquad (25)$$

Transform the tree T into a new tree T_1, by removing segments of length δ from each end point a_1, b_1, c_1 from the segments a_1a_2, b_1b_2, c_1c_2, and move a_h and b_i a distance δ along the internal bisectors of $\angle a_{h-1}a_h k$ and $\angle b_{i-1}b_i k$ respectively. Then

$$\Lambda(T_1) < \Lambda(T) - (3 + \sqrt{3})\delta + O(\delta^2),$$
$$\mu(T_1) \geqslant \mu(T) - 2\delta,$$

and again we have a contradiction with (13). Case II cannot occur.

Case III. One arc, say α, is a single segment and the other two arcs each contain more than one segment. The orders of $b_1, \ldots, b_i$ and $c_1, \ldots, c_j$ are such that all these points belong to the sector whose angle is $\frac{2}{3}\pi$ and which is bounded by half-rays containing kb_i and kc_j respectively and terminating at k.

In this case the vertices b_1 and c_1 are P-adjacent. (See Fig. 10.) We show firstly that the line b_1b_2 meets the line c_1c_2 at a point which lies on the same side of b_1c_1 as k and that, of the four sectors into which the lines b_1b_2 and c_1c_2 divide the plane, the sector containing k has an angle greater than or equal to $\frac{1}{3}\pi$. Remove from T two segments of length δ, one from b_1b_2, with end point at b_1, and one from c_1c_2 with end point at c_1. Denote the subtree of T which remains by T_1. Now there are parallel support lines of P through b_1 and c_1 by *13* and b_1b_2 cannot be parallel to c_1c_2 by *19* (with an appropriate change of notation). Thus b_1b_2 meets c_1c_2 at a point on the same side of b_1c_1 as k.

Let P_1 be the convex cover of T_1, and l_1, l_2 be a pair of parallel support lines of P. If one or other of l_1 or l_2 is a support line of P_1

then the distance apart of the two parallel support lines of P_1 is at least $\mu(T) - \delta$. If neither l_1 nor l_2 is a support line of P_1, they pass, one each, through c_1 and b_1. The two parallel support lines of P_1 are at a distance apart which is equal to that of l_1 from l_2

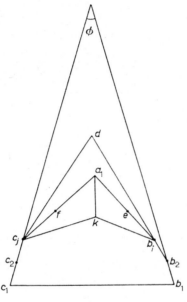

Fig. 10.

decreased by x where x is the sum of the lengths of the projections of the two segments removed from T, in the direction concerned.

Thus if the angle of the sector formed by $b_1 b_2$ and $c_1 c_2$ and containing k is ϕ we have

$$\mu(T_1) \geqslant \mu(T) - \max (\delta, 2\delta \sin \tfrac{1}{2}\phi).$$

We assume that $\phi < \tfrac{1}{3}\pi$. Then

$$\mu(T_1) = \mu(T) - \delta$$

Also,

$$\Lambda(T_1) = \Lambda(T) - 2\delta$$

As in *13* this implies that T_1 is another extremal figure. Let the end points of T_1 be b_1' in place of b_1 and c_1' in place of c_1. One pair of parallel support lines of P_1 through b_1' and c_1' are minimal support lines by *13*. But their distance apart is at least

$$\mu(T) - 2\delta \sin \tfrac{1}{2}\phi > \mu(T) - \delta$$

But since by (13)

$$\frac{\mu(T_1)}{\Lambda(T_1)} \leqslant \frac{\mu(T)}{\Lambda(T)}$$

we have $\mu(T_1) = \mu(T) - \delta$. Thus there is no pair of parallel minimal support lines of P_1 through b_1' and c_1'. This contradiction shows that $\phi \geqslant \frac{1}{3}\pi$.

Now, as in Case I,

$$\angle a_1 c_j k \leqslant \tfrac{1}{2}\pi - \tfrac{1}{2}\angle kc_j c_{j-1} \quad \angle a_1 b_i k \leqslant \tfrac{1}{2}\pi - \tfrac{1}{2}\angle kb_i b_{i-1}. \qquad (26)$$

Let $c_{j-1}c_j$ produced meet $b_{i-1}b_i$ in d. Then

$$\angle kc_j c_{j-1} = \angle c_j dk + \angle dkc_j \qquad \angle kb_i b_{i-1} = \angle b_i dk + \angle dkb_i.$$

Hence, since $\angle c_j db_i \geqslant \phi \geqslant \tfrac{1}{3}\pi$,

$$\angle kc_j c_{j-1} + \angle kb_i b_{i-1} = \angle c_j db_i + \tfrac{4}{3}\pi \geqslant \tfrac{5}{3}\pi. \qquad (27)$$

Thus by (26) and (27)

$$\angle a_1 c_j k + \angle a_1 b_i k \leqslant \tfrac{1}{6}\pi,$$

and finally

$$\angle c_j a_1 b_i = (\tfrac{1}{3}\pi - \angle a_1 c_j k) + (\tfrac{1}{3}\pi - \angle a_1 b_i k) \geqslant \tfrac{1}{2}\pi. \qquad (28)$$

Next $a_1 c_j$ is a minimal support line of P. For if it were not we could move c_j along $c_j c_{j-1}$ towards c_{j-1} into the position c_j'. In T replace segments kc_j, $c_j c_{j-1}$ by kc_j', $c_j' c_{j-1}$ respectively and denote the new tree by T_1. Then if c_j' is sufficiently close to c_j, $\mu(T) = \mu(T_1)$. Since $\Lambda(T_1) < \Lambda(T)$ we have a contradiction with (13). Thus $a_1 c_j$ is a minimal support line of P.

By the remark after *13* the support line of P parallel to $a_1 c_j$ passes through b_1. If f is the foot of the perpendicular from b_1 to line $a_1 c_j$ then by property (B) f belongs to segment $a_1 c_j$ and the segment $b_1 f$ is of length $\mu(T)$. For the parallel support line through b_1 cannot contain c_1 (or we should have $\Lambda(\gamma) > \mu(T)$ in contradiction with *14*) nor can it contain b_2 (since $b_1 b_2$ meets $c_1 c_2$ on the same side of $b_1 c_1$ as k). Thus this support line through b_1 meets P in the single point b_1. Similarly if e is the foot of the perpendicular from c_1 to $a_1 b_i$ then e belongs to the segment $a_1 b_i$ and the length of the segment $c_1 e$ is equal to $\mu(T)$.

The support line parallel to $b_1 c_1$ passes through a_1. Thus the perpendicular distance from a_1 to $b_1 c_1$ is greater than or equal to $\mu(T)$. Hence

$$\angle fa_1 b_1 \leqslant \angle a_1 b_1 c_1 \qquad \angle ea_1 c_1 \leqslant \angle a_1 c_1 b_1 \qquad (29)$$

But

$$\angle fa_1 e = \angle fa_1 b_1 + \angle ea_1 c_1 - \angle c_1 a_1 b_1$$

and thus from (28) and (29)

$$\angle a_1b_1c_1 + \angle a_1c_1b_1 - \angle c_1a_1b_1 \geqslant \angle fa_1e \geqslant \tfrac{1}{2}\pi .$$

But from triangle $a_1b_1c_1$

$$\angle a_1b_1c_1 + \angle a_1c_1b_1 + \angle c_1a_1b_1 = \pi .$$

Thus by addition

$$\angle a_1b_1c_1 + \angle a_1c_1b_1 > \tfrac{3}{4}\pi .$$

This implies that ϕ, the angle of the sector bounded by lines b_1b_2 and c_1c_2 and containing k, is less than $\tfrac{1}{4}\pi$. This is in contradiction with the fact, already established, that ϕ is not less than $\tfrac{1}{3}\pi$. The case cannot occur.

Case IV. One arc, say α, *is a single segment and the other two arcs are not single segments. The vertices* $b_1, \ldots, b_i$, $c_1 \ldots, c_j$ *are in order on the frontier of P.*

Either the three pairs a_1, c_j; c_1, b_i; b_1, a_1 are P-adjacent or the three pairs a_1, c_1; c_j, b_1; b_i, a_1 are P-adjacent. We suppose that the first alternative holds: the argument when the second alternative holds is the same with b's and c's interchanged.

By the argument used in Case III c_1b_i and a_1c_j are minimal support lines of P. Produce c_1b_i in both directions to meet a_1c_j produced in e and a_1b_1 produced in f.

Now each of the angles ea_1f, a_1fe, a_1ef is not greater than $\tfrac{1}{2}\pi$. For, since c_1b_i is a minimal support line and the parallel support line through a_1 meets P in the single point a_1 (otherwise we should have $\Lambda(\beta) > \mu(T)$ in contradiction with *14*) it follows from (*B*) that the perpendicular from a_1 to ef intersects the segment b_ic_1 and therefore

$$\angle a_1ef < \tfrac{1}{2}\pi, \qquad \angle a_1fe < \tfrac{1}{2}\pi .$$

Also by *19* b_1b_2 is not parallel to a_1e and thus, by a similar argument, the perpendicular from b_1 to a_1e meets segment a_1c_j, thus

$$\angle fa_1e \leqslant \tfrac{1}{2}\pi .$$

By *12* $\angle kc_jc_{j-1} \geqslant \tfrac{2}{3}\pi$ and by the argument used in Case I $\angle a_1c_jk \leqslant \angle ec_jc_{j-1}$. Thus $\angle a_1c_jk \leqslant \tfrac{1}{6}\pi$ and this implies, from triangle a_1kc_j that $\angle ea_1k \geqslant \tfrac{1}{6}\pi$. Also $\angle kb_ie \leqslant \tfrac{1}{6}\pi$.

Project the polygonal line a_1, k, b_i in the direction of c_1b_i. We have

$$a_1k + \tfrac{1}{2}kb_i \geqslant \mu(T).$$

Project the polygonal line $c_1, c_2, \ldots, c_j, k, b_i, b_{i-1}, \ldots, b_1$ in the direction a_1b_i. We have

$$kc_j + \ldots + c_2c_1 + kb_i \sin \angle kb_ia_1 + b_ib_{i-1} + \ldots + b_1b_2 \geqslant \mu(T).$$

Now if $kb_i > ka_1$, then $\angle kb_ia_1 < \frac{1}{6}\pi$ and on adding the above inequalities we obtain

$$\Lambda(T) > 2\,\mu(T)$$

in contradiction with (*). Thus $kb_i \leqslant ka_1$.

But in triangle kc_jb_i

$$\angle kb_ic_j < \angle kb_ie \leqslant \tfrac{1}{6}\pi, \qquad \angle kc_jb_i + \angle kb_ic_j = \tfrac{1}{3}\pi.$$

Thus

$$\angle kb_ic_j < \angle kc_jb_i,$$

and this implies that

$$kc_j < kb_i.$$

Similarly

$$ka_1 \leqslant kc_j.$$

Thus

$$ka_1 < kb_i$$

and we have a contradiction.

This case cannot occur.

Case V. Two of the arcs are single segments and one is composed of more than one segment.

We assume without loss of generality that the arc α is the only arc with more than one segment and that the points $a_ha_{h-1}, \ldots,$ a_1, b_1, c_1 are in the clockwise order round the frontier of P (see Fig. 11).

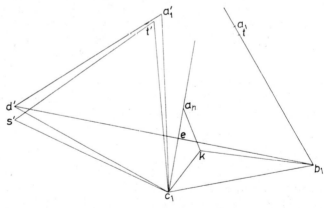

Fig. 11.

As in the previous case c_1a_h is a minimal support line and the perpendicular distance from b_1 to c_1a_h is $\mu(T)$. We show first that a_1b_1 is a minimal support line of P. By *17* if this is not the case the line through a_1 perpendicular to a_1a_2 is a minimal support line. It cannot therefore coincide with a_1b_1 and must meet P in the single point a_1. By property (B) the line a_1a_2 meets P in a segment of length $\mu(T)$ i.e. the length of segment a_1a_2 is $\mu(T)$. This is in contradiction with 14. Thus a_1b_1 is a minimal support line of P.

The perpendicular distances of b_1 and c_1 from a_hc_1 and a_1b_1 respectively are both equal to $\mu(T)$. Thus $\angle a_hc_1b_1 = \angle a_1b_1c_1$. If these angles are less than $\frac{1}{3}\pi$ the perpendicular distance of a_1 from b_1c_1 is less than $\mu(T)$. This is not so. If these angles are equal to $\frac{1}{3}\pi$, then a_1 must be the third vertex of an equilateral triangle $a_1b_1c_1$. There are then no other vertices $a_2, \ldots, a_h$. This case is considered later (see Case VI). Thus in fact

$$\angle a_hc_1b_1 = \angle a_1b_1c_1 > \tfrac{1}{3}\pi.$$

Since the perpendicular distance from a_1 to b_1c_1 is greater than or equal to that of c_1 from a_1b_1 we have

$$a_1b_1 \geqslant c_1b_1$$

On a_1b_1 let t be such that $tb_1 = c_1b_1$. Let a_1', t' be the reflections of a_1, t in a_hc_1 respectively. On $a_1'c_1$ erect the equilateral triangle where third vertex d' lies on the side of $a_1'c_1$ opposite to b_1, and on c_1t' erect the equilateral triangle where third vertex s' lies on the side of $t'c_1$ opposite to b_1. Let s and d be the reflections of s' and d' respectively in a_hc_1. Then by the lemma

$$\Lambda(T) \geqslant d'b_1.\dagger$$

Let $d'b_1$ meet line a_hc_1 in e. Now, since $\angle tb_1c_1 > \tfrac{1}{3}\pi$ and $b_1t = b_1c_1$ we have

$$\angle c_1tb_1 = \angle tc_1b_1 < \tfrac{1}{3}\pi$$

Therefore b_1 is a point of the triangle c_1ts. The vector $\boldsymbol{sd}$ is equal to the vector $\boldsymbol{ta_1}$ rotated in the clockwise sense through an angle of $\frac{1}{3}\pi$. Since $\angle a_hc_1b_1 = \angle a_1b_1c_1 > \tfrac{1}{3}\pi$ it follows that the perpendicular distance of d from a_hc_1 is greater than that of s from a_hc_1 and since b_1 is a point of triangle c_1st this last distance is greater than $\mu(T)$. Thus

$$de > \mu(T).$$

Since $b_1e \geqslant \mu(T)$ we have

$$\Lambda(T) \geqslant b_1d' = b_1e + ed > 2\mu(T).$$

This is in contradiction with (*).

This case cannot occur.

$\dagger$ $\angle a_1'c_1b_1 < \tfrac{2}{3}\pi$, for otherwise $\Lambda(T) > c_1a_1' + c_1b_1 = c_1a_1 + c_1b_1 > 2\mu(T)$; $\angle a_1'b_1c_1 < \angle a_1b_1c_1 \leqslant \tfrac{1}{2}\pi$; $\angle c_1a_1'b_1 < \pi - \angle a_1'c_1b_1 < \pi - \angle a_hc_1b_1 < \tfrac{2}{3}\pi$.

Case VI. Each arc α, β, γ *is a single segment.*

On the largest side of $a_1b_1c_1$, say on b_1c_1 erect the equilateral triangle whose third vertex d lies on the side of b_1c_1 opposite to a_1. Triangle b_1c_1d has area greater than or equal to that of triangle $a_1b_1c_1$. Thus the perpendicular distance of d from b_1c_1 is greater than or equal to that of a_1 from b_1c_1. If $a_1b_1c_1$ is not equilateral we have

$$\Lambda(T) = a_1d > 2\mu(T).$$

This is in contradiction with (*). Thus $a_1b_1c_1$ is equilateral.

This concludes the proof that $\mu(T) \leqslant \frac{1}{2}\Lambda(T)$ and that the only extremal figure whose convex cover is a polygon is formed from three equal equally inclined segments.

§4. E is a simple arc

Let $A_{(n)}$ be the class of all simple polygonal arcs of unit length composed of at most n segments. Define k by

$$\kappa = (\sec\alpha + 2\tan\alpha + \pi - 4\beta - 2\alpha)$$

where

$$\tfrac{1}{2} + \sin\alpha = 4\cos^2\alpha/(1 + 4\cos^2\alpha)$$

and

$$\tan\beta = \tfrac{1}{2}\sec\alpha.$$

By Theorem 3 of §2 it is sufficient to show that for any member E of $A_{(n)}$

$$\frac{1}{\mu(E)} \geqslant \kappa$$

Write

$$\inf_{E \in A_{(n)}} \frac{1}{\mu(E)} = \tau$$

By the arguments used by P. A. P. Moran [6] there is a member T of $A_{(n)}$ for which $\mu(T) = \tau^{-1}$.

We shall assume that

$$\kappa \geqslant \tau \tag{31}$$

and show that this assumption leads to a contradiction. The method is similar to that used in §3 in that it depends upon appropriately chosen variations of T.

Denote the polygon which is the convex cover of T by P, and let the end points of the segments of T be $t_1, t_2, \ldots, t_n$ in order.

1. *The points common to two segments of T and the two end-points of T are vertices of P.*

    Obvious: Cf. §3.4.

2. *Every vertex of P is either a point common to two segments of T or is an end-point of T.*

Obvious: Cf. §3.1.

3. *The polygon P subtends an angle of not more than $\frac{1}{2}\pi$ at each end-point of T.*

By the same argument as that used in §3.*15*, t_1 and t_2 are P-adjacent. Suppose that t_h is the other vertex of PP-adjacent to t_1. If $\angle t_2t_1t_h > \frac{1}{2}\pi$ let t_1' be a point on the line t_ht_1 such that t_1 lies between t_1' and t_h and $\angle t_2t_1't_h \geqslant \frac{1}{2}\pi$. In T replace segment t_2t_1 by segment t_2t_1'. We suppose that t_1' is so close to t_1 that the new connected set T' is an arc. Then

$$\Lambda(T') < \Lambda(T) \qquad \mu(T') \geqslant \mu(T)$$

Since $T' \in A(n)$ we have a contradiction with the minimal property of T. Hence $\angle t_2t_1t_h \leqslant \frac{1}{2}\pi$.

4. *There are parallel support lines of P, one through each of the end points t_1, t_n of T.*

This is an immediate consequence of 3.

5. *Let t_i be a vertex of P which is not an end point of T, such that of the vertices t_{i-1}, t_{i+1} at most one, say t_{i-1}, is P-adjacent to t_i. Let t_j be the other vertex of P P-adjacent to t_i, then*

$$\angle t_{i+1}t_it_j + \angle t_{i-1}t_it_j \leqslant \pi$$

On the line t_jt_i let p be a point such that t_i lies between p and t_j. Then if $\angle t_{i+1}t_it_j + \angle t_{i-1}t_it_j > \pi$ it follows that

$$\angle t_{i+1}t_it_j > \angle t_{i-1}t_ip.$$

But if we move t_i along t_ip towards p through a small distance to the position t_i' and in T replace segments $t_{i-1}t_i$, t_it_{i+1} by $t_{i-1}t_i'$, $t_i't_{i+1}$ respectively we obtain a new member T' of $A(n)$ for which

$$\Lambda(T') < \Lambda(T) \qquad \mu(T') \geqslant \mu(T)$$

This is impossible because of the extremal property of T. Thus *5* is established.

6. *It is possible to find two vertices of T say t_i, t_j, $i < j$, with the following properties.*

  (a) *t_i and t_j are P-adjacent.*
  (b) *The support line of P parallel to t_it_j, other than the line t_it_j itself, meets P in a vertex t_h with $i < h < j$.*

Consider two vertices for which (a) is true (there are such vertices).

Denote by $T(i, j)$ the subarc $t_i t_j$ of T and by $K(i, j)$ the set of points of intersection of the line joining t_i to t_j with support lines of P that pass through some vertex t_k of $T(i, j)$ other than t_i or t_j. If t_i, t_j do not satisfy (a) we define $K(i, j)$ to be the void set.

If $K(i, j)$ is non-void and unbounded then t_i, t_j satisfy (b). We shall assume that each non-void $K(i, j)$ is bounded and show that this assumption leads to a contradiction.

If t_i, t_j are P-adjacent $i < j$, then distinct consecutive members of $t_{i+1}, \ldots, t_{j-1}$ are also P-adjacent (if there are any). For if for example t_k was not P-adjacent to t_{k+1} then the segment $t_k t_{k+1}$ would divide P into two domains. Of these domains one must contain both t_i and t_j since they are P-adjacent. The other domain contains a vertex t_r with either $r < k$ or $r > k+1$. If $r < k$, $T(r, i)$ which joins t_r to t_i, cuts $t_k t_{k+1}$. This is not so since T is an arc. Similarly we cannot have $r > k + 1$ and in fact t_k and t_{k+1} are P-adjacent.

It follows that two members of $t_{i+1}, \ldots, t_{j-1}$ which are not T-adjacent are also not P-adjacent. For if there were two such members at t_h and t_g, $h < g$, then, in the sequence $t_h, t_{h+1} \ldots, t_{g-1}$, t_g, t_h each consecutive pair is P-adjacent and thus the segments $t_h t_{h+1}, \ldots, t_{g-1} t_g, t_g t_h$ would comprise the whole of the frontier of P. This is not so since t_i belongs to the frontier of P and to none of these segments. Thus since $K(g, g + 1)$ is void for all g we see that $K(g, h)$ is void for all g, h satisfying $i \leqslant g < h \leqslant j$ except $g = i, h = j$.

If $K(i, j)$ is non-void and bounded it is a closed segment. For it is the union of segments one corresponding to each t_k with $i < k < j$ and $t_k t_{k+1}$ is a support line of P and thus intersects $t_i t_j$ in a point belonging to the segment corresponding to t_k and to the segment corresponding to t_{k+1}. Thus these segments abut to form one segment.

The end points t_1, t_n of T are each end points of exactly one segment say $K(l, i_1)$ and $K(j_1, n)$ respectively since $t_1 t_2$ and $t_{n-1} t_n$ are P-adjacent pairs. Now an end point e of $K(i, j)$ other than t_1 or t_n lies on $t_i t_j$ and on a support line through t_k, $i < k < j$. This support line must pass through a second vertex t_l of P or e would not be an end point of $K(i, j)$. If $i < l < j$ then t_k and t_l are T-adjacent i.e. $l = k - 1$ or $k + 1$ but then this again contradicts the fact that e is an end point of $K(i, j)$. Thus either $l < i < k$ or $k < j < l$. Suppose the former. Then $K(l, k)$ is not void; it contains e. Now no three of the segments $K(i, j)$ can meet for if they did it would imply that three support lines of P would be concurrent. Also no two segments $K(i, j)$, $K(g, h)$ can meet except possibly at end points of each. For if they did each of the segments $K(i, j)$, $K(g, h)$ would be on support lines of P and since there are at most two support lines through any one point the line containing $K(g, h)$ would be a line used in the definition of $K(i, j)$, i.e. it would meet P in a vertex t_k with $i < k < j$. But any non-end point of $K(i, j)$ lies on a support line of P that meets P exclusively in points of $T(i, j)$. Thus $i \leqslant g < h \leqslant j$ and as remarked above this implies that $K(g, h)$ is void. Thus $K(g, h)$ meets $K(i, j)$ in an end point of $K(i, j)$. Similarly this end point is an end point of $K(g, h)$.

It follows that the union of all the non-void sets $K(i, j)$ contains a simple arc joining t_1 to t_n.

By 4 there are two parallel support lines of P one each through t_1 and t_n. Denote the open strip bounded by these support lines by U. We may assume that t_1 and t_n are not P-adjacent for if they are then (b) obviously holds with $i = 1, j = n$.

The line $t_1 t_n$ divides the frontier of P into two arcs which are disjoint except for the fact that they both have t_1 and t_n as end points. Denote these two arcs by X_1 and X_2. Of the two P-adjacent vertices $t_i t_j$ $(i < j)$ either both belong to X_1 or both to X_2 or one is t_1 or t_n and in any case the segment $t_i t_j$ of the frontier of P is contained in X_1 or X_2. If $t_i t_j$ is contained in X_1 and $K(i, j)$ is non-void then all vertices t_k $(i < k < j)$ belong to X_2 and vice-versa. In any case the part of the line $t_i t_j$ contained in U is separated from t_k by $t_1 t_n$. Thus no part of the line $t_i t_j$ in U can belong to $K(i, j)$ for such a point is joined to t_k by a segment which on the one hand is contained in U and on the other cannot meet the part of $t_1 t_n$ contained in U.

Hence

$$K(i, j) \cap U = \emptyset.$$

But U separates t_1 from t_n and $\bigcup K(i, j)$ joins t_1 to t_n thus for some pair (i, j) $K(i, j) \cap U \neq \emptyset$. This contradiction shows that for some i, j $K(i, j)$ is unbounded and (b) holds.

We can now complete the proof of the inequality $\tau \geqslant \kappa$ by considering two possible cases and by showing that in each case the assumption (31) leads to a contradiction.

Case I. There is a pair of integers i, j such that $t_i t_j$ satisfy 6 and one of t_i, t_j is not an end point of T.

Suppose for definiteness that $1 \leqslant i < j < n$. Let t_k, $i < k < j$, be the vertex of P at which a support line is parallel to $t_i t_j$. If

$$\angle t_k t_j t_i \leqslant \tfrac{1}{4}\pi$$

the length of the segment $t_k t_j$ is at least $\sqrt{2}\mu(T)$ and since that of $t_i t_k$ is at least $\mu(T)$ we see that

$$\Lambda(T) \geqslant (1 + \sqrt{2})\mu(T)$$

since calculation shows that

$$\mu(T) = \frac{1}{\tau} \geqslant \frac{1}{\kappa} > \frac{1}{2\cdot28}$$

we have

$$\Lambda(T) > 1$$

By our original assumption this is not so. Thus $\angle t_k t_j t_i > \frac{1}{4}\pi$.
   Since, by 5

$$\angle t_i t_j t_{j+1} + \angle t_{j-1} t_j t_{j+1} \leqslant \pi$$

and

$$\angle t_{j-1} t_j t_i \geqslant t_k t_j t_i > \frac{1}{4}\pi$$

we have

$$\angle t_{j-1} t_j t_{j+1} \leqslant \frac{3}{8}\pi$$

Now construct a new arc from T by removing a segment of length δ from the end of $t_{n-1}t_n$ at t_n and moving t_j along the internal bisector of $\angle t_{j-1} t_j t_{j+1}$ a distance δ to t'_j and replacing segments $t_{j-1}t_j$, $t_j t_{j+1}$ by $t_{j-1}t'_j$ and $t'_j t_{j+1}$. If δ is small we do in fact obtain a new arc. We denote it by T_1. Then since there are not two parallel support lines of P through t_j and t_n† we have

$$\mu(T_1) \geqslant \mu(T) - \delta$$

Also

$$\Lambda(T_1) \leqslant \Lambda(T) - \delta - 2\,\delta \cos \frac{3\pi}{16} + O(\delta^2)$$

But these inequalities imply, if δ is small,

$$\frac{\mu(T_1)}{\Lambda(T_1)} \geqslant \frac{\mu(T)}{\Lambda(T)}$$

and this is impossible by the extremal property of T.
   This case cannot occur.

Case II. The only pair of integers i, j for which t_i, t_j satisfy 6 are $i = 1$ and $j = n$.

In this case t_1, t_n are P-adjacent and this implies that the whole arc T lies in the frontier of P. Let t_k be the vertex of T, $1 < k < n$, at which there is a support line parallel to $t_1 t_n$.
   Denote the common part of the two circular discs whose centres are t_1 and t_n and whose radii are $\mu(T)$ by D. The part of D on the same side of $t_1 t_n$ as t_k is contained in P. Denote it by D_1. Denote

---

† If there were each subarc $T(i, k)$, $T(k, j)$, $T(j, n)$ of T would be of length greater than or equal to $\mu(T)$. Hence

$$\Lambda(T) \geqslant 3\mu(T) > 1$$

a contradiction since $\Lambda(T) = 1$.

the convex cover of t_1, t_k, t_n and D_1 by P_1 and the length of the frontier of P_1 excluding the segment t_1t_n by $X(P_1)$.

Steiner symmetrisation† about the perpendicular bisector of t_1t_n shows that $X(P_1)$ is least when t_k lies on the perpendicular

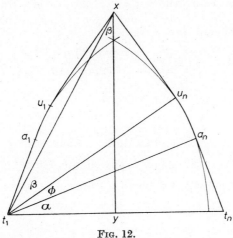

FIG. 12.

bisector of t_1t_n. Also $X(P_1)$ is least when the distance of t_k from t_1t_n is $\mu(T)$. Denote this position of t_k by x and the corresponding convex cover of t_1, x, t_n, D_1 by P_2. Let the points of contact of the lines of support from x to D_1 be u_1 and u_n and those from t_1 and t_n to be a_1 and a_n respectively where the point u_1 is on the same side of the perpendicular bisector of t_1t_n as is t_1. Denote the length of the frontier of P_2 excluding t_1t_n by L and letting y be the mid-point of t_1t_n. (See Fig. 12.)

Suppose the points $t_1a_1u_1xu_na_nt_n$ are in order on the frontier of P_2.

If δ is a small positive number and we move t_1 along t_1t_n a distance δ to t_1' and t_n along t_nt_1 a distance δ to t_n' and then form P_2 and L' from t_1', t_n', x in exactly the same way that P_2 and L were formed from t_1, t_n, x, we have

$$L' = L + 2\delta \sin \angle yxu_n - 4\delta \sin \angle a_nt_1t_n + o(\delta),$$

since, to within a term in $o(\delta)$ the effect is to translate u_n, a_n by δ in the sense $\overrightarrow{t_1t_n}$ parallel to t_1t_n and u_1, a_1 by an equal amount in the opposite sense. Thus L is least when either

† If a line parallel to t_1t_n meets P_1 in a segment then this segment is moved along this line until its mid-point lies on the perpendicular bisector of t_1t_n. This process applied to all lines parallel to t_1t_n is called Steiner symmetrisation. It transforms a convex set into a convex set and reduces the length of its perimeter.

(i) x, t_1, t_n are all distant $\dfrac{2}{\sqrt{3}}\mu(T)$ from one another, or

(ii) t_1, t_n are distant $\mu(T)$ from one another, or

(iii) $\sin \angle yxu_n = 2 \sin \angle a_n t_1 t_n$.

In the third case write β for $\angle xt_1u_n = \angle yxt_1$ (this equality is because $xy = t_1 u_n = \mu(T)$), and α for $\angle a_n t_1 t_n$. Then calculating $t_1 t_n$ in two different ways we have,

$$t_1 t_n = t_1 a_n \sec \alpha = \mu(T) \sec \alpha$$
$$t_1 t_n = 2xy \tan \beta = 2\mu(T) \tan \beta$$

thus

$$\tan \beta = \tfrac{1}{2} \sec \alpha \tag{32}$$

also

$$\angle yxu_n = \angle u_n t_1 y = \phi + \alpha$$

where $\phi = \angle u_n t_1 a_n$. Thus by (iii)

$$\sin (\phi + \alpha) = 2 \sin \alpha.$$

But from triangle xyt_1 we have

$$\beta = \tfrac{1}{2}\pi - (\beta + \alpha + \phi).$$

Hence,

$$\cos 2\beta = 2 \sin \alpha$$

Substituting for β from (32) we have

$$\tfrac{1}{2} + \sin \alpha = \frac{4 \cos^2 \alpha}{1 + 4 \cos^2 \alpha} \tag{33}$$

Also

$$L = (2 \tan \alpha + 2\phi + 2 \tan \beta)\mu(T)$$
$$= (2 \tan \alpha + \sec \alpha + \pi - 4\beta - 2\alpha)\mu(T)$$

Calculation shows that in the third case $L = 2 \cdot 273\mu(T)$ approximately and that in (i) $L = 2 \cdot 309\mu(T)$ in (ii) $L = 2 \cdot 28\mu(T)$. Thus L is least in the third case, and we have proved that

$$\Lambda(T) \geqslant L \geqslant \kappa\mu(T) > 1$$

But this is not so by assumption. Thus (31) leads to a contradiction in all cases and must itself be false.

Thus the required inequality is established.

§5. Further problems

There are many other problems of the same type as those considered in §3 and §4. If T is any connected set of finite linear measure and $f(X)$ an increasing functional of the convex set X then the number

$$\sup_T \frac{f(H(T))}{\Lambda(T)} = \mu_f$$

(where $H(T)$ is the convex cover of T) conveys certain information about the relationship between a connected set and its convex cover. Examples of the function $f(X)$ are the area of X, the inradius of X, the circumradius of X, the perimeter of X, the diameter of X, the moment of inertia of X about its centroid, etc. Of these some lead only to trivial results either because an extremal figure is obvious or because the ratio $f(H(T))/\Lambda(T)$ is not an invarient under similarity transformations.

We consider here the case when $f(X)$ is the square root of the area of X. This problem can be replaced by another one as follows. Consider a finite set of n points in R^2, say the set E. Let A be the area of the convex cover of E. What is the least measure of any connected set which contains E, expressed in terms of A and n? We shall show that

$$\Lambda(K) \geqslant 2[A(n-1)\tan\pi/(2(n-1))]^{\frac{1}{2}} \quad n > 3 \qquad (34)$$

$$\Lambda(K) \geqslant 2[A\sqrt{3}]^{\frac{1}{2}} \qquad\qquad\qquad n = 3. \qquad (35)$$

Since as $n \to \infty$ the right-hand side of (34) decreases to $(2\pi A)^{\frac{1}{2}}$ it follows that μ_f calculated for f equal to the square root of the area is $(2\pi)^{-\frac{1}{2}}$. This is an immediate consequence of Theorem 3.2. In turn the fact that $\mu_f = 1/(2\pi)^{\frac{1}{2}}$ implies a result of P. A. P. Moran who proved a conjecture of S. Ulam, namely that the convex cover of an arc of unit length has area less than or equal to $1/2\pi$. This result is best possible since equality is attained when the arc is a semi-circle, whether this is the only extremal curve is not known. The results given in (34) and (35) are also best possible. In (34) equality is attained when E is a set of consecutive vertices of a regular $2(n-1) - gon$ and K is the arc joining them. In (35) equality holds when E is the set of vertices of an equilateral triangle and K is formed from three equal segments inclined at an angle of $\frac{2}{3}\pi$ with one another.

The proof of (34) and (35) is quite simple. As in §3 let $\mathscr{L}(n)$ be the class of closed connected plane sets which are of finite positive linear measure and whose convex covers are polygons with at most n vertices. Denote the area of the convex cover of T by $A(T)$. Write

$$K_n = \sup_{T \in \mathscr{L}(n)} \frac{[A(T)]^{\frac{1}{2}}}{\Lambda(T)}.$$

It is not difficult to prove that there is a member T_0 of $\mathscr{L}(n)$ for which

$$K_n = \frac{[A(T_0)]^{\frac{1}{2}}}{\Lambda(T_0)}.$$

6

There may be more than one such member of $\mathscr{L}(n)$. If there is we select one whose convex cover has the least possible number of vertices. Denote this set by T^* and the convex cover of T^* by P^*.

As in the problem considered in §3, T^* is a polygonal tree and is a connected set of the least possible measure containing the vertices of P^*. Every end point of T^* is a vertex of P^* and every node of T^* is an interior point of P^*.

Next, the segment joining any two end-points of T^* lies in the frontier of P^*. For suppose that there were two end points p_1, p_2 of T^* such that the segment p_1p_2 met the interior of P^*. Let p_1q_1 and p_2q_2 be the segments of T^* which terminate at p_1 and p_2 respectively. Take points p_1' on line p_1q_1 distant x_1 from p_1, where x_1 is positive if p_1 lies between p_1' and p_1 and negative otherwise, and p_2' on line p_2q_2 distant x_2 from p_2'. Both x_1 and x_2 are not greater than the least length of segments p_1q_1 and p_2q_2. In T^* replace p_1q_1 by $p_1'q_1$ and p_2q_2 by $p_2'q_2$. Denote the new polygonal tree by $T^*(x_1, x_2)$ and its area by $A(x_1, x_2)$. Now if $x_1 > 0$ is small

$$\Lambda(T^*(x_1, -x_1)) = \Lambda(T^*)$$

Thus $A(x_1, -x_1) \leqslant A(T^*)$. But if $A(x_1, -x_1) < A(T^*)$, then $A(-x_1, x_1) > A(T^*)$. This is impossible. Hence

$$A(x_1, -x_1) = A(T^*)$$

We increase x_1 until either $p_1'p_2'$ lies in the frontier of P^* or p_2' coincides with q_2. This is impossible. In each case we obtain an extremal figure whose convex cover has less vertices than P^*. This is impossible by the choice of P^*. Thus every segment joining two end points of T^* lies in the frontier of P^*.

Thus T^* has either three end points or two end points. If T^* has three end points the segments joining them in pairs lie in the frontier of P^* thus P^* is a triangle and T^* is formed from three segments inclined to one another at an angle of $\frac{2}{3}\pi$. If T^* has two end points it is an arc and must lie entirely in the frontier of P^*.

Consider the first alternative. Let the lengths of the three segments be l_1, l_2, l_3. Then

$$\begin{aligned} A(T^*) &= \tfrac{1}{4}\sqrt{3} \cdot (l_1l_2 + l_2l_3 + l_3l_1) \\ &= [2(\Lambda(T^*))^2 - (l_1 - l_2)^2 - (l_1 - l_3)^2 - (l_2 - l_3)^2]/8\sqrt{3} \\ &\leqslant [\Lambda(T^*)]^2/4\sqrt{3}. \end{aligned}$$

Thus (35) (and *a fortiori* (34)) is true in this case.

Consider the second alternative. Let the arc T^* be $p_1p_2 \ldots p_k$ where each p_i is a vertex of P^*. Then segment p_ip_{i+1} is of equal length to segment $p_{i-1}p_i$ $i = 2, \ldots, k - 1$. For otherwise we can symmetrize the triangle $p_{i-1}p_ip_{i+1}$ about the perpendicular bisector of segment $p_{i-1}p_{i+1}$ to reduce $\Lambda(T^*)$ without affecting $A(T^*)$. This is impossible by the definition of T^*. If P^* has only three vertices, then T^* is the sum of the lengths of the two shortest sides of P^*. Since T^* is the connected set of least length that contains the vertices of P^* this implies that one of the angles of P^* is at least $\frac{2}{3}\pi$ and T^* is the two sides adjacent to this angle. But then $A(T^*)$ can be increased without altering $\Lambda(T^*)$ by rotating one of these sides relative to the other until they form an angle equal to $\frac{1}{3}\pi$. By the extremal property of T^* this is impossible. Thus P^* has at least four vertices. We consider any four consecutive vertices of T^*, say p_1, p_2, p_3, p_4 for definiteness. We shall show that p_2p_3 is parallel to p_1p_4, and thus, since p_1p_2 and p_3p_4 are segments of equal length, that $\angle p_1p_2p_3 = \angle p_2p_3p_4$. If now p_2p_3 is not parallel to p_1p_4 suppose that p_3 is nearer to p_1p_4 than is p_2. Let the line through p_3 parallel to the line p_1p_4 cut the segment p_1p_2 in p_2'. Symmetrize the trapezium $p_1p_2'p_3p_4$ about the perpendicular bisector of p_1p_4 to obtain the trapezium $p_1p_2^*p_3^*p_4$. On $p_2^*p_3^*$ construct a triangle $tp_2^*p_3^*$ congruent to and similarly situated to $p_2p_2'p_3$. Now since p_3 is nearer to p_1p_4 than is p_2, we have $\angle p_2p_1p_4 > \angle p_3p_4p_1$ and thus $\angle tp_2^*p_3^* > \angle p_2^*p_1p_4$. It follows that p_2^* is an interior point of the convex cover of p_1, t, p_3^*, p_4. In T^* we replace p_1p_2, p_2p_3, p_3p_4 by $p_1t, tp_3^*, p_3^*p_4$. The effect is to reduce $\Lambda(T^*)$ and to increase $A(T^*)$, since however the new polygonal tree still is a member of $\mathscr{L}(n)$ we have a contradiction with the extremal property of T^*. It follows that all the angles $p_{i-1}p_ip_{i+1}$ are equal, $i = 2, \ldots k - 1$, and therefore that all the points $p_1, \ldots, p_k$ lie on a circle say C. Now p_1p_k is a diameter of C for if $\angle p_1p_2p_k \neq \frac{1}{2}\pi$ we could increase the area of triangle $p_2p_1p_k$ by a suitable small rotation of p_1p_2 about p_2. This is not so by the extremal property of T^*. Thus p_1p_k is a diameter of C. Direct calculation now leads to (34).

§6. Remarks

Although the arguments used in the three preceding paragraphs are both long and complicated they do not completely solve the problems concerned. They fail to characterize completely the extremal figures. In each case we are able to give one extremal figure but our methods are such that we are unable to say whether or not the figure is unique. Our method is to classify some of the possible figures into classes which are not difficult to deal with and then to obtain the final result by an approximation argument. In §4 it is not surprising that we are unable to define all the extremal figures since the one which we actually specify does not belong to any of the classes that we argue with, its convex cover is not a polygon. In §3 the extremal figure belongs to all these classes and is almost certainly unique. The methods used here are by no means exhausted. There are many other possible variations available and it may be possible to establish the uniqueness of the extremal set without using any really new ideas.

The argument in §3 could have been substantially simplified by the assumption $\mu(T) > \frac{1}{2}\Lambda(T)$ instead of $\mu(T) \geqslant \frac{1}{2}\Lambda(T)$. For the two key steps in the argument are to show that T has 3 end points and that every two end points lie on a pair of minimal support lines. Now (14) implies that T has at most 3 end points (if we assume $\mu(T) > \frac{1}{2}\Lambda(T)$ and the arguments given in *9* and *10* are unnecessary. Similarly (18) and (19) together imply the second key property of T without the complicated succeeding argument in *13*. But of course such a procedure abandons any hope of finding all the extremal figures.

There are many other problems similar to those solved here. For example we can consider the analogues of the problem of §§1, 3, 4, 5 in $R.^3$ The analogues of §5 in R^3 (i.e. to find the largest volume of the convex cover of a connected set of given length) is particularly interesting. The case when the connected set is restricted to be an arc, that is to say the three dimensional analogues of Ulam's conjecture has not been solved. It is likely that the solution is a certain equi-angular spiral (see Egerváry [4]), and that unlike the situation in R^2, the solution of the connected set problem does not imply that of the arc problem.

References

1. A. S. Besicovitch; "On the fundamental geometrical properties of linearly measurable plane sets of points II." *Math. Annalen* **115** (1938) 296–329.
2. A. S. Besicovitch; "On the fundamental geometrical properties of linearly measurable plane sets of points III." *Math. Annalen* **116** (1938–9) 349–57.
3. W. Blaschke; *Kreis and Kugel.* Leipzig (1916).
4. E. Egerváry; "On the smallest convex cover of a simple arc of space-curve." *Publ. math. Debrecen* **1** (1949) 65–70.
5. O. Hanner and H. Radström; "A generalization of a theorem of Fenchel." *Proc. American Math. Soc.* **2** (1951) 589–93.
6. P. A. P. Moran; "On a problem of S. Ulam." *J. London Math. Soc.* **21** (1946) 175–179.

CHAPTER II

PROBLEMS WHICH CAN BE REDUCED TO PROBLEMS ON CONVEX SETS

4TH PROBLEM. COVERING A THREE DIMENSIONAL
SET WITH SETS OF SMALLER DIAMETER

Introduction

It has been conjectured by K. Borsuk [1]† that every point set in real n-dimensional Euclidean space whose diameter is D can be regarded as the union of $n + 1$ sets each of diameter less than D. This conjecture has been established by H. Hadwiger [3], [4], [5], in the case in which the set can be enclosed in a convex set whose diameter is D and which has a smooth boundary, i.e. through every boundary point of which there passes exactly one support hyperplane‡. This condition of smoothness is essential to Hadwiger's argument but seems to have no intrinsic connection with the truth of the conjecture. Nor can the general case be deducted from Hadwiger's result by a limiting or approximation process. In the present paper we consider only three-dimensional space but in that space we prove Borsuk's conjecture without any restriction on the set involved.

To clarify the situation in three dimensions we give a summary of the solutions of the corresponding problem in two dimensions. In this case there are a very large number of solutions, which may be divided into three classes as follows.

(a) Methods which depend upon circumscribing a simple geometrical figure about the convex set. The figure is made as small as possible and is then divided into three sets each of diameter less than D. This subdivision implies a corresponding subdivision of the original set. An example of this method is the following. Let X be a set of diameter D. Then X may be enclosed§ in a set Y of constant width D which itself may be enclosed‖ in a regular hexagon Z whose minimal width is D. This hexagon can be split into three congruent parallelograms by joining alternate vertices

---

† The references are on p. 92.
‡ For notation see Bonnesen and Fenchel [6].
§ [6], p. 130.
‖ [6], p. 131.

77

to the centre. Each of these parallelograms is of diameter D and the part of X inside each of them is of diameter less than D unless Y is a Reuleaux triangle. In this last case we either use a different argument or redivide Z by joining to its centre the three vertices not previously employed. The resulting three parallelograms contain parts of X of diameter less than D.

Another example of this type is the method used by D. Gale in [2]. This method enables Gale to show that every plane set of diameter D is the union of three sets each of diameter less than or equal to $\frac{1}{2}\sqrt{3D}$, and that the factor $\frac{1}{2}\sqrt{3}$ cannot be improved upon.

(b) Methods depending upon some figure inscribed in the set. This figure is made as large as possible and is used as a basis for the subdivision of the original set.

(c) Methods which depend upon the fact that two points of a convex set X which is of diameter D, are at a distance D apart only if they lie on the frontier of X and if there exist two parallel support lines of X, one passing through each of the two points.

An example which combines both the ideas in (b) and (c) is the following. We need only consider sets of constant width D. Any such set X contains an inscribed circle with centre C that meets the frontier of X in points L, M, N, such that C is an interior point of the triangle $L\,M\,N$. The three segments CL, CM, CN divide X into three sets each of diameter less than D.

The difficulty of applying methods of type (a) or (b) or combinations of them in three-dimensional space is that the approximating figures which are available, approximate to the given convex set too crudely for the required result to be obtained.† On the other hand methods of type (c) can still be used and it is a method of this type that we actually follow. But of course one cannot hope to get a best possible result analogous to Gale's by such a method.

Although the method used here seems unduly intricate it does give an indication as to why the problem is so much easier when we make the restriction which Hadwiger imposed. It is because a certain continuous mapping on which our whole argument is based becomes, in this particular case, a homeomorphism. The method also draws attention to some interesting problems concerned with the characterization of convex sets of constant width and with certain classes of continuous mappings of spheres.

† This method has recently been used successfully by Mr. Grünbaum. It is of course much simpler than the method that I give here but throws no light on the problem itself nor does it seem likely that it can be extended to higher dimensional space. Mr. Grünbaum shows that a set of diameter D in R^3 can be divided into 4 sets each of diameter less than $0.9887D$.

§1. The continuous mapping

Since every set of diameter D is contained in a set of constant width D it is sufficient to establish the result for this latter class of sets. Let K be a set of constant width D in three-dimensional space. Let S be a sphere whose centre is the point O and let $x = f(s)$ be the continuous mapping of the surface of S onto the surface of K by means of corresponding parallel support planes,† that is to say, if σ is the tangent plane to S at s, then we define $f(s)$ to be that point on the surface of K at which the support plane to K, say τ, is parallel to σ and is such that K lies on the same side of τ as does S of σ. Since K is a set of constant width, every support plane meets it in a single point and thus $f(s)$ is uniquely defined for all points s on the surface of S.

It is sufficient to divide the surface of K into four sets K_1, K_2, K_3, K_4, each of diameter less than D. For if there is such a subdivision and x is any interior point of K then the four sets which are the convex covers of the sets $x \cup K_i$, $i = 1, 2, 3, 4$, cover the whole of K and are each of diameter less than D. In what follows we shall be exclusively concerned with the surfaces that bound K and S and we shall use the same symbols to denote these surfaces instead of the sets themselves.

If L is a subset of S then by L' we mean the reflection L in O. For any $x \in K$ we write $f^{-1}(x) = X$ so that $X \subset S$.

The mapping f has six properties that we require. The first three depend upon its being a continuous mapping defined over a compact space; the last three depend upon the particular way in which it is defined. These properties are as follows.

(i) For any $x \in K$, X is a closed subset of S.

(ii) If $x_1 \neq x_2$, then $X_1 \cap X_2 = \emptyset$.

(iii) The sets X form an upper semi-continuous decomposition of S.

(iv) X is a convex‡ subset of S.

(v) Any two points of X subtend at O an angle which is not greater than $\frac{1}{3}\pi$.

Let $X \in K$ and let τ be a support plane of K at x. Let the support plane parallel to τ and distinct from τ meet K in y. The segment xy is of length D and is perpendicular to τ (because K is of constant width D). The sphere whose centre is y and which is of radius D, contains K and touches τ at x. It follows that if s_1 and s_2 are two points of X, then K is contained in each of two spheres of radius D

---

† [6], p. 15.

‡ Convex in the spherical sense, with small arcs of great circles used instead of segments. See [6], p. 14. There are no difficulties about this definition since no set X contains antipodal points of S. We always use "arc" to mean 'small arc of a great circle," throughout this problem.

whose centres c_1 and c_2 are at a distance $2D \sin (\frac{1}{2} \angle s_1 O s_2)$ apart. The width of the set K in the direction $c_1 c_2$ is less than or equal to the width of the common part of the two spheres in the same direction Thus

$$D \leqslant 2D - 2D \sin (\tfrac{1}{2} \angle s_1 O s_2),$$

and hence $\angle s_1 O s_2 \leqslant \frac{1}{3}\pi$.

  (vi) For any two points of K, x_1 and x_2, either
    (a) $X_1 \cap X_2' = \emptyset$, or
    (b) $X_1 \cap X_2'$ is a single point which is an extremal† point of both X_1 and X_2', or
    (c) one at least of X_1 or X_2 is a single point.

We show firstly that $X_1 \cap X_2'$ contains at most one point. For suppose that this intersection contained two points s_1 and s_2. Of the two parallel support planes of K that are parallel to the tangent plane to S at s_1 one passes through x_1 and the other through x_2. Similarly of the two parallel support planes of K that are parallel to the tangent plane to S at s_2 one passes through x_1 and the other through x_2. Since K is of constant width this is impossible.

To complete the proof of (vi) we suppose that X_1' contains an arc ab and X_2 an arc cd where c is an interior point of ab and d does not lie on the great circle through ab. We show that this supposition leads to a contradiction. Since X_1' contains an arc ab and since two parallel support planes to K meet K in points which lie on the line perpendicular to the two planes, it follows that K contains a circular arc of points say yz where $y = f(a)$ and $z = f(b)$, which arc is part of a circle whose centre is x_1 and whose radius is D. Further as c is a point of ab, x_2 lies on the arc yz. If x_2 were one of the end-points of yz, then X_2 would contain one of a, b as well as c. Since c is an interior point of ab, X_2 would contain [by (iv)] a subarc of ab. This is impossible by the argument given above. Thus x_2 is an interior point of the arc yz. But since X_2 contains two distinct points, there are two distinct support planes to K at x_2, say τ_1 and τ_2. Let σ denote the plane of arc yz. Let P and T be the two spheres of radius D that touch τ_1 and τ_2 respectively at x_2 and each of which contains K. Denote the circles $T \cap \sigma$ and $P \cap \sigma$ by γ_T and γ_P. In σ we have an an arc yz of radius D, x_2 an interior point of this arc, and two circles γ_T, γ_P each passing through x_2 and each of radius not more than D. But then yz cannot lie on or inside both γ_T and γ_P. This is the required contradiction, since $yz \subset K$ and must therefore lie inside or on both γ_T and γ_P. Thus (iv) is proved.

† i.e. if α is an arc with $p \in \alpha \subset X$ then p is an extremal point of X if and only if for each p and α, p is an end point of α.

Notation. We use $d(X)$ to denote the diameter of the set X. For subsets of S we also use the term angular diameter of X to mean the upper bound of angles subtended by pairs of points X at O. It is denoted by ang. $d(X)$.

§2. Description of method

The aim of the method is to divide S into four sets $S_1 S_2 S_3 S_4$ which are closed and such that each of the sets $f^{-1}(f(S))$, $i = 1, 2, 3, 4$, does not contain antipodal points of S. In these circumstances the sets $f(S_i)$ are closed and $d(f(S_i)) < D$.† Thus the four sets $f(S_i)$ provide the required subdivision of K.

Write g for $f^{-1}f$ and F for the operation $F(K_0) = f[(f^{-1}(K_0))']$ where K_0 is a subset of K. Write $F_n(K_0)$ for the n-th iteration of F operating on K_0.

The set $g(S_i)$ contains S_i and the difficulty of the application of this method is that of finding a method of limiting the size of $g(S_i)$ relative to that of S_i. The means used here is to construct a simple Jordan curve which divides S into two antipodal sets and which is of a particular form. In the first case it will consist of a finite number of arcs which will all belong to sets either of the form $f^{-1}(x)$ or of the form $[f^{-1}(x)]'$. This curve then constitutes a barrier such that if $f^{-1}(y)$ meets it, then either y is one of a certain finite number of points, or $f^{-1}(y)$ is a single point. This enables us to divide the set S as required. In the second case we cannot construct such a curve but we proceed by constructing a curve with similar properties.

§3.

Case 1. For some point x of K and some integer n, $d(F^n(x)) = D$.

We use this condition to establish the existence of a curve as described in §2. Write

$$T_n = \{x | x \in K \quad \text{and} \quad d(F^n(x)) = D\}$$

and let m be the least integer for which $T_n \neq \emptyset$. Let z be a point of T_m. The set $f^{-1}(z)$ contains more than one point, for otherwise $F(z)$ would be a single point, say w, and we should have

$$d(F_{m-1}(w)) = d(F_m(z)) = D$$

This relation however contradicts the minimal property of m. Hence the convex set $f^{-1}(z)$ contains more than one point and therefore contains non-extremal points. Let s be one such point.

---

† Because if $d(f(S_i)) = D$ there are two points x_1, x_2 of $f(S_i)$ at which the support planes to K are parallel and thus some point of $f^{-1}(x_1)$ is antipodal to some point of $f^{-1}(x_2)$.

Since $f^{-1}(z)$ is convex each point of it can be joined to s by an arc in $f^{-1}(z)$.

The set $f^{-1}(F(z))$ consists of the set Z' together with all the sets Y for which $Y \cap Z' \neq \emptyset$.† Thus each point of $f^{-1}(F(z))$ can be joined to s' by a curve formed of one or two arcs. If it is formed of two arcs, one is contained in Z' and the other in a set of the form Y.

We proceed similarly and see that each point of $f^{-1}(F^p(z))$ can be joined to s if p is even and to s' if p is odd, by a curve of at most $p + 1$ arcs which belong alternately to sets of the form X' and sets of the form Y. Each of these arcs is a genuine arc and does not degenerate to a point since otherwise we should have two distinct sets $f^{-1}(z)$ that intersect and this is in contradiction with (ii).

The set $f^{-1}(F^m(z))$ contains at least one pair of antipodal points of S. Suppose that m is even; if m were odd the argument would be the same with s and s' interchanged. Let t and t' be one such pair of points. Join both of them to s by curves as described above. The minimal property of m implies that one of these curves is made up of $m + 1$ subarcs, but the other curve may be made up of a smaller number of arcs. Let these curves be $s, a_1, a_2, \ldots, a_{m+1} = t$ and $s, b_1, b_2, \ldots, b_r = t'$ where a_i and b_i are the vertices of the arcs involved. Replace the two arcs sa_1 and sb_1 by a single arc a_1b_1. Since $f^{-1}(z)$ is convex, $a_1b_1 \subset f^{-1}(z)$. Denote the resulting curve $a_{m+1}, a_m, \ldots, a_1b_1, \ldots, b_r$ by γ. We shall suppose that γ contains no other pair of antipodal points apart from t and t', for if it did there would be a subcurve γ_1 of γ irreducible with respect to the property of joining a pair of antipodal points of S and we should use γ_1 in place of γ.

Consider the union of γ and its reflection in O, γ'. The intersection $\gamma \cap \gamma'$ is made up of the two points a_{m+1} and b_r. At a_{m+1} there are two arcs $a_{m+1}a_m$ and $a_{m+1}b'_{r-1}$. If these arcs both belong to one set of the form $f^{-1}(x)$ or $[f^{-1}(x)]'$ we replace them by the single arc $a_m b'_{r-1}$. Similarly if $a'_m b_r$ and $b_r b_{r-1}$ both belong to one set of the form $f^{-1}(x)$ or $[f^{-1}(x)]'$ we replace them by the single arc $a'_m b_{r-1}$. Otherwise these arcs are not altered. Write δ for the final curve. It has the two properties:

3(i): δ divides S into two open antipodal sets U and V.

3(ii): δ is composed of a finite number of arcs which belong alter-
       nately to sets of the form $f^{-1}(x)$ and of the form $[f^{-1}(x)]'$.

It is clear that δ is composed of an even number of arcs say $2r$. From the class of all curves with properties 3(i) and 3(ii) we select one curve for which r has its least possible value. The condition (v) on f implies that $r \geqslant 3$. Denote by Γ this selected curve and suppose

† Where $Z' = (f^{-1}(z))'$ and $Y = f^{-1}(y)$ for some y of K.

that Γ has exactly $2r$ arcs. We write the vertices of Γ as $P_0, P_1, \ldots,$ P_{2r-1} where

$$P_i = P'_{i+r}, \qquad i = 0, 1, \ldots, r-1.$$

It follows that we can choose our notation such that $P_i P_{i+1}$ is a great circle arc contained in $f^{-1}(x_{i/2})$ provided i is even, $i = 0, 2, 4,$ $\ldots, 2r-2$, and the arcs $P_1 P_2, P_3 P_4, P_5 P_6, \ldots$ lie in sets of the form $[f^{-1}(x)]'$. We remark that r is odd; otherwise x_0 and x_r violate (vi). Further if two antipodal points of S can be joined by a curve made up of s arcs each contained in a set $f^{-1}(x)$ or a set $[f^{-1}(x)]'$ it follows from the minimal property of Γ that $s \geqslant r$. Thus Γ is a simple Jordan curve.

We now consider two alternatives. Either

      (a) for some x ang. $d(f^{-1}(x)) = \tfrac{1}{3}\pi$, or

      (b) for every x ang. $d(f^{-1}(x)) < \tfrac{1}{3}\pi$.

Case (a)

Let s_1, s_2 be two points of $f^{-1}(x_0)$ for which $\angle s_1 O s_2 = \tfrac{1}{3}\pi$. Let τ_1, τ_2 be the two support planes of K that pass through x_2 and are parallel respectively to the two tangent planes to S at s_1 and s_2. Let x_1 be the point distant D from x_0 along the perpendicular to τ_1 at x_0 and on the same side of τ_1 as K. Similarly define x_2 with respect to τ_2. Both x_1 and x_2 belong to K and moreover since $\angle x_1 x_0 x_2 = \tfrac{1}{3}\pi$ the points x_0, x_1, x_2 are all at a distance of D from one another. The projection of K onto the plane x_0, x_1, x_2 is a set of constant width D which contains the points x_0, x_1, x_2, and thus it is the Reuleaux triangle with vertices x_0, x_1, x_2. It follows that the plane through O parallel to the plane x_0, x_1, x_2 cuts S in a great circle which can be regarded as made up of six arcs with the properties 3(i) and 3(ii). This curve automatically has the minimal property that distinguishes Γ and we take it as our curve Γ. The arcs of Γ are $P_0 P_1, P_1 P_2, P_2 P_3, P_3 P_4, P_4 P_5, P_5 P_0$ where

$$P_0 P_1 \subset f^{-1}(x_0), \quad P_2 P_3 \subset f^{-1}(x_1), \quad P_4 P_5 \subset f^{-1}(x_2),$$
$$P_1 P_2 \subset [f^{-1}(x_2)]', \quad P_3 P_4 \subset [f^{-1}(x_0)]', \quad P_5 P_0 \subset [f^{-1}(x_1)]'.$$

(See Fig. 13.)

Each of these arcs is of angular diameter $\tfrac{1}{3}\pi$.

Denote the two open hemispheres into which S is divided by Γ, by H and J. Consider the two closed sets $(H \cup \Gamma) \cap [f^{-1}(x_0)]'$ and $(J \cup \Gamma) \cap (f^{-1}(x_0)]'$.

Let R_ε denote the union of the spherical caps with centres P_3, P_4 and angular radii $\tfrac{1}{3}\pi - \varepsilon$, where ε is a small positive number. There is an ε, $\tfrac{1}{6}\pi > \varepsilon > 0$ such that either R_ε contains the whole of $(H \cup \Gamma) \cap [f^{-1}(x_0)]'$ or R_ε contains the whole of $(J \cup \Gamma) \cap [f^{-1}(x_0)]'$. For if this were not so the property (v) would not hold for $[f^{-1}(x_0)]'$ and thus would not hold for $f^{-1}(x_0)$. Suppose the first alternative holds. Let T_1 be the part of $(H \cup \Gamma) \cap [f^{-1}(x_0)]'$ in the closed cap centre P_3 and angular radius $\frac{1}{3}\pi - \varepsilon$ and let T_2 be the part of $(H \cup \Gamma) \cap [f^{-1}(x_0)]'$ in the closed cap centre P_4 and angular radius $\frac{1}{3}\pi - \varepsilon$. Then $(H \cup \Gamma) \cap [f^{-1}(x_0)]' = T_1 \cup T_2$; ang. $d(T_1) < \frac{1}{3}\pi$, ang. $d(T_2) < \frac{1}{3}\pi$, where T_1 and T_2 are closed.

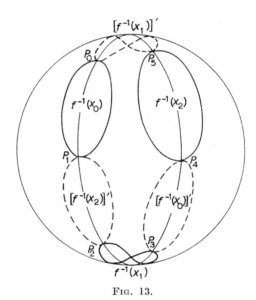

Fig. 13.

We divide K into four sets as follows.

$x \in K_1$ if $f^{-1}(x)$ meets T_1, i.e. $K_1 = f(T_1)$.

$x \in K_2$ if $f^{-1}(x)$ meets T_2, i.e. $K_2 = f(T_2)$.

$x \in K_3$ if $f^{-1}(x)$ meets $H \cup \Gamma$ and does not meet T_1 or T_2, i.e.

$$K_3 = f(H \cup \Gamma) - f(T_1) - f(T_2).$$

$x \in K_4$ if $f^{-1}(x)$ does not meet $H \cup \Gamma$, i.e. $K_4 = K - K_1 - K_2 - K_3$.

We shall show that each of the four sets K_i is such that $f^{-1}(K_i)$ is a set that does not contain two antipodal points.

Consider K_1. Since, for every x, ang. $d(X) \leqslant \frac{1}{3}\pi$, and ang. $d(T_1) < \frac{1}{3}\pi$, it follows that ang. $d(f^{-1}(K_1)) < \pi$. Thus $f^{-1}(K_1)$ does not contain a pair of antipodal points of S.

Similarly K_2 does not contain an antipodal pair of points.

Consider next K_3. For $x \in K_3$ either $f^{-1}(x) \subset H$ or $f^{-1}(x)$ meets Γ. In the latter case either $f^{-1}(x)$ is an interior point of arc P_1P_2 or of arc P_0P_5 or x is x_0. Suppose if possible that there exist y_1, $y_2 \in K_3$ and $s_1 \in f^{-1}(y_1)$, $s_2 \in f^{-1}(y_2)$ such that $\angle s_1 O s_2 = \pi$. Of the two points s_1, s_2 one at least does not belong to H. Suppose that $s_1 \notin H$, then $s_2 \in H \cup \Gamma$, and $f^{-1}(y_1)$ meets Γ. Thus s_1 is either an interior point of arc P_1P_2 or of arc P_0P_5 or it is a point of $f^{-1}(x_0)$. Thus s_2 since $\angle s_1 O s_2 = \pi$, is either an interior point of arc P_2P_3 or of arc P_4P_5 or is a point of $[f^{-1}(x_0)]'$. Thus either y_2 is x_1 or x_2 or $f^{-1}(y_2)$ meets $(H \cup \Gamma) \cap [f^{-1}(x_0)]'$ in s_2. None of these possibilities are permissible since they all imply that $f^{-1}(y_2)$ meets T_1 or T_2.

Finally, since $H \cup \Gamma$ is a closed hemisphere it follows that $f^{-1}(K_4)$ does not contain a pair of antipodal points.

Since K_1 and K_2 are closed we can assert immediately that $d(K_1) < D$ and $d(K_2) < D$. The sets K_3 and K_4 are not closed but for these sets we proceed as follows. The set $K_3 \cup K_1 \cup K_2$ is closed and there are two open sets Y_1 and Y_2 such that $Y_1 \supset K_1$, $Y_2 \supset K_2$, $d(Y_1) < D$, $d(Y_2) < D$. Thus the set $K_3 - Y_1 - Y_2$ is closed and as the set $f^{-1}(K_3 - K_1 - Y_2)$ does not contain an antipodal pair of points on S we have $d(K_3 - Y_1 - Y_2) < D$. Finally there is an open set Y_3 such that $Y_3 \supset K_3 - Y_1 - Y_2$ and $d(Y_3) < D$. Then $K_4 - Y_1 - Y_2 - Y_3$ is closed and hence $d(K_4 - Y_1 - Y_2 - Y_3) < D$. Write $Y_4 = K_4 - Y_1 - Y_2 - Y_3$.

The four sets Y_1, Y_2, Y_3, Y_4 constitute a subdivision of K into four sets each of diameter less than D.

Case (b)

Consider the curve Γ as constructed previously. The minimal property of Γ implies that at most one arc of Γ lies in any one set $f^{-1}(x)$, i.e. the points x_0, x_1, $\ldots$, x_{r-1} are distinct. For suppose that there were two or more arcs of Γ in (say) $f^{-1}(x_0)$. Let Γ_0 be an irreducible subcurve of Γ that joins $f^{-1}(x_0)$ to $[f^{-1}(x_0)]'$ and which meets $f^{-1}(x_0)$ in the point A and $[f^{-1}(x_0)]'$ in the point B. If A is B' let Λ be the curve composed of Γ_0 from A to B and Γ_0' from B to A.† If A is not B' let Λ be the curve composed of Γ_0 from A to B; the arc BA'; Γ_0' from A' to B'; arc $B'A$. The points A, B, A', B', are vertices of Γ, i.e. are some of the points P_j. The number of arcs of Λ outside the set $f^{-1}(x_0) \cup [f^{-1}(x_0)]'$ does not exceed the number of arcs of Γ outside the same set. Inside this set Λ has less arcs than Γ. Thus Λ is formed from fewer arcs than is Γ. Also Λ is connected, $\Lambda = \Lambda'$ and the arcs of Λ are contained

---

† Actually if this case were possible Γ would not be a simple Jordan curve, and we have already remarked that the minimal property of Γ implies that it is a simple curve.

in sets that are alternately of the form $f^{-1}(x)$ and $[f^{-1}(x)]'$. But this means that Λ belongs to the class of curves with properties 3(i) and 3(ii). Since Λ is formed from a smaller number of arcs than Γ we have a contradiction with the minimal property of Γ. Thus our original assumption was false and in fact Λ has only one arc in each of the sets $f^{-1}(x_i)$.

The closure of the set of points of Γ that do not belong to $f^{-1}(x_0)$ or to $[f^{-1}(x_0)]'$ is a set formed of the two curves $P_1P_2 \ldots P_r$ and $P_{r+1} \ldots P_{2r-1}P_0$ which we denote by Θ and Θ' respectively. (See Fig. 14.) A property of these arcs which we require is that x_0 and

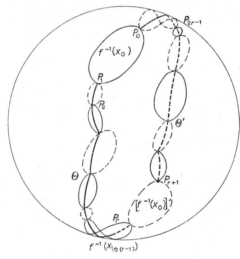

Fig. 14

$x_{\frac{1}{2}(r-1)}$ are the only points of K for which $f^{-1}(x)$ meets both Θ and $[f^{-1}(f(\Theta))]'$. For if $f^{-1}(x)$ meets Θ either

(α) $f^{-1}(x)$ is a single point interior to one of the arcs

$$P_1P_2,\ P_3P_4,\ \ldots,\ P_{r-2}P_{r-1}$$

or

(β) x is x_i where $i = 0, 1, \ldots, (r-1)/2$.

Now the set $[f^{-1}(f(\Theta))]'$ consists of the arc Θ' together with the sets $[f^{-1}(x_i)]'$, $i = 0, 1, \ldots, (r-1)/2$. Thus in case ($\alpha$) $f^{-1}(x)$ can only meet $[f^{-1}(f(\Theta))]'$ if it actually belongs to one of the sets $[f^{-1}(x_i)]'$, since $\Theta \cap \Theta' = 0$. But it belongs to one of the arcs $P_1P_2, \ldots$, $P_{r-2}P_{r-1}$ and thus to one of the sets $[f^{-1}(x_i)]'$ $i = (r+1)/2, \ldots$, $r-1$. Since it can belong to only one set of the form $[f^{-1}(x)]'$

this implies that two of the points x_i are identical. We have shown above that this is impossible.

In case (β) $f^{-1}(x)$ can meet $[f^{-1}(f(\Theta))]'$ only if either there are two antipodal points of S one belonging to

$$\Phi_1 = \Theta \cup f^{-1}(x_0) \cup f^{-1}(x_1) \cup \ldots \cup f^{-1}(x_{\frac{1}{2}(r-1)})$$

and the other to

$$\Phi_2 = \Theta \cup f^{-1}(x_1) \cup f^{-1}(x_2) \cup \ldots \cup f^{-1}(x_{\frac{1}{2}(r-3)})$$

or if $x = x_0$ or $x = x_{\frac{1}{2}(r-1)}$. Now any point of Φ_1 can be joined to any point of Φ_2 by a curve made up at most of $r - 1$ arcs contained in sets of the form $f^{-1}(x)$ or $[f^{-1}(x)]'$. By a remark made earlier this contradicts the minimal property by which Γ was selected. Thus $x = x_0$ or $x = x_{\frac{1}{2}(r-1)}$.

The curve Γ divides S into two open antipodal sets. We denote one of these sets by H. The sets K_1, K_2, K_3, K_4 are next defined.

$x \in K_1$ if $f^{-1}(x)$ meets $(H \cup \Gamma) \cap [f^{-1}(x_0)]'$.

$x \in K_2$ if $f^{-1}(x)$ meets $(H \cup \Gamma) \cap [f^{-1}(f(\Theta))]'$ and does not meet
$$(H \cup \Gamma) \cap [f^{-1}(x_0)]'.$$

$x \in K_3$ if $f^{-1}(x)$ meets $H \cup \Gamma$ and does not meet
$$(H \cup \Gamma) \cap [f^{-1}(f(\Theta))]'.$$

$x \in K_4$ if $f^{-1}(x)$ does not meet $H \cup \Gamma$.

Consider the set K_1. K_1 is closed and ang. $d(f^{-1}(x_0)) < \frac{1}{3}\pi$. Thus, by an argument similar to that used for K_1 in case (a) we have $d(K_1) < D$.

Next consider K_2. If $x \in K_2$ either $f^{-1}(x) \subset H$ or $f^{-1}(x)$ meets Γ. In the latter case either $f^{-1}(x)$ does not meet Θ or $x = x_0$ or $x_{\frac{1}{2}(r-1)}$. (For $f^{-1}(x)$ does meet $[f^{-1}(f(\Theta))]'$.) But $x_{\frac{1}{2}(r-1)} \in K_1$ and thus $x_{\frac{1}{2}(r-1)} \notin K_2$. Thus if $f^{-1}(x)$ meets Γ it must meet the open subcurve of Γ

$$P_r P_{r+1} \ldots P_{2r-1} P_0 P_1.$$

However it cannot meet arcs $P_r P_{r+1}$, $P_{r+1} P_{r+2}$ by the definition of K_2. Thus either $f^{-1}(x)$ is either a single point of one of the arcs

$$P_{r+2} P_{r+3}, \ P_{r+4} P_{r+5}, \ \ldots, \ P_{2r-1} P_0$$

or x is one of the points $x_{\frac{1}{2}(r+3)}, \ldots, x_{r-1}, x_0$. Now no two points on the curve $P_{r+2} P_{r+3} \ldots P_{2r-1} P_0 P_1$ are antipodal, and the reflection of this curve is contained in the union of Θ and the arc $P_r P_{r+1}$. Suppose now that there were two points of S say s_1, s_2 such that $s_1 \in f^{-1}(y_1)$ and $s_2 \in f^{-1}(y_2)$; y_1, $y_2 \in K_2$ and the points s_1 and s_2 were antipodal. One at least of these points, say, s_1, does not belong to H. Then $f^{-1}(y_1)$ meets Γ. Now s_1 cannot belong to $f^{-1}(x_0)$, for if it did, s_2 would belong to $[f^{-1}(x_0)]'$, but s_2 also belongs to $H \cup \Gamma$, and thus $f^{-1}(y_2)$ would meet $(H \cup \Gamma) \cap [f^{-1}(x_0)]'$ in the point s_2. This is impossible by the definition of K_2. Since $f^{-1}(y_1)$ meets Γ we have that s_1 is either a point of one of the arcs

$$P_{2r-1}P_0; \quad P_iP_{i+1}, \; i = r + 2, r + 4, \ldots, 2r - 3,$$

or of one of the sets $f^{-1}(x_{\frac{1}{2}(r+3)}), \ldots, f^{-1}(x_{r-1})$. But by the definition of K_2 the set $f^{-1}(y_2)$ meets $f^{-1}(f(\Theta))]' \cap (H \cup \Gamma)$ and does not meet

$$(H \cup \Gamma) \cap [f^{-1}(x_0)]'.$$

Thus it either meets $(H \cup \Gamma) \cap [f^{-1}(x_i)]'$, $i = 1, \ldots, (r-1)/2$ or y_2 is $x_{\frac{1}{2}(r+3)}, \ldots, x_{r-1}$. Thus s_1 and s_2 can be joined by a curve made up of at most $r-1$ arcs each contained in a set of the form $f^{-1}(x)$ or $[f^{-1}(x)]'$. By the remark made about the minimal property of Γ this is impossible. Thus two such points s_1 and s_2 do not exist.

Let Y_1 be an open set such that $Y_1 \supset K_1$ and $d(Y_1) < D$. Then $K_2 - Y_1$ is closed and thus since this set is such that $f^{-1}(K_2 - Y_1)$ contains no pair of antipodal points we conclude that $d(K_2 - Y_1) < D$.

Next consider the set K_3. For $x \in K_3$ either $f^{-1}(x) \subset H$ or $f^{-1}(x)$ meets Γ and in the last case it must by the definition of K_3, meet the open subcurve of Γ, $P_1P_2 \ldots P_{r-1}$. In this second case either $f^{-1}(x)$ is a single point of one of the arcs $P_1P_2, P_3P_4, \ldots, P_{r-2}P_{r-1}$ or x is one of the points $x_1, x_2, \ldots, x_{\frac{1}{2}(r-3)}$. Now if s_1 and s_2 belong to $f^{-1}(K_3)$ and are antipodal, one at least say s_1 does not belong to H. The points antipodal to the arcs $P_1P_2, P_2P_3, \ldots, P_{r-2}P_{r-1}$ do not belong to $f^{-1}(K_3)$. Thus s_1 must belong to a set $f^{-1}(x_i)$, $i = 1, 2, \ldots, (r-3)/2$. But in this case $s_2 \in [f_1(x_i)]'$ and $s_2 \in H \cup \Gamma$; thus $s_2 \in (H \cup \Gamma) \cap [f^{-1}(f(\Theta))]'$. If $s_2 \in f^{-1}(y)$ (say) we conclude that $y \notin K_3$ and $s_2 \notin f^{-1}(K_3)$. This contradiction shows that no pair of points of $f^{-1}(K_3)$ are antipodal.

Let Y_2 be an open set for which $Y_2 \supset K_2 - Y_1$ and $d(Y_2) < D$. Then $K_3 - Y_2 - Y_1$ is a closed set and does not contain a pair of points at which the support planes to K are parallel. Thus as before

$$d(K_3 - Y_2 - Y_1) < D.$$

Let Y_3 be an open set with $Y_3 \supset K_3 - Y_2 - Y_1$ and $d(Y_3) < D$. Then $K_4 - Y_3 - Y_2 - Y_1$ is closed and as in case (a) we have

$$d(K_4 - Y_3 - Y_2 - Y_1) < D.$$

Write $Y_4 = K_4 - Y_3 - Y_2 - Y_1$. The sets $Y_1, \; Y_2, \; Y_3, \; Y_4$

constitute a decomposition of K into four sets each with a diameter of less than D.

This completes the proof of the result in Case 1.

§4.

Case 2. For every point of x of K and every integer n, $d(F^n(x)) < D$.

If, for every x of K, $f^{-1}(x)$ is a single point then $f(x)$ is a homeomorphism and the result follows from Hadwiger's argument. Suppose then that for some x, $f^{-1}(x)$ is not a single point. Consider a triad of points x_1, x_2, x_3 such that $f^{-1}(x_1)$ and $f^{-1}(x_3)$ both meet $[f^{-1}(x_2)]'$. There are two points s_1 of $f^{-1}(x_1)$ and s_3 of $f^{-1}(x_3)$ such that $\angle s_1 O s_3$ has its largest possible value. By the Blaschke selection theorem and a property of upper semi-continuous decompositions,[†] there is amongst all the triads x_1, x_2, x_3 as described above, at least one for which the largest value $\angle s_1 O s_3$ attains its upper bound. We select one such triad.

Since $\angle s_1 O s_3 < \pi$, there is a unique great circle γ through s_1 and s_3. Define points P_i, $i = 0, 1, 2, \ldots, 7$ on S as follows. (See Fig. 15.)

$$P_0 = f^{-1}(x_2)]' \cap f^{-1}(x_1);$$
$$P_1 = s_1;$$
$$P_2 = s_3';$$
$$P_3 = [f^{-1}(x_3)]' \cap f^{-1}(x_2);$$
$$P_4 = f^{-1}(x_2) \cap [f^{-1}(x_1)]';$$
$$P_5 = s_1';$$
$$P_6 = s_3;$$
$$P_7 = [f^{-1}(x_2)]' \cap f^{-1}(x_3).$$

It may happen that P_0 is P_1 and that P_4 is P_5 or that P_2 is P_3 and that P_6 if P_7 or that both of these sets of coincidences occur.

We next define points Q_1, Q_2, Q_5, Q_6 on the great circle γ as follows. $Q_1 Q_2$ lie on the subarc $P_1 P_2$ of γ in order $P_1 Q_1 Q_2 P_2$; Q_5 is Q_1', Q_6 is Q_2' and Q_1 is so close to P_1 and Q_2 to P_2 that if α is the union of the great circle arcs $Q_2 P_2$, $P_2 P_3$, $P_3 P_4$, $P_4 P_5$, $P_5 Q_5$, then

$$d f[f^{-1}(f(\alpha))]' < D.$$

Denote the circular polygon $P_0 P_1 P_2 \ldots P_7 P_0$ by Γ and one of the two open subsets of S that are bounded by Γ by H. Let R be an interior point of arc $Q_1 P_1$ and let β be the arc $Q_2 R$ of Γ.

† [7], p. 122.

7

Define subsets K_1, K_2, K_3, K_4 of K as follows.

$x \in K_1$ if $f^{-1}(x)$ meets $(H \cup \Gamma) \cap [f^{-1}(f(\alpha))]'$.

$x \in K_2$ if $f^{-1}(x)$ meets $(H \cup \Gamma) \cap [f^{-1}(f(\alpha \cup \beta))]'$ and does not meet

$$(H \cup \Gamma) \cap [f^{-1}(f(\alpha))]'.$$

$x \in K_3$ if $f^{-1}(x)$ meets $H \cup \Gamma$ and does not meet

$$(H \cup \Gamma) \cap [f^{-1}(f(\alpha \cup \beta))]'.$$

$x \in K_4$ if $f^{-1}(x)$ does not meet $H \cup \Gamma$.

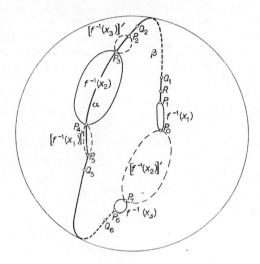

FIG. 15.

Consider the set K_1. Since $x \in K_1$ implies that $f^{-1}(x)$ meets $[f^{-1}(f(\alpha))]'$, we have $x \in f([f^{-1}(f(\alpha))]')$. Thus $K_1 \subset f([f^{-1}(f(\alpha))]')$ $d(K_1) < D$.

Consider the set K_2. If $x \in K_2$ either $f^{-1}(x) \subset H$ or $f^{-1}(x)$ meets Γ. If $f^{-1}(x)$ meets Γ it must meet subcurve $Q_1Q_2P_2P_3P_4P_5Q_5Q_6$ of Γ by the definition of K_2. Now $x_2 \notin K_2$, for if it did belong to K_2, $f^{-1}(x_2)$ would meet $[f^{-1}(f(\beta))]'$ and thus there would exist $y \in K$ such that $[f^{-1}(y)]'$ meets both $f^{-1}(x_2)$ and β', i.e. arc $R'Q_6$. But then the triad y, x_2, x_3 would violate the maximal property of x_1, x_2, x_3, since any point of arc $R'Q_6$ subtends at O with the point P_2 an angle which is greater than $\angle P_2OP_5$. $f^{-1}(x)$ cannot meet the open arcs P_2P_3, P_4P_5 if these exist. For if it did it would be a single point and the set $[f^{-1}(x_i)]'$ to which it belonged would meet arc Q_6R'. Thus $\angle P_5OP_2$ would not be the largest angle subtended at O by a pair of points of the set $[f^{-1}(x_1)]' \cup [f^{-1}(x_2)] \cup [f^{-1}(x_3)]'$. Nor can $f^{-1}(x)$ meet Γ in a point of Q_1P_2 for if it did it would (since $x \in K_2$) meet say $[f^{-1}(y)]'$ where $[f^{-1}(y)]'$ meets arc Q_6R'. But then the pair of points x, y form a degenerate triad which violates the maximal property of x_1, x_2, x_3. If now $s_1 \in f^{-1}(y_1)$, $s_2 \in f^{-1}(y_2)$, $y_1 \in K_2$, $y_2 \in K_2$ and s_1, s_2 are antipodal points, then one at least of the sets, say $f^{-1}(y_1)$, meets Γ and therefore meets arc $P_5Q_5Q_6$. Consider the set $[f^{-1}(y_1)]'$. This set meets both $f^{-1}(y_2)$ and arc $P_1Q_1Q_2$. Further by the definition of K_2, $f^{-1}(y_2)$ meets a set $[f^{-1}(y_3)]'$ that meets arc $R'Q_6$. Then the triad y_1, y_2, y_3 violates the maximal property of the triad x_1, x_2, x_3. Thus no two points of $f^{-1}(K_2)$ are antipodal.

Let Y_1 be an open set containing K_1 with $d(Y_1) < D$. The set $K_2 - Y_1$ is closed and thus $d(K_2 - Y_1) < D$.

Consider the set K_3. If $x \in K_3$ either $f^{-1}(x) \subset H$ or $f^{-1}(x)$ intersects Γ. Now if it were the case that two points s_1, s_2 of S were antipodal and $s_1 \in f^{-1}(y_1)$, $s_2 \in f^{-1}(y_2)$, $y_1 \in K_3$, $y_2 \in K_3$, then one of the points say s_1 would not belong to H. Thus $f^{-1}(y_1)$ meets Γ. By the definition of K_3, $f^{-1}(y_1)$ does not meet $(H \cup \Gamma) \cap [f^{-1}(f(\alpha \cup \beta))]' \supset \alpha' \cup \beta'$. But $\alpha \cup \beta \supset \Gamma - (\alpha' \cup \beta')$ thus $f^{-1}(y_1)$ meets $\alpha \cup \beta$. Hence $f^{-1}(y_1) \subset f^{-1}[f(\alpha \cup \beta)]$ and since s_1 and s_2 are diametrically opposite points $s_2 \in [f^{-1}(f(\alpha \cup \beta))]'$. But since $s_1 \notin H$, and s_1 and s_2 are antipodal, $s_2 \in H \cup \Gamma$. Thus $f^{-1}(y_2)$ meets $(H \cup \Gamma) \cap [f^{-1}(f(\alpha \cup \beta))]'$ in contradiction with the definition of K_3.

Let Y_2 be an open set containing $K_2 - Y_1$ such that $d(Y_2) < D$. The set $K_3 - Y_1 - Y_2$ is closed and as K_4 does not contain an antipodal pair of points we have $d(K_4 - Y_1 - Y_2 - Y_3) < D$. Write

$$Y_4 = K_4 - Y_1 - Y_2 - Y_3.$$

The four sets Y_1, Y_2, Y_3, Y_4 constitute a decomposition of K into four sets of diameter less than D.

§5. Remarks

The method given here is undoubtedly complicated and if one is content simply to prove the result that any three-dimensional set can be split into four sets of smaller diameter then Mr. Grünbaum's method is preferable. His method is to circumscribe a regular octahedra of width equal to the diameter of the given set and then remove three tetrahedra. The remaining polyhedron can then be split into four sets each of diameter less than that of the given set. The method, though simple, is really a lucky fluke.

It just happens that this polyhedra can be divided in this particular way. Borsuk's conjecture should be based on more fundamental properties of Euclidean space and this is what I have attempted to do. It is possible that this method extends to higher dimensional spaces, whereas any method based on approximation by simple geometrical figures becomes progressively and rapidly more unmanageable as the dimension of the embedding space increases.

The function f defined in Section 1 induces an upper-semi-continuous decomposition of the sphere S. An important and difficult problem is that of characterizing all such decompositions of S. Such a characterisation would be valuable in other problems concerning sets of constant width. There is an analogous problem in two dimensions. Here the solution is both simple and less important, because we have a great deal of knowledge concerning the structure of two dimensional sets of constant width for which the analogous results in three dimensions are missing.

References

1. K. Borsuk; "Drei Satze über die n-dimensionale Euklidisch Sphäre," *Fundamenta Math.*, **20** (1933) 177–190.
2. D. Gale; "On inscribing n dimensional sets in a regular n simplex," *Proc. American Math. Soc.* **4** (1953) 222–5.
3–4. H. Hadwiger; "Uberdeckung einer Menge durch Mengen kleineren Durchmessers," *Comm. Math. Helv.*, **19** (1946–7) 72–3, and *ibid*, **18** (1945–6) 73–5.
5. H. Hadwiger; "Uber die Zerstücking eines Eikörpers," *Math. Zeitschrift*, **51** (1947–9) 161–5.
6. T. Bonnesen und W. Fenchel; *Theorie der Konvexen Körper* (Reprint, New York, 1948).
7. G. T. Whyburn; *Analytic Topology* (New York, 1942).
8. H. G. Eggleston; "Covering a three dimensional set with sets of smaller diameter." *J. London Math. Soc.* **30** (1955) 11–24.

CHAPTER III

PROBLEMS ON CONVEX SETS

In this chapter the problems are defined only for convex sets. It is true that the definition of the problem could be extended to some wider class of sets but with the problems which concern us here this extension is unnatural and leads to unsolved, and uninteresting problems.

The next problem, Problem 5, is an important one both in itself and in applications to packing problems in the geometry of numbers. It is worth observing that in the last part of the solution of this problem we are compelled to take a step which is typical of this type of work. We are interested to the closeness of approximation of convex polygons to convex sets and yet we are forced to consider approximation by a sort of double convex polygon, in order to obtain the result we desire. We have to consider a wider class than the one with which we are really concerned. Another good example of this will be found in Problem 7.

5TH PROBLEM. APPROXIMATION TO PLANE CONVEX CURVES

Introduction

Of the many methods of measuring the " closeness" of two plane convex sets X and Y to one another, there are three which are particularly important. They are defined as follows.

(i) The area deviation $\tau_A(X, Y)$, defined to be the area of the set of points which belong to one but not to both of X and Y.

(ii) The perimeter deviation $\tau_P(X, Y)$ defined to be the positive difference between the lengths of the frontiers of the union $X \cup Y$ and of the intersection $X \cap Y$.

(iii) The distance deviation $\tau_D(X, Y)$ defined as $\rho_1 + \rho_2$ where ρ_1 is the largest of the distances of any point of X from the set Y and ρ_2 is the largest of the distances of any point of Y from the set X.

In these definitions and in what follows it is always assumed that the sets concerned are both bounded and closed.

Suppose next that X is a fixed convex set and that three classes of convex polygons are defined as follows.

(a) $\mathscr{P}(n)$ the class of all proper m-sided convex polygons, $m \leqslant n$.

(b) $\mathscr{P}_i(n\colon X)$ the subclass of those members of $\mathscr{P}(n)$ which are contained in X.

(c) $\mathscr{P}_c(n; X)$ the subclass of those members of $\mathscr{P}(n)$ which contain X.

Write

$$T_A(X; n) \quad = \inf. \, \tau_A(X, Y) : Y \in \mathscr{P}(n),$$

$$T_A(X; n; i) = \inf. \, \tau_A(X, Y) : Y \in \mathscr{P}_i(n; X),$$

$$T_A(X; n; c) = \inf. \, \tau_A(X, Y) : Y \in \mathscr{P}_c(n; X)$$

Similar definitions are made using the perimeter deviation or the distance deviation in place of the area deviation.

A theorem of Dowker, which has proved to be important in packing and covering problems, asserts that $T_A(X; n; i)$ and $T_A(X; n; c)$ are convex functions of n (see (1), (2))† and the question has been raised by Fejes Tóth (2) as to whether or not this is true of the other seven functions $T_A(X; n)$, $T_P(X; n)$, $T_P(X; n; i)$, $T_P(X; n; c)$, $T_D(X; n)$, $T_D(X; n; i)$, $T_D(X; n; c)$.

In this paper we show that $T_D(X; n)$, $T_D(X; n; c)$ and $T_D(X; n; i)$ need not be convex and that Dowker's argument can be modified to establish the convexity of $T_P(X; n; i)$ and $T_P(X; n; c)$. The two really interesting functions are $T_P(X; n)$ and $T_A(X; n)$. We show firstly that $T_P(X; n)$ is equal to $T_P(X; n; i)$, a result which is of interest on its own account and secondly that $T_A(X; n)$ is convex as a function of n. This last result is by far the most difficult to establish.

§1. The functions $T_D(X; n)$, $T_D(X; n; i)$ and $T_D(X; n; c)$

In this paragraph we use X_m to denote a regular m-sided polygon of side-length k. We shall consider different values of m but all the polygons will have the same side-length.

We need the following lemmas:

LEMMA 1. *If $f(n)$ is a convex function of the integral variable n and $f(p) = 0$, then*

$$f(p - r) \geqslant r f(p - 1), \quad r = 1, 2, \, \ldots, p - 1. \tag{1}$$

The proof is a simple induction argument.

LEMMA 2.

$$T_D(X_{2r}; r; i) \leqslant k \sin (\pi/2r) \tag{2}$$

$$T_D(X_{2r}; r; c) \leqslant \tfrac{1}{2} k \tan (\pi/r). \tag{3}$$

To prove (2) let W be the polygon formed by joining r alternate vertices of X_{2r}. Then $W \in \mathscr{P}_i(r; X_{2r})$ and

$$\tau_D(X, W) = k \sin (\pi/2r)$$

thus (2) is proved.

† For references see p. 121

For (3) let Z be the polygon formed by producing r alternate sides of X_{2r}. Then $Z \in \mathscr{P}_c(r; X_{2r})$ and

$$\tau_D(X, Z) = \tfrac{1}{2}k \tan (\pi/r),$$

and thus (3) is proved.

LEMMA 3.

$$T_D(X_{2r};\ 2r - 1) \geqslant \frac{k \sin (\pi/r)}{4(1 + \cos^2(\pi/2r))} \qquad (4)$$

Let X' and X'' be two polygons similar to and similarly situated to X_{2r} such that $X' \subset X_{2r} \subset X''$. Further let the distance apart of corresponding parallel sides of X' and X_{2r} and those of X_{2r} and X'' be δ where δ is the expression on the right-hand side of the inequality (4). In order for it to be possible to construct X' the distance apart of any two parallel sides of X_{2r} must be greater than 2δ. This will be the case if r is sufficiently large. We suppose in what follows that r is large enough and that X' is a genuine convex polygon.

The value of δ has been chosen so that the polygon formed by joining the mid-points of adjacent sides if X'' is also the polygon formed by the external bisectors of the angles at the vertices of X'.

Consider a polygon K whose distance deviation from X_{2r} is less than δ. Let a be a vertex of X'', and let b, c be the mid-points of the two sides of X'' that pass through a. Let d be the vertex of X' on bc, i.e. the mid-point of bc. The triangle abc contains a vertex of X_{2r} and also contains all the points whose distance from this vertex are less than δ. Thus the interior of abc contains points of K. Of the three sides of abc two lie in the frontier of X'', namely ab and ac. Since these sides are at a distance δ from X_{2r}, K does not meet them. Thus either K lies inside abc or K lies partly inside abc and partly outside and meets the frontier of abc in points of bc only.

The first alternative cannot arise for there are $2r - 1$ triangles with the same properties as abc obtained by taking different vertices of X'' instead of a. All these $2r$ triangles have interiors which are disjoint and each of these interiors meets K. The second alternative implies that K has a vertex in the interior of abc.

Thus K has at least $2r$ vertices and we deduce that for any polygon L with $2r - 1$ vertices or less,

$$\tau_D(L,\ X_{2r}) \geqslant \delta, \qquad (5)$$

and this implies the statement of the lemma.

We can now prove the required result. Clearly

$$T_D(X; n) \leqslant T_D(X; n; i), \qquad (6)$$

$$T_D(X; n) \leqslant T_D(X; n; c). \qquad (7)$$

Thus if $T_D(X_{2r}; n)$ were convex we should have from (2), (3), and (6)

$$k \sin (\pi/2r) \geqslant T_D(X_{2r}; r; i) \tag{8}$$
$$\geqslant T_D(X_{2r}; r)$$
$$\geqslant r\, T_D(X_{2r}; 2r - 1)$$
$$\geqslant r\, \frac{k \sin (\pi/r)}{4(1 + \cos^2(\pi/2r))} \,.$$

But (8) is clearly false if r is large: thus $T_D(X_{2r}; n)$ is not convex. Similarly it may be shown that $T_D(X_2; n; i)$ and $T_D(X_{2r}; n; c)$ are not convex.

§2. The functions $T_P(X; n)$, $T_P(X; n; i)$, $T_P(X; n; c)$

We prove first the following lemma.

LEMMA 4. $T_P(X; n) = T_P(X; n; i)$.

Denote the diameter of X by d and let $X(R)$ be the set formed by the intersection of all the circular discs of radius R, $R > d$, which contain X. Let $X(R; r)$ be the set of all points whose distance from $X(R)$ is not more than r. Through every point of the boundary of $X(R; r)$ it is possible to draw two circles, one of radius r that is contained in $X(R; r)$ and one of radius $R + r$ that contains $X(R; r)$.

We show first that it is sufficient to prove the lemma for sets of the form $X(R; r)$. If the class of all bounded plane convex sets is made into a metric space by the distance function $\tau_D(X, Y)$, then $\tau_P(X, Y)$ is a continuous function of X and Y. Further the class of all sets of the form $X(R; r)$ for varying X, R, r is dense in the space of all bounded convex sets. Thus if the lemma is true for sets of the form $X(R; r)$ it is also true for all bounded convex sets X.

We next prove the lemma for the set $X(R; r)$. To avoid a clumsy notation this set is denoted by X and we recall that through every point of its frontier there pass two circles, one of radius r which is contained in X and one of radius $R + r$ which contains X. Thus every support line to X is a tangent line to the frontier of X.

By the Blaschke selection theorem there is a polygon Y of the class $\mathscr{P}(n)$ such that

$$\tau_P(X, Y) = T_P(X; n). \tag{9}$$

Let the vertices of Y be $a(1)$, $a(2)$, . . . , $a(n)$ in clockwise order round Y. Our aim is to show that these vertices belong to X.

Each closed segment that is a side of Y meets X, for if, for example, $a(1)\, a(2)$ did not meet X then it could be given a small displacement parallel to itself into a new position such that the new polygon Y' obtained from Y by this process has the properties

$$Y' \cap X = Y \cap X, \quad Y' \subset Y. \tag{10}$$

Because $Y' \in \mathscr{P}(n)$ and because of the way in which it is obtained from Y we conclude that

$$\tau_P(X, \, Y') < \tau_P(X, \, Y). \tag{11}$$

By (9) this last inequality is impossible and thus each side of Y meets X.

Next we show that each side of Y meets X in a point which is not a vertex of Y. Suppose $a(1) \, a(2)$ met X only in the one point $a(2)$. If the line of which $a(1) \, a(2)$ is part were not a support line of X at $a(2)$, a small rotation of $a(1) \, a(2)$ about $a(2)$ in the appropriate

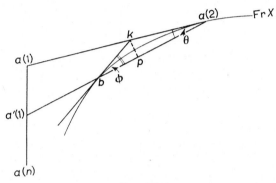

Fig. 16.

sense would reduce $\tau_P(X, \, Y)$. If however $a(1) \, a(2)$ is part of the support line to X at $a(2)$, then X and Y both lie on the same side of this line. Suppose that $a(1) \, a(2)$ is rotated about $a(2)$ into the position $a'(1) \, a(2)$ where $a'(1)$ lies on the segment $a(n) \, a(1)$. We choose $a'(1)$ so near to $a(1)$ that $a'(1) \, a(2)$ meets the frontier of X in the point b which lies between $a'(1)$ and $a(2)$. Let the tangent at b to the frontier of X meet $a(1) \, a(2)$ in k. As $a'(1)$ tends to $a(1)$ k tends to $a(2)$ from the direction of $a(1)$. Thus we may assume that k lies between $a(1)$ and $a(2)$. (See Fig. 16.)

Denote the polygon $a'(1) \, a(2) \ldots a(n) \, a'(1)$ by Y', angles $\angle k \, a(2)b$ and $\angle k \, ba(2)$ by θ and ϕ respectively, and let p be the foot of the perpendicular from k to $ba(2)$. (We use the symbol $ba(2)$ both for the segment joining b to $a(2)$ and for the length of this segment.)

We need to show that $\phi = O(\theta)$ as $\theta \to 0$. Suppose that θ is so small that $ba(2) < r$. Since X contains b and $a(2)$ and since further X can be regarded as an intersection of discs of radius $R + r$, it follows that X contains the circular arcs of radius $R + r$ which join b to $a(2)$. Thus

$$\sin \theta \geqslant \tfrac{1}{2}ba(2)/(R + r). \tag{12}$$

Further the circles of radius r which pass through b and touch bk, either do not contain $a(2)$ or do so as a frontier point. Thus

$$\sin \, \phi \leqslant \tfrac{1}{2}ba(2)/r. \tag{13}$$

Hence

$$\phi \leqslant \frac{\pi}{2} \sin \phi \leqslant \frac{\pi(R + r)}{2r} \theta \tag{14}$$

We use the symbol $\widehat{x_1 x_2}$ for two points on the frontier of X to denote the smaller length of the two arcs of the frontier of X joining these two points. Then

$$b\widehat{a}(2) < bk + ka(2) \tag{15}$$
$$= bp \sec \phi + pa(2) \sec \theta$$
$$= ba(2) + O(\theta^2).$$

But

$$\tau_P(X, \, Y') = \tau_P(X, \, Y) + a'\,(1)b + b\widehat{a}(2) - a'(1)\,a(1) - a(1)\,a(2)$$
$$+ b\widehat{a}(2) - ba(2). \tag{16}$$

and substituting from (15) we obtain

$$\tau_P(X, \, Y') < \tau_P(X, \, Y)$$
$$- a(1)a'(1)\,(1 + \cos \, \angle a(n)a(1)a(2)) + O(\theta^2) \tag{17}$$

Now $a'(1)\,a(1)$ is of the same order as θ, and so $\tau_P(X, \, Y')$ is less than $\tau_P(X, \, Y)$ when θ is small unless $\angle a(n)a(1)a(2) = \pi$, i.c. $a(1)$ is not a vertex. This is a contradiction with the hypotheses and it follows that every side of Y meets X in a point which is not a vertex of Y.

Thus there are five possible ways in which each side of Y can be disposed in regard to X. For example for the side $a(1)\,a(2)$ one of the following five alternatives holds.

(i) $a(1)\,a(2)$ is tangent to the frontier of X at a point which is neither $a(1)$ nor $a(2)$.

(ii) $a(1)\,a(2)$ cuts the frontier of X in two distinct points neither of which is $a(1)$ or $a(2)$.

(iii) $a(1)\,a(2)$ cuts the frontier of X in two distinct points one of which is $a(2)$ and the other is not $a(1)$, or vice versa.

(iv) $a(1)\,a(2)$ cuts the frontier of X in one point which is neither $a(1)$ nor $a(2)$.

(v) $a(1)\,a(2)$ is contained in X.

Our aim is to show that every segment which is a side of Y is of type (v). We assume that this is not the case and that the vertices $a(i_1), a(i_2), \ldots, a(i_k), 1 \leqslant i_1 < i_2 \ldots < i_k \leqslant n$ are exterior to X.

Let the interior angle made by the two sides of Y at the vertex $a(i_j)$ be θ_j. Let the point of X on $a(i_j)a(i_j - 1)$ nearest to $a(i_j)$ be b_j and the point of X on $a(i_j) a(i_j + 1)$ nearest to $a(i_j)$ be c_j, and let the angle made by $a(i_j)a(i_j - 1)$ with the tangent to the frontier of X at b_j be β_j and the angle made by $a(i_j) a(i_j + 1)$ with the tangent to the frontier of X at c_j be γ_j (see Fig. 17). We choose these angles so that

$$\beta_j \leqslant \angle a(i_j) b_j c_j \qquad \gamma_j \leqslant \angle a(i_j) c_j b_j$$
$$\theta_j + \beta_j + \gamma_j < \pi \tag{18}$$

(In this and in what follows there is the usual gloss that if $i_1 = 1$ then $i_1 - 1 = n$ and if $i_k = n$ then $i_k + 1 = 1$.)

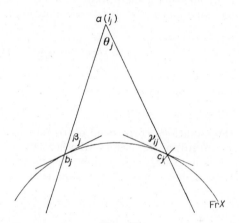

$a(i_j)$

θ_j

β_j

γ_{ij}

b_j

c_j

FrX

FIG. 17.

We now consider each segment which is a side of Y and which has an end point exterior to X. Consider for example $a(i_1)a(i_1 + 1)$. If this segment is of type (ii) then $i_1 + 1 = i_2$. We give the segment a small displacement by an amount δ perpendicular to itself. Suppose that the new polygon is Y' and that $Y' \subset Y$. Then if $\delta > 0$

$$\tau_P(X, \ Y') = \tau_P(X,Y) - \delta \{2 \cot \beta_2 - 2 \operatorname{cosec} \beta_2$$
$$+ \operatorname{cosec} \theta_2 + \cot \theta_2 + 2 \cot \gamma_1 - 2 \operatorname{cosec} \gamma_1$$
$$+ \cot \theta_1 + \operatorname{cosec} \theta_1\} + O(\delta^2). \tag{19}$$

This formula holds for all δ sufficiently small whether positive or negative. Thus the coefficient of δ must be zero and on rearrangement this gives

$$\cot \tfrac{1}{2}\theta_1 + \cot \tfrac{1}{2}\theta_2 = 2\{\tan \tfrac{1}{2}\beta_2 + \tan \tfrac{1}{2}\gamma_1\} \tag{20}$$

Next if $a(i_1)a(i_1 + 1)$ is of type (i) a displacement as above with δ positive so that $Y' \subset Y$ would give in place of (19)

$$\tau_P(X, \ Y') = \tau_P(X, \ Y) - \delta\{\text{cosec } \theta_2 + \cot \theta_2$$
$$+ \text{ cosec } \theta_1 + \cot \theta_1\} + O(\delta^{3/2}). \qquad (21)$$

But in this expression the coefficient of $-\delta$ is positive and thus for δ sufficiently small,

$$\tau_P(X, \ Y') < \tau_P(X, \ Y).$$

This is impossible by the minimal property of Y. Thus there are no sides of Y of type (i).

Finally, if $a(i_1) \ a(i_1 + 1)$ is of type (iii) or (iv) with $a(i_1 + 1)$ contained in X, we consider a small rotation of $a(i_1) \ a(i_1 + 1)$ about $a(i_1 + 1)$ through an angle θ, say. If the new polygon is Y', we have

$$\tau_P(X, \ Y') = \tau_P(X, \ Y) + \theta\{(\text{cosec } \gamma_1 - \cot \gamma_1)2g$$
$$- (\text{cosec } \theta_1 + \cot \theta_1)f\} + O(\theta^2), \qquad (22)$$

where $g = c_1 a(i_1 + 1)$ and $f = a(i_1) \ a(i_1 + 1)$. Thus, by the minimal property of Y, the coefficient of θ is zero, i.e.,

$$(f/g) \cot \tfrac{1}{2}\theta_1 = 2 \tan \tfrac{1}{2}\gamma_1, \qquad f/g > 1. \qquad (23)$$

We obtain the equations corresponding to (20) or (23) for each side of Y of type (ii) (iii) or (iv). Since all other sides are of type (v), each angle θ_j occurs in exactly two of these equations and each angle β_j, γ_j in exactly one. If we add all these equations we have

$$\sum_{j=1}^{k} \eta_j \cot \tfrac{1}{2}\theta_j = 2 \sum_{j=1}^{k} (\tan \tfrac{1}{2}\beta_j + \tan \tfrac{1}{2}\gamma_j) \qquad (24)$$

where $\eta_j \geqslant 2$. Now from (18)

$$\tan \tfrac{1}{2}\beta_j + \tan \tfrac{1}{2}\gamma_j < \tan \tfrac{1}{2}(\beta_j + \gamma_j)$$
$$\leqslant \tan (\tfrac{1}{2}\pi - \tfrac{1}{2}\theta_j) = \cot \tfrac{1}{2}\theta_j. \quad j = 1, \dots, k \qquad (25)$$

From (25) it follows that (24) is impossible.

Hence there are no vertices of Y exterior to X and the lemma is proved.

The behaviour of the perimeter deviation is next shown to be similar to that of the area deviation by using arguments due to Dowker and Fejes Tóth.

The function $T_P(X; n; i)$

It is sufficient to show that if we are given an $n - 1$-sided polygon Q and an $n + 1$ sided polygon R both inscribed in X then we can construct two inscribed n-sided polygons U and V such that

$$\tau_P(X, Q) + \tau_P(X, R) \geqslant \tau_P(X, U) + \tau_P(X, V). \qquad (26)$$

Denote the length of the frontier of the convex set Y by $l(Y)$. Then since we have relations such as

$$\tau_P(X, Q) = l(X) - l(Q) \tag{27}$$

it is sufficient to show that U and V can be found such that

$$l(Q) + l(R) \leqslant l(U) + l(V). \tag{28}$$

We consider two polygons Q, $Q \in \mathscr{P}_i(n-1; X)$ and R, $R \in \mathscr{P}_i(n+1; x)$ for which $l(Q)$ and $l(R)$ are maximal. If X is a member of $\mathscr{P}(n)$ then we take X for U and for V. Since $Q \subset X$ and $R \subset X$ the inequality (28) is trivially true. Suppose then that X is not a member of $\mathscr{P}(n)$. In this case Q has $n-1$ distinct vertices and R has $n+1$ distinct vertices and they all lie on the frontier of X.

There are two possible cases.

(i) For a suitable choice of the notation of $a_1 a_2 \ldots$ as vertices of Q and $b_1 b_2 \ldots$ of R both in the clockwise sense round the frontier of X, then $\widehat{a_1 a_2}$ contains three vertices $b_1 b_2 b_3$ of R.†

Let U be the n-sided polygon $a_1 b_2 a_2 a_3 \ldots a_{n-1} a_1$, and let V be the n-sided polygon $b_1 b_3 b_4 \ldots b_{n-1} b_1$. Then

$$l(U) + l(V) = l(R) + l(Q) + a_1 b_2 + b_2 a_2 + b_1 b_3$$
$$- a_1 a_2 - b_1 b_2 - b_2 b_3, \tag{29}$$

and (28) will be true if

$$a_1 b_2 + b_2 a_2 + b_1 b_3 \geqslant a_1 a_2 + b_1 b_2 + b_2 b_3. \tag{30}$$

The segment $b_1 b_3$ meets both the segments $a_1 b_2$ and $b_2 a_2$ in, say, c_1 and c_2 respectively. Then we have

$$b_3 c_2 + c_2 b_2 \geqslant b_2 b_3, \qquad b_1 c_1 + c_1 b_2 \geqslant b_1 b_2$$
$$a_1 c_1 + c_1 c_2 + c_2 a_2 \geqslant a_1 a_2.$$

If we add these inequalities we obtain (30).

(ii) Arc $\widehat{a_1 a_2}$ contains vertices $b_1 b_2$ of R and arc $\widehat{a_{s-1} a_s}$ contains the vertices $b_s b_{s+1}$.

Let U be the polygon whose vertices are $a_1 b_2 \ldots b_s a_s \ldots a_{n-1} a_1$ and let V be the polygon whose vertices are $b_1 a_2 \ldots a_{s-1} b_{s+1} \ldots b_{n+1} b_1$. Then

$$l(U) + l(V) = l(Q) + l(R) + a_1 b_2 + a_2 b_1 - a_1 a_2$$
$$- b_1 b_2 + a_s b_s + a_{s-1} b_{s+1} - a_{s-1} a_s - b_s b_{s+1}. \tag{31}$$

Since

$$a_1 b_2 + a_2 b_1 \geqslant a_1 a_2 + b_1 b_2, \quad a_s b_s + a_{s-1} b_{s+1} \geqslant a_{s-1} a_s + b_s b_{s+1}$$

it follows that (28) is true in this case also.

Hence the function $T_P(X; n; i)$ is a convex function of n.

† By $\widehat{a_1 a_2}$ here we mean the arc in the clockwise sense from a_1 to a_2.

The function $T_P(X; n; c)$

Let Q be an $n - 1$ sided polygon circumscribing X with sides $h_1 h_2, \ldots, h_{n-1}$ and let R be an $n + 1$-sided polygon circumscribing X with sides $k_1 k_2, \ldots, k_{n-1}$. On each h_i, k_j let a_i and b_j respectively denote points of X. Our aim is to construct from Q and R two n-sided polygons U and V circumscribing X such that

$$l(U) + l(V) \leqslant l(Q) + l(R). \tag{32}$$

We shall suppose that Q and R have the least possible length, i.e.

$$\tau_P(X, Q) = T_P(X; n - 1; c), \quad \tau_P(X, R) = T_P(X; n + 1; c), \tag{33}$$

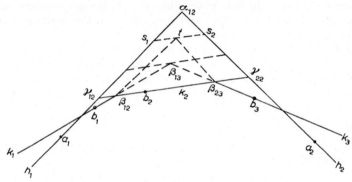

FIG. 18.

If X is a polygon with not more than n sides then take $U = X$, $V = X$ and (32) is obviously true since $X \subset Q$, $X \subset R$. Otherwise Q and R are polygons with exactly $n - 1$ and $n + 1$ genuine sides.

There are two possible cases

(i) For a suitable choice of notation $\overparen{a_1 a_2}$ contains the points b_1, b_2, b_3.

Let U be the n-sided polygon h_1, k_2, h_2, $\ldots$, h_{n-1} and let V be the n-sided polygon k_1, k_3, k_4, $\ldots$, k_{n+1}. Then denote the points of intersection of $h_i h_j$ by α_{ij}; of $k_i k_j$ by β_{ij} and of $h_i k_j$ by γ_{ij}. We have

$$l(U) + l(V) = l(Q) + l(R) + \gamma_{12}\beta_{12} + \beta_{23}\gamma_{22}$$
$$+ \beta_{12}\beta_{13} + \beta_{13}\beta_{23} - \gamma_{12}\alpha_{12} - \alpha_{12}\gamma_{22}. \tag{34}$$

Through β_{23} and β_{12} draw lines parallel respectively to h_2 and h_1 to meet in t. Through t draw a line parallel to k_2 to meet h_1 in s_1 and to meet h_2 in s_2. (See Fig. 18.) Since β_{13} is a point of the triangle $t\beta_{12}\beta_{23}$ we have

$$\beta_{12}\beta_{13} + \beta_{13}\beta_{23} \leqslant \beta_{12}t + t\beta_{23} = \gamma_{12}s_1 + \gamma_{22}s_2.$$

Also

$$\gamma_{12}\beta_{12} + \beta_{23}\gamma_{22} = s_1 s_2 \leqslant s_1 \alpha_{12} + \alpha_{12} s_2.$$

Thus on adding we obtain

$$\gamma_{12}\beta_{12} + \beta_{12}\beta_{13} + \beta_{13}\beta_{23} + \beta_{23}\gamma_{22} \leqslant \alpha_{12}\gamma_{12} + \alpha_{12}\gamma_{22}.$$

From (34) we conclude that

$$l(U) + l(V) \leqslant l(Q) + l(R).$$

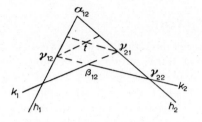

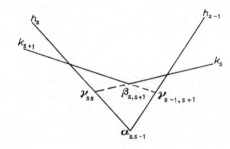

FIG. 19.

(ii) Arc $\widehat{a_1 a_2}$ contains points $b_1 b_2$ and arc $\widehat{a_{s-1} a_s}$ contains points $b_s b_{s+1}$.

Let U be the n-sided polygon $h_1 k_2, \ldots k_s h_s \ldots h_{n-1} h_1$ and let V be the n-sided polygon $k_1 h_2 \ldots h_{s-1} k_{s+1} \ldots k_{n+1} k_1$. Using the same notation as in (i) above, (32) will be true provided

$$\gamma_{21}\beta_{12} + \beta_{12}\gamma_{12} \leqslant \gamma_{21}\alpha_{12} + \alpha_{12}\gamma_{12} \tag{35}$$

and

$$\gamma_{ss}\beta_{s,s+1} + \beta_{s,s+1}\gamma_{s-1,s+1} \leqslant \gamma_{s,s}\alpha_{s,s-1} + \alpha_{s,s-1}\gamma_{s-1,s+1} \tag{36}$$

To prove (35) draw the lines through γ_{21} and γ_{12} parallel respectively to k_2 and k_1 to meet in t. (See Fig. 19.) Since

$$\angle \alpha_{12}\gamma_{21}\gamma_{12} = \angle \gamma_{21}\gamma_{12}\beta_{12} + \angle \gamma_{21}\gamma_{22}\gamma_{12} \geqslant \angle \gamma_{21}\gamma_{12}\beta_{12}$$

and similarly,

$$\angle \alpha_{12}\gamma_{12}\gamma_{21} \geqslant \angle \gamma_{12}\gamma_{21}\beta_{12}$$

it follows that t lies inside the triangle $\alpha_{12}\gamma_{21}\gamma_{12}$.

Thus

$$\gamma_{21}\beta_{12} + \beta_{12}\gamma_{12} = \gamma_{21}t + t\gamma_{12} \leqslant \gamma_{21}\alpha_{12} + \alpha_{12}\gamma_{12}$$

and (35) is proved.

The inequality (36) can be proved similarly and we conclude that (32) is correct and that $T_P(X; n; c)$ is a convex function of n.

§3. The function $T_A(X; n)$

We first define the area deviation between two sets C and K each of which consists of a finite number of oriented closed curves. For each point p of the plane that does not lie on C or on K we consider the angle through which the directed segment $\overrightarrow{pz}$ rotates as z describes C in the prescribed sense. This angle, measured positively in the clockwise sense is an integral multiple of 2π and is denoted by $f_c(p)$. Similarly we define $f_k(p)$. Then the area deviation between C and K is

$$\tau_A^*(C, K) = \frac{1}{2\pi} \int\!\!\int |f_c(p) - f_k(p)|\, d\mu \tag{37}$$

where μ is Lebesgue plane measure. Questions of measurability will be trivial because of the simplicity of the sets C and K that we actually consider.

We use the definition only for two special types of curves. C will be the frontier of an open convex set X described twice in the clockwise sense, so that $f_c(p) = 4\pi$ if $p \in X$.

K will be a member of a certain class of polygonal curves to define which we need some further notation.

An ordered segment with end points p and q will be denoted by pq and it will be understood in this notation that the ordering is from p to q. A polygonal line formed from the ordered segments $p_1p_2, p_2p_3, \ldots, p_{k-1}p_k$ will be denoted by $p_1p_2 \ldots p_k$. The segment pq lies in a line which divides the plane into two open disjoint half planes. Of these two half planes one, which we denote by $L(pq)$, has the property that if $r \in L(pq)$ and s describes pq in the sense from p to q then the segment rs rotates about r in the clockwise sense. If Z is a finite number of closed polygonal curves then we use $L(Z)$ to denote the intersection of all the half spaces $L(pq)$ for each segment pq of Z. We denote by $Q(2n)$ the class of all unions of a finite number of closed polygonal curves formed from a total of not more than $2n$ segments and such that if $Z \in Q(2n)$ then $L(Z)$ is not empty and if $p \in L(Z)$ then $f_Z(p) = 4\pi$.

The definition of deviation given in (37) will be used only when $K \in Q(2n)$.

For convenience (and without sacrificing any generality) we suppose that C does not contain any linear segment, that $n \geqslant 4$ and that the area of X is unity.

We define τ^* by

$$\tau^* = \inf. \, \tau_A^*(C, K), \, K \in Q(2n).$$

We show that there is a member K of $Q(2n)$ for which $\tau_A^*(C, K)$ is equal to τ^* and then develop the properties of this set K. We conclude finally that this set is either an n-sided convex polygon described twice in the clockwise sense or two convex n-sided polygons each described once in the clockwise sense. This result implies that $T_A(X; n)$ is a convex function of n.

LEMMA 5. $\tau^* \leqslant 2(\pi - 2)/\pi$.

Proof. It is possible to inscribe in C a quadrilateral Q which covers an area not less than the area of a square inscribed in a circle of unit area. Now Q described twice in the clockwise sense is a member of $Q(2n)$, thus

$$\tau^* \leqslant \tau_A^*(C, Q) \leqslant 2 \, (\text{area } C - \text{area } Q) \leqslant 2(\pi - 2)/\pi.$$

LEMMA 6. *There exists a member, say Z, of $Q(2n)$ such that* $\tau_A^*(C, Z) = \tau^*$.

Proof. There is certainly a sequence of members of $Q(2n)$ say $P_1, P_2, \ldots$ such that

$$\tau^* = \lim_{i \to \infty} \tau_A^*(C, P_i)$$

and we may suppose that the sets P_i are uniformly bounded. To see the truth of this last statement we observe firstly that if P is a member of $Q(2n)$ and if two segments of P have more than one point in common then they must be described in the same sense along the line containing them both. For otherwise $L(P)$ would be empty. The set CP is an open set and $f_P(p)$ is constant on each component of it. If two points q_1, q_2 of CP are such that $q_1 q_2$ meets P in a single point then $f_P(q_1)$ differs from $f_P(q_2)$ and if further the segment $q_1 q_2$ meets the segment $p_1 p_2$ of P such that $q_1 \in L(p_1 p_2)$, $q_2 \notin L(p_1 p_2)$ then $f_P(q_1) > f_P(q_2)$. It follows that any half-ray ending at a point p of $L(P)$ meets P in at most 2 points and that as q moves along this half-ray, $f_P(q)$ is a decreasing function. Thus it takes only the values 0, 2π, 4π. If the unbounded component of CP is denoted by B then CB is connected and star-like with respect to each point of $L(P)$. The set $L(P)$ is convex since it is an intersection of half-spaces. Now

$$\tau_A^*(C, P) \geqslant \text{Area } (X - L(P)).$$

8

Thus given $\varepsilon > 0$ there exists an integer i_0 such that

$$\text{Area } (X - L(P_i)) \leqslant 2(\pi - 2)/\pi + \varepsilon, \qquad i > i_0.$$

Hence

$$\text{Area } (L(P_i) \cap X) \geqslant 1 - 2(\pi - 2)/\pi - \varepsilon, \qquad i > i_0.$$

With a suitable choice of ε this implies that

$$\text{Area } (L(P_i) \cap X) \geqslant \tfrac{1}{2}\{1 - 2(\pi - 2)/\pi\} \qquad i > i_0. \qquad (38)$$

If d is the diameter of X, (38) implies that the minimal width Δ_i of $L(P_i) \cap X$, satisfies

$$\Delta_i \geqslant (1 - 2(\pi - 2)/\pi)/2d. \qquad (39)$$

Now if the set CB contains a point s distant y, $y > d$, from a point p of $L(P) \cap X$, then $L(P)$ contains a segment of length Δ_i perpendicular to sp and distant from s at least $y - d$ and at most $y + d$. Since CB is a star domain with respect to each point of this segment it follows that CB contains a triangle, exterior to X, of area at least

$$\tfrac{1}{2}\Delta_i \cdot \frac{(y-d)^2}{(y+d)} \qquad (40)$$

But at each point q of this triangle $f_c(q) = 0$, $f_P(q) \geqslant 2\pi$. Hence from (39) and (40),

$$\tau_A^*(C, P) > \frac{(1 - 2(\pi - 2)/\pi)}{4d} \cdot \frac{(y - d)^2}{(y + d)} . \qquad (41)$$

From Lemma 5, it follows that for i sufficiently large P_i lies inside a circle whose centre is a fixed point of X and radius $15d$.

Thus we can suppose, by the Blaschke selection theorem that P_i converges to a set P. Clearly the closure of $L(P_i)$ converges to a set, say T, and for every point x not belonging to $P, f_{P_i}(x)$ tends to a limit as i tends to infinity. The interior of T is non-void since its area is greater than or equal to $\tfrac{1}{2}\{1 - 2(\pi - 2)/\pi\}$. P is composed of at most $2n$ oriented segments and the interior of T is the set $L(P)$. For $p \in L(P)$, $f_P(p) = 4\pi$. Thus $P \in Q(2n)$ and since $\tau_A^*(C, P) = \tau^*$ the lemma is proved with P for Z.

Remarks. We shall always use Z for a member of $Q(2n)$ that satisfies Lemma 6. We observe that the set $L(Z) \cap X$ is non-void.

An end point common to two consecutive segments of P will be called a vertex of P, for any $P \in Q(2n)$.

The line containing the segment pq will be denoted by $l(pq)$. The distance between two points p, q will be denoted by $\rho(p,q)$.

LEMMA 7. (i) *Every vertex of Z is exterior to X.* (ii) *Any segment of Z, say z_1z_2, meets C in points x_1, x_2 such that*

$$\rho(z_1, x_1) = \rho(x_2, z_2) = \tfrac{1}{4}\rho(z_1, z_2)$$

We suppose that $z_0z_1z_2z_3$ are consecutive vertices of Z where z_0 may coincide with z_3. Let $l(pq: \eta)$ be the line parallel to $l(pq)$ at a distance η from $l(pq)$ and choose the sign of η so that

$$l(pq: \eta) \subset L(pq) \quad \text{if} \quad \eta > 0 \quad \text{and} \quad l(pq: \eta) \not\subset L(pq) \quad \text{if} \quad \eta < 0.$$

Write

$$z_1(\eta) = l(z_0z_1) \cap l(z_1z_2: \eta)$$

$$z_2(\eta) = l(z_2z_3) \cap l(z_1z_2: \eta)$$

Denote the length of that part of z_1z_2 that is contained in X by I and the length of the remainder by J. Denote by $Z(\eta)$ the member of $Q(2n)$ obtained from Z by replacing z_0z_1, z_1z_2, z_2z_3 by $z_0z_1(\eta)$, $z_1(\eta)z_2(\eta)$, $z_2(\eta)z_3$ respectively. This new set is a member of $Q(2n)$ if η is small. Then

$$\tau_A^*(C, Z(\eta)) = \tau_A^*(C, Z) + (I - J)\eta + O(\eta^2).$$

Hence by the minimal property of Z, $I = J$.

Thus the segment z_1z_2 intersects X. Let the end-points of the segment $z_1z_2 \cap X$ be x_1 and x_2 where the order on z_1z_2 is $z_1x_1x_2z_2$. Of course we may have x_1 coinciding with z_1 or x_2 with z_2, but x_1 is certainly distinct from x_2. Let b be the mid-point of the segment x_1x_2 and $l(\theta)$ be a line through b making an angle θ, measured positively in the clockwise sense, with z_1z_2. Write

$$z_1(\theta) = l(\theta) \cap l(z_0z_1) \qquad z_2(\theta) = l(\theta) \cap l(z_2z_3).$$

If θ is small the polygon $Z(\theta)$ obtained by replacing z_0z_1, z_1z_2, z_2z_3 by $z_0z_1(\theta)$, $z_1(\theta) z_2(\theta)$, $z_2(\theta) z_3$ belongs to $Q(2n)$. Now

$$\tau_A^*(C, Z(\theta)) = \tau_A^*(C, Z) + \tfrac{1}{2}\theta\{\rho(z_1, b)^2 - \rho(z_2, b)^2\} + O(\theta^2).$$

Hence

$$\rho(z_1, b) = \rho(z_2, b)$$

and thus

$$\rho(x_1, z_1) = \rho(x_2, z_2).$$

Since we have already shown that $\rho(x_1x_2) = \rho(z_1x_1) + \rho(x_2z_2)$, the two parts of the lemma are proved.

It is convenient to refer to a point of $L(p, q)$ as being on the positive side of pq. A point that does not belong to $L(pq)$ or to $l(pq)$ is said to lie on the negative side of pq.

LEMMA 8. *If $z_0z_1z_2z_3$ are four consecutive vertices of Z, then z_0 and z_3 lie on the positive side of z_1z_2.*

Proof. Consider the three vertices $z_1 z_2 z_3$. By Lemma 7 there is a point of X on $z_2 z_3$. Denote one such point by b. Let p be a point of $L(Z) \cap X$ and k be the point $l(z_1 z_2) \cap l(pb)$. It is assumed that p is chosen so that $l(pb)$ is not parallel to $l(z_1 z_2)$. If z_3 lies on the negative side of $z_1 z_2$ so does b. Since p lies on the positive side it follows that k is a point of pb and thus of X. Further in this case z_1 lies on the negative side of $z_2 z_3$. Thus p lies on the opposite side of $z_2 z_3$ to z_1 and hence $z_1 z_2$ lie on the same side of pb. Thus either z_1 lies between z_2 and k or z_2 lies between z_1 and k. Since there is a point of $z_1 z_2$ belonging to X we should have, in either case a vertex of Z belonging to X.

This is in contradiction with Lemma 7 and thus z_3 lies on the positive side of $z_1 z_2$. Similarly z_0 lies on the positive side of $z_1 z_2$.

LEMMA 9. *Z has exactly $2n$ segments.*

Proof. If Z had $r < 2n$ segments suppose that $z_1 z_2$, $z_2 z_3$ were two consecutive segments. Since z_2 does not belong to the closure of X there are points z_2' and z_2'' on $z_2 z_3$ such that the triangle $z_2' z_2 z_2''$ is completely exterior to X. If we replace in Z the segments $z_1 z_2$, $z_2 z_3$ by $z_1 z_2'$, $z_2' z_2''$, $z_2'' z_3$ then the new polygon Z' also belongs to $Q(2n)$ but

$$\tau_A^*(C, Z') < \tau_A^*(C, Z)$$

in contradiction with the minimal property of Z.

Hence the lemma is proved.

LEMMA 10. *If one vertex of Z is a double vertex (i.e. the end point of four segments formed from two consecutive pairs of segments), then Z is an n-sided convex polygon described twice in the clockwise sense.*

Proof. From Lemma 7 it is sufficient to show that for any point y exterior to X there are at most two lines through y say $yx_1 x_2$, $yx_3 x_4$ meeting the frontier of X in $x_1 x_2$ and $x_3 x_4$ respectively so that

$$\rho(yx_1) = \tfrac{1}{2}\rho(x_1 x_2), \qquad \rho(yx_3) = \tfrac{1}{2}\rho(x_3 x_4).$$

If there were three such lines let the third be $yx_5 x_6$ and suppose this line meets $x_1 x_3$ in a point x_5' and $x_2 x_4$ in a point x_6'. Then

$$\rho(yx_5') = \tfrac{1}{2}\rho(x_5' x_6')$$

by similar triangles. But

$$\rho(yx_5) < \rho(yx_5'), \qquad \rho(x_5' x_6') < \rho(x_5 x_6)$$

thus $yx_5 x_6$ does not have the required properties. Thus there are at most two such lines and the lemma is proved.

Our aim is to show that Z is an n-sided convex polygon described twice or is two n-sided convex polygons. We shall assume that this is not the case and show that this assumption leads to a contradiction. From Lemma 10 we shall assume that Z has no double vertices without further explicit reference to the fact.

LEMMA 11. *If b_1b_2 are two points of C on the segment z_1z_2 of Z then there are two parallel lines one each through b_1 and b_2 which bound a strip containing the part of X on the negative side of z_1z_2.*

Proof. Let z_3 be the vertex of Z next after z_2. Let z_2z_3 meet C in b_3b_4 and suppose that the orders of the points on z_1z_2, z_2z_3 are $z_1b_1b_2z_2$ and $z_2b_3b_4z_3$ respectively. Then $l(b_1b_4)$, $l(b_2b_3)$ have the required property.

Let z be a vertex of Z. Of the two segments of Z which terminate at z we denote that of which z is the final point by $s_1(z)$ and that of which z is an initial point by $s_2(z)$. The point of C on $s_1(z)$ nearest to z is denoted by $c_1(z)$ and that on $s_2(z)$ by $c_2(z)$. The point of C on $s_1(z)$ furthest from z is denoted by $d_1(z)$ and that on $s_2(z)$ is denoted by $d_2(z)$. The arc of C described once positively from $c_1(z)$ to $c_2(z)$ is denoted by $\alpha(z)$ and the open domain bounded by $c_1(z)z$, $zc_2(z)$ and $\alpha(z)$ described negatively is denoted by $A(z)$. The open single sector bounded by $l(zc_1(z))$, $l(zc_2(z))$ and containing $A(z)$ is denoted by $K(z)$.

LEMMA 12. *If z_1 is a vertex of Z there is no other vertex in $A(z_1)$*

Proof. The argument of Lemma 10 shows that the sector $K(z_1)$ is characterized by the property that any half-ray terminating at z_1 and lying in $K(z_1)$ meets C in two points say c', c'' where c' lies between z_1 and c'' and where

$$\rho(z_1c') < \tfrac{1}{2}\rho(c'c'').$$

Suppose then that a vertex, say z^* of Z belonged to $A(z_1)$. The half lines terminating at z^* and containing $d_1(z_1)$ or $d_2(z_1)$ both have the property characterising half-rays of $K(Z^*)$. Thus the half-ray terminating at z^* and containing $c_1(z^*)$ meets either $z_1d_1(z_1)$ or $z_1d_2(z_1)$, and similarly the half-ray terminating at z^* and containing $c_2(z^*)$ meets either $z_1d_2(z_1)$ or $z_1d_1(z_1)$.

Now Z cannot consist of two convex polygons P_1, P_2 of which one, say P_1, is completely contained in the closure of triangle $z_1c_1(z_1)c_2(z_1)$. For in this case we could translate P_1 until it became P_1' lying in the open domain bounded by $d_1(z_1)c_1(z_1)$, $c_1(z_1)c_2(z_1)$, $c_2(z_1)d_2(z_1)$, $d_2(z_1)d_1(z_1)$. Denote the new member of $Q(2n)$ thus obtained by taking P_1' and P_2, by Z'. Now in this case $\tau_A^*(C, Z)$ is the sum of the area deviations of P_1, P_2 from C, i.e.

$$\tau_A^*(C, Z) = \tau_A(C, P_1) + \tau(C, P_2),$$

and

$$\tau_A(C, P') < \tau_A(C, P).$$

Hence

$$\tau_A^*(C, Z') < \tau_A^*(C, Z).$$

Since this last inequality is impossible on account of the minimal property of Z it follows that Z does not consist of two polygons, one of which is contained in the closure of triangle $z_1 c_1(z_1) c_2(z_1)$.

Thus there is a largest sequence of consecutive vertices of Z that are all contained in $A(z_1)$. Denote the first by z_i^* and the last by z_j^*. Then z_{i-1}^* and z_{j+1}^* lie outside $A(z_1)$ and thus each of $z_{i-1}^* z_i^*$ and $z_j^* z_{j+1}^*$ must meet one or other of $z_1 d_1(z_1)$, $z_1 d_2(z_1)$. If $z_{i-1}^* z_i^*$ and $z_{j+1}^* z_j^*$ both meet $z_1 d_1(z_1)$ let the vertex of $z_i^* z_{i+1}^* \ldots z_j^*$ nearest to $l(z_1 d_2(z_1))$ be z_k^*. Then if the line through z_k^* parallel to $z_1 d_2(z_1)$ is m we have $A(z_k^*)$ lying on one side of m whilst $z_k^* d_2(z)$ lies on the other. This is impossible. Thus we cannot have $z_{i-1}^* z_i^*$ and $z_j^* z_{j+1}^*$ both meeting $z_1 d_1(z_1)$. Similarly they cannot both meet $z_1 d_2(z_1)$. If $z_{i-1}^* z_i^*$ intersects $z_1 d_2(z_1)$ then z_1 lies on the positive and $d_2(z_1)$ on the negative side of $z_{i-1}^* z_i^*$. But $A(z_1^*)$ which contains $d_2(z_1)$ lies on the positive side of $z_{i-1}^* z_i^*$. Thus we have a contradiction. Similarly $z_j^* z_{j+1}^*$ does not meet $d_1(z_1) z_1$ and we conclude finally that $z_{i-1}^* z_i^*$ meets $d_1(z_1) z_1$ and $z_j^* z_{j+1}^*$ meets $z_1 d_2(z_1)$.

Produce $z_{i-1}^* z_i^*$ to meet $z_1 d_2(z_1)$ in k_2 and $z_i^* z_{i+1}^*$ to meet $z_1 d_1(z_1)$ in k_1. Then k_2 belongs to $z_1 c_2(z_1)$ and k_1 to $z_1 c_1(z_1)$ for otherwise z_i^* would not be exterior to X.

We obtain a new member of $Q(2n)$ from Z by replacing segments as follows. Suppose that $z_0 z_1 z_2$ are consecutive vertices of Z. Then replace $z_0 z_1$ by $z_0 k_1$, $z_i^* z_{i+1}^*$ by $k_1 z_{i+1}^*$, $z_{i-1}^* z_i^*$ by $z_{i-1}^* k_2$ and $z_1 z_2$ by $k_2 z_2$ so that the new member has vertices in the order $z_0 k_1 z_{i+1}^* \ldots z_{i-1}^* k_2 z_2 \ldots z_0$. Denote this new set by Z'. Then $L(Z') = L(Z)$. Z' has no end points and it is clear that $Z' \in Q(2n)$. If Z is two closed polygons then Z' is one polygonal line and vice versa.

Denote the area of the convex quadrilateral $z_1 k_1 z_i^* k_2$ by A, then

$$\tau_A^*(C, Z) = \tau_A^*(C, Z') + A$$

This is impossible by the minimal property of Z. Thus no such vertices as z_i^* exist and the lemma is proved.

LEMMA 13. *There is no vertex of Z on any segment of Z apart from the end points of the segment.*

Proof. Suppose that $z_0 z_1$ is a segment of Z so that z_i^* is also a vertex of Z lying on this segment. There is no real loss of generality in supposing that z_i^* lies on the segment $c_1(z_1) z_1$.

Then the segment $d_1(z_1) d_2(z_1)$ is contained in $K(z_i^*)$ and this implies that z_{i-1}^* lies outside $K(z_1)$ and that $z_{i-1}^* z_i^*$ produced meets $z_1 c_2(z_1)$ in say k. In Z replace $z_0 z_1$ by $z_0 z_i^*$, $z_{i-1}^* z_i^*$ by $z_{i-1}^* k$, and $z_1 z_2$ by $k z_2$ to obtain a new member Z' of $Q(2n)$. If A denotes the area of the triangle $z_1 z_i^* k$ we have

$$\tau_A^*(C, Z') = \tau_A^*(C, Z) - A.$$

This is impossible. Thus no such vertices as z_i^* exist and the lemma is proved.

LEMMA 14. *No two vertices of Z lie on the negative side of any segment of Z.*

Proof. We show firstly that we need consider only that case in which the vertices are consecutive vertices of Z.

Suppose that $z_0 z_1$ is a segment of Z. If Z is two polygons they are both convex and all the vertices of the polygon to which $z_0 z_1$ belong lie on the positive side of $z_0 z_1$ by Lemma 8. For the other polygon of Z either at most one vertex lies on the negative side of $z_0 z_1$ or the vertices which lie on the negative side of $z_0 z_1$ contain two consecutive vertices of Z. If on the other hand Z is a single polygon and if the three vertices stu in order on Z are such that t lies on the negative and s, u on the positive side of $z_0 z_1$ where stu are consecutive vertices, then we can suppose that $z_0 z_1$ meets at least one of st, tu. For otherwise either it lies entirely on the negative side of st or of tu in which case we have two consecutive vertices z_0, z_1 on the negative side of a segment of Z or it lies entirely in the sector common to the two positive sides of st and tu, i.e. in $K(t)$. In this case $l(z_0 z_1)$ cannot meet $c_1(t)t$ or $tc_2(t)$, for if it did so we should have z_0 or z_1 in $A(t)$, a contradiction with Lemma 12. Thus $l(z_0 z_1)$ meets $sc_2(s)$ and $c_1(u)u$. Suppose $l(z_0 z_1)$ meets $sc_2(s)$ in p and r is the vertex preceding s, then since z_0, $z_1 \notin A(s)$ and z_0, z_1 lie on the same side of st as r, we have sr meeting $l(z_0 z_1)$ in say k lying between p and z_0 or z_1. But this implies that $L(z_0 z_1) \cap X \cap K(s) = \emptyset$. This is not so and therefore $z_0 z_1$ meets one at least of st, tu; suppose it meets st in w. Replace st, $z_0 z_1$ by sw, wz_1, $z_0 w$, wt. Then Z becomes two polygons one of which is convex and the other is convex except at the point w. It follows that no vertices of Z apart from t lie on the negative side of $z_0 z_1$. Thus there is no loss of generality in assuming that if two vertices of Z lie on the negative side of $z_0 z_1$, then there are two such vertices which are consecutive. We shall denote two such vertices by $z_i^* z_{i+1}^*$.

Next, it is not possible that both z_0 and z_1 should lie on the negative side of $z_i^* z_{i+1}^*$. There is a point p of X on the positive sides of both $z_0 z_1$ and $z_i^* z_{i+1}^*$ and other points of X on $z_0 z_1$ (say q) and on $z_i^* z_{i+1}^*$ (say q^*). p and q^* lie on opposite sides of $l(z_0 z_1)$ and q lies between z_0 and z_1. Thus the triangle qq^*p contains one of z_0, z_1. This is impossible since z_0, z_1 are both exterior to X whilst $qq^*p \subset X$.

Thus there are two cases to consider:

(a) One of $z_0 z_1$ lies on the negative side of $z_i^* z_{i+1}^*$ and the other either on $l(z_i^* z_{i+1}^*)$ or on the positive side of $z_i^* z_{i+1}^*$.

(b) Both of $z_0 z_1$ lie on either $l(z_i^* z_{i+1}^*)$ or on the positive side of $z_i^* z_{i+1}^*$.

Case (a).

We divide this case into two such subcases as follows:

(i) z_0 lies on the negative side of $z_i^* z_{i+1}^*$.

(ii) z_1 lies on the negative side of $z_i^* z_{i+1}^*$.

These two subcases are essentially similar and we consider only case (i).

Let $l(z_i^* z_{i+1}^*)$ meet $z_0 z_1$ in k. k belongs either to $z_0 c_2(z_0)$ or $c_1(z_1) z_1$, for otherwise we should have $k \in X$ and therefore $z_i^* \in X$. This is

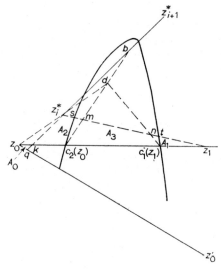

FIG. 20.

not so by Lemma 7. If k belongs to $c_1(z_1) z_1$, $p \in L(z_i^* z_{i+1}^*) \cap L(z_0 z_1)$ and $q \in l(z_i^* z_{i+1}^*) \cap X$ then the segment $z_i^* z_{i+1}^*$ contains q and pq meets $l(z_0 z_1)$ in r where $r \notin X$ and hence $p \notin X$. Thus

$$L(z_i^* z_{i+1}^*) \cap K(z_1) \cap X = \emptyset$$

a contradiction with the fact that $L(Z) \cap X \neq \emptyset$ (see the remark after Lemma 6). Thus $k \in z_0 c_2(z_0)$.

Further, the points of $X \cap s_1(z_0)$ and $X \cap z_0 z_1$ lie on the same side of $z_i^* z_{i+1}^*$ for otherwise we should have $z_i^* \in X$. Thus $l(z_i^* z_{i+1}^*)$ intersects $s_1(z_0)$ in say q. (See Fig. 20.)

In Z let z_0' be the vertex immediately preceding z_0. Replace $z_0' z_0$ by $z_0' q$; $z_i^* z_{i+1}^*$ by $q z_{i+1}^*$ and $z_0 z_1$ by $z_i^* z_1$. The new set of oriented segments taken in proper order is called Z'. Z' is a member of $Q(2n)$, it is a single polygon if Z is two polygons and it is two polygons if Z is one. Denote the point of X on z^*z_1 nearest z_i^* by s and that nearest z_1 by t.

Now
$$\tau_A^*(C,\, Z') = \tau_A^*(C,\, Z) - A_0 + A_1 + A_2 - A_3$$
where

A_0 is the area of triangle qz_0k,

A_1 is the area bounded by $c_1(z_1)z_1$, z_1t and the positive arc $tc_1(z_1)$ of C,

A_2 is the area bounded by $c_2(z_0)k$, kz_i^*, z_i^*s and the negative arc $sc_2(z_0)$ of C,

A_3 is the area bounded by $c_2(z_0)c_1(z_1)$, the negative arc $c_1(z_1)t$ of C, ts, and the negative arc $sc_2(z_0)$ of C. All the numbers A_0, A_1, A_2, A_3 are positive, they are not signed areas.

Let b be a point of $X \cap z_i^*z_{i+1}^*$ and let $l(z_0z_1^*)$ meet $bc_2(z_0)$ in d. Let $dc_2(z_0)$ meet $z_i^*z_1$ in m and $dc_1(z_1)$ meet $z_i^*z_1$ in n. Then, since n, and m belong to st and C is convex and contains no straight lines,

A_1 is less than area of triangle $nc_1(z_1)z_1 = A_1'$,

A_2 is less than area of quadrilateral $z_0c_2(z_0)mz_i^* = A_2'$,

A_3 is greater than area of quadrilateral $mc_2(z_0)c_1(z_1)n = A_3'$.

Make an area preserving affine transformation such that $\angle z_0z_i^*z_1$ is transformed into a right angle. Use the same symbols in the transformed figure. Take z_i^* as the origin of rectangular Cartesian coordinates z_0 as $(1,0)$ and z_1 as $(0,1)$. Then $c_2(z_0)$ is $(\frac{3}{4},\frac{1}{4})$, $c_1(z_1)$ is $(\frac{1}{4},\frac{3}{4})$ and if d is $(-X, 0)$, then m is $(0, X/(3 + 4X))$, n is $(0, 3X/(1 + 4X))$. Thus

$$z_1n + mz_i^* = \left(1 - \frac{3X}{1 + 4X}\right) + \frac{X}{3 + 4X}$$

$$> \frac{3X}{1 + 4X} - \frac{X}{3 + 4X}$$

$$= mn$$

Thus area dmn, is less than the sum of areas dmz_i^* and dnz_1.

Hence, since area $dz_0c_2(z_0)$ and area $dz_1c_1(z_1)$ together equal area $dc_2(z_0)c_1(z_1)$ it follows that

$$A_3' > A_2' + A_1'$$

Thus finally

$$\tau_A^*(C,\, Z') < \tau_A^*(C,\, Z),$$

a contradiction which shows that Case (a) cannot occur.

Case (b).

Both of z_0, z_1 lie either on $l(z_i^*z_{i+1}^*)$ or on the positive side of $z_i^*z_{i+1}^*$.

Firstly we observe that it is not possible for both of z_0 and z_1 to lie on $l(z_i^* z_{i+1}^*)$ because then the mid-points of $z_0 z_1$ and $z_i^* z_{i+1}^*$ would coincide (each being coincident with the mid-point of the segment $X \cap z_i^* z_{i+1}^*$), and thus either z_0 is z_i^*, in which case by Lemma 10, Z is a convex n-sided polygon described twice, or either $z_0 \in z_i^* z_{i+1}^*$ or $z_i^* \in z_0 z_1$. Both these last two alternatives are in contradiction with Lemma 13, and we are assuming that Z is not a convex n-sided polygon described twice. Thus we may suppose that either z_0 or z_1 is on the positive side of $z_i^* z_{i+1}^*$. We assume that this is true of z_1 (the argument in the other case is similar).

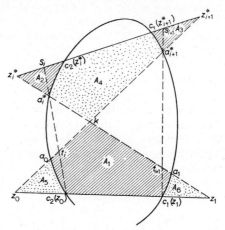

FIG. 21.

Next, if z_0 lies on $l(z_i^* z_{i+1}^*)$ we can apply exactly the same argument as in Case (1). Here q, k coincide with z_0. We are led to a contradiction with the minimal property of Z.

Suppose then that both z_0 and z_1 lie on the positive side of $z_i^* z_{i+1}^*$. Denote the point of intersection of $z_i^* z_1$ with $z_{i+1}^* z_0$ by k. k may lie inside or outside X. Let the points C on $z_i^* z_1$ be a_i^* nearest to z_i^* and a_1 nearest to z_1. Let the points of C on $z_{i+1}^* z_0$ nearest to z_{i+1}^* be a_{i+1}^* and nearest to z_0 be a_0. Then if we denote by Z' the member of $Q(2n)$ obtained by replacing $z_0 z_1$ by $z_0 z_{i+1}^*$ and $z_i^* z_{i+1}^*$ by $z_i^* z_1$, we have

$$\tau_A^*(C, Z') = \tau_A^*(C, Z) - (A_1 + A_2 + A_3) + (A_4 + A_5 + A_6)$$

where if $k \in X$, (see Fig. 21),

A_1 is the area bounded by $c_2(z_0) c_1(z_1)$; the negative arc $c_1(z_1) a_1$ of C; $a_1 k$; $k a_0$; the negative arc $a_0 c_2(z_0)$ of C,

A_2 is the area bounded by $c_2(z_i^*)z_i^*$; $z_i^*a_i^*$; the positive arc $a_i^*c_2(z_i^*)$ of C.

A_3 is the area bounded by $a_{i+1}^*z_{i+1}^*$; $z_{i+1}^*c_1(z_{i+1}^*)$; the positive arc $c_1(z_{i+1}^*)a_{i+1}^*$ of C,

A_4 is the area bounded by a_i^*k; ka_{i+1}^*; the negative arc $a_{i+1}^*c_1(z_{i+1}^*)$ of C; $c_1(z_{i+1}^*)c_2(z_i^*)$; the negative arc $c_2(z_i^*)a_i^*$ of C,

A_5 is the area bounded by $z_0c_2(z_0)$; the positive arc $c_2(z_0)a_0$ of C; a_0z_0,

A_6 is the area bounded by $c_1(z_1)z_1$; z_1a_1; the positive arc $a_1c_1(z_1)$ of C.

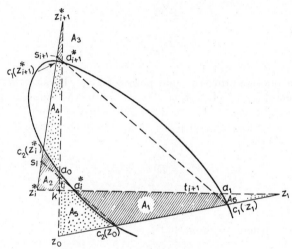

FIG. 22.

If k lies outside X say $k \in z_0a_0$ and $k \in z_i^*a_i^*$, then (see Fig. 22),

A_1 is the area bounded by $c_2(z_0)c_1(z_1)$; the negative arc $c_1(z_1)a_1$ of C; $a_1a_i^*$; the negative arc $a_i^*c_2(z_0)$ of C,

A_2 is the area bounded by $c_2(z_i^*)z_i^*$; z_i^*k; ka_0; the positive arc $a_0c_2(z_i^*)$ of C,

A_3 is the area bounded by $a_{i+1}^*z_{i+1}^*$; $z_{i+1}^*c_1(z_{i+1})$; the positive arc $c_1(z_{i+1})a_{i+1}^*$ of C,

A_4 is the area bounded by $a_0a_{i+1}^*$; the negative arc $a_{i+1}^*c_1(z_{i+1}^*)$ of C; $c_1(z_{i+1}^*)c_2(z_i^*)$; negative arc $c_2(z_i^*)a_0$ of C,

A_5 is the area bounded by $z_0c_2(z_0)$; the positive arc $c_2(z_0)a_i^*$ of C; a_i^*k; kz_0,

A_6 is the area bounded by $c_1(z_1)z_1$; z_1a_1 the positive arc $a_1c_1(z_1)$ of C.

If k lies on $a_{i+1}^*z_{i+1}^*$ and on a_1z_1 there are further changes in the definitions of $A_1, A_2, \ldots, A_6$. But this case is effectively the same as the one described immediately above and we shall only consider further the two cases which have been written out explicitly.

Our aim is to show that

$$A_1 + A_2 + A_3 > A_4 + A_5 + A_6$$

Write

$$s_i = z_i^* z_{i+1}^* \cap l(c_2(z_0)a_i^*),$$

$$s_{i+1} = z_i^* z_{i+1}^* \cap l(c_1(z_1)a_{i+1}^*),$$

$$t_i = z_0 z_{i+1}^* \cap s_i c_2(z_0),$$

$$t_{i+1} = z_i^* z_1 \cap s_{i+1} c_1(z_1).$$

The lines $l(s_i t_i)$ and $l(s_{i+1} t_{i+1})$ divide the plane into four sectors[†] of which one contains the mid-point of $z_0 z_1$. Denote the frontier of this sector by C'. Let A_1', $i = 1, \ldots, 6$ be the numbers obtained (as above in place of A_i, $i = 1, \ldots, 6$) when we use C' in place of C, t_i in place of a_0, t_{i+1} in place of a_1, s_i in place of $c_2(z_i^*)$ and s_{i+1} in place of $c_1(z_{i+1}^*)$.

Then

$$A_1' + A_2' + A_3' < A_1 + A_2 + A_3$$

$$A_4' + A_5' + A_6' > A_4 + A_5 + A_6$$

and it is sufficient to show that

$$A_1' + A_2' + A_3' \geqslant A_4' + A_5' + A_6'.$$

We have

$$\rho(z_i^*, s_i) \leqslant \tfrac{1}{4}\rho(z_i^*, z_{i+1}^*), \; \rho(z_{i+1}^*, s_{i+1}) \leqslant \tfrac{1}{4}\rho(z_i^*, z_{i+1}^*).$$

It also follows from Lemma 11 that $l(s_i t_i)$ meets $l(ls_{i+1} t_{i+1})$ on the negative side of $z_0 z_1$. This in turn implies that

$$kz_i^* \cdot kz_{i+1}^* \leqslant kz_0 \cdot kz_1. \tag{42}$$

For if we make an affine transformation such that the angles $z_i^* z_{i+1}^* z_0$ and $z_0 z_1 z_i^*$ transform into equal angles then the length of the transform of $z_i^* z_{i+1}^*$ is less than or equal to that of $z_0 z_1$. This implies that the area of $kz_i^* z_{i+1}$ is less than or equal to that of $kz_0 z_1$. Thus (42) is proved.

† Or three sets if they are parallel but Lemma 11 shows that they are not parallel.

We next make an affine transformation such that, using appropriate rectangular Cartesian axes we have the following correspondences

$$k \to O = (0,0) \qquad z_1 \to B = (4,0) \qquad z_0 \to A = (0,4)$$

$$z_i^* \to C = (-X, 0) \quad z_{i+1}^* \to D = (0, -Y) \quad c_2(z_0) \to H = (1,3)$$

$$c_1(z_1) \to G = (3,1) \qquad s_i \to E = (E_1, E_2) \quad s_{i+1} \to F = (F_1, F_2)$$

$$t_i \to T_1 \qquad a_{i+1}^* \to L_1 \qquad t_{i+1} \to T_2$$

$$a_i^* \to L_2$$

(see Fig. 23.)

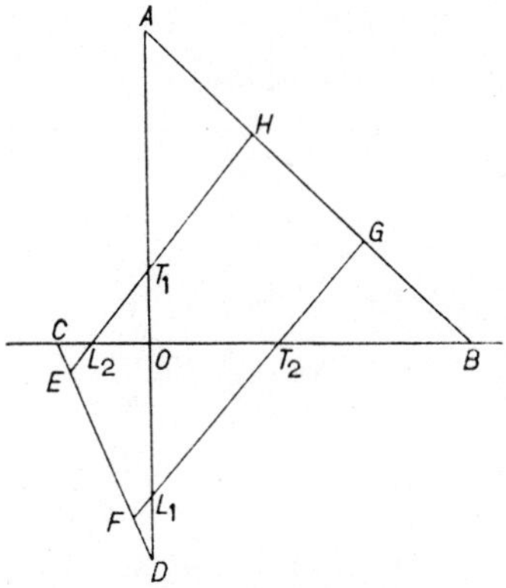

FIG. 23. (case $k \in X$).

The coordinates of T_1, L_1, T_2, L_2 are

$$T_1 = \left(0, \frac{3E_1 - E_2}{E_1 - 1}\right), \qquad L_1 = \left(0, \frac{F_1 - 3F_2}{F_1 - 3}\right),$$

$$T_2 = \left(\frac{3F_2 - F_1}{F_2 - 1}, 0\right), \qquad L_2 = \left(\frac{3E_1 - E_2}{3 - 0E_2}, 0\right).$$

We consider variations of the position of CD subject to the following restrictions:

C lies on BO and D on AO such that O lies between B and C and also between A and D;

$OC \cdot OD \leqslant 16$;

CD meets HT_1L_2 in a point E and GT_2L_1 in a point F such that $CE \leqslant \frac{1}{4}CD$, $FD \leqslant \frac{1}{4}CD$;

The points C, D, E, F vary whilst all the other named points are fixed. Under these conditions we select that (or one of those) position (s) of CD which maximalises the function, $\Phi(C, D)$, defined to be

$$\text{Area } EL_2OL_1F - \text{Area } CEL_2 - \text{Area } FL_1D$$

if $k \in X$ and the function

$$\text{Area } ET_1L_1F - \text{Area } CET_10 - \text{Area } FL_1D$$

if $k \notin X$; $k \in z_0a_0$, $k \in z_i^*a_i^*$.

Denote the positions of C, D, E, F for which this maximum is attained by $C'D'E'F'$. Of course it is not immediately obvious that the figure does not degenerate. It is possible that $C'D'E'F'$ all lie at O or that either C' or D' lie at O. In either case $\Phi(C, D) = 0$. In the first case, $k \in X$, the function $\Phi(C, D)$ is positive if $C = L_2$ and $D = L_1$ thus the maximal figure $C'D'$ is not a degenerate one. In the second case we assume that the maximal figure $C'D'$ gives $\Phi(C'D')$ a positive value. For otherwise,

$$A_4' \leqslant A_2' + A_3'.$$

Join H to L_1 cutting OB in S. Then by the argument used in case (a)

$$\text{Area } HGT_2S \geqslant \text{Area } AHSO + \text{Area } GT_2B.$$

Hence

$$A_1' \geqslant A_5' + A_6'$$

the required result

$$A_1' + A_2' + A_3' \geqslant A_4' + A_5' + A_6'$$

is true.

Thus we may assume that the extremal figure $C'D'$ is non-degenerate.

We next show that either $OC' . OD' = 16$ or $C'E' = F'D' = \frac{1}{4}C'D'$. Suppose that $OC' . OD' < 16$. If $D'F' < \frac{1}{4}C'D'$ let $C''D''$ be a line through E' meeting $C'O$ in C'' and OD' in D'' with C'' between O and C'. If C'' is close to C', $C''D''$ is again a possible position of the line CD and $\Phi(C'', D'') > \Phi(C, D)$. Thus $D'F' = \frac{1}{4}C'D'$ and similarly $C'E' = \frac{1}{4}C'D'$.

We are thus led to consider two cases.

Case I. $OC' . OD' = 16$

Apply the affine transformation sending $\angle ABC'$ and $\angle AD'C'$ into equal angles. Let l be the interior bisector of the angle formed by the transforms of AB' and $C'D'$ or if these are parallel lines let l be the parallel line midway between them. In the first case the transformed figure is symmetrical in l (since $OC' . OD' = 16$ the triangles AOB and COD' have equal area). Since $CE \leqslant \tfrac{1}{4}CD$, $FD \leqslant \tfrac{1}{4}CD$, Lemma 11 implies that HE and GF are parallel and if O lies between HE and GF, then

$$\text{Area } AHT_1 = \text{area } CL_2E, \quad \text{area } FDL_1 = \text{area } BGT_2$$
$$\text{Area } EL_2Ol_1F = \text{area } GT_2OT_1H.$$

Thus in the case $k \in X$, we have

$$A_1' + A_2' + A_3' \geqslant A_4' + A_5' + A_6'.$$

The case $k \notin X$, $k \in a_i^* z_i^*$, $k \in a_0 z_0$ is similar. If on the other hand the transforms of AB and $C'D'$ are parallel then so are AB and $C'D'$ and the result required is again true.

Case II. $C'E' = F'D' = \tfrac{1}{4}C'D'$.

Direct calculation shows that the function Ψ defined by

$$\Psi = \text{Area } HT_1OT_2G + \text{Area } L_2C'E' + \text{Area } L_1F'D'$$
$$- \text{Area } OL_2E'F'L_1 - \text{Area } AHT_1 - \text{Area } GT_2B$$

when $k \in X$

$$\Psi = \text{Area } HL_2T_2G + \text{Area } C'OT_1E' + \text{Area } F'L_1D'$$
$$- \text{Area } E'F'L_1T_1 - \text{Area } AOL_2H - \text{Area } GT_2B$$

when $k \notin X$, $k \in a_i^* z_i^*$, $k \in a_0 z_0$, is equal to

$$\tfrac{3}{4}(16 - XY)\left\{\frac{9X - Y}{(4 + 3X)(Y + 12)} + \frac{9Y - X}{(4 + 3Y)(X + 12)}\right\}$$

where $\rho(0, C) = X$, $\rho(0, D) = Y$. This expression can be written as

$$\tfrac{3}{4}(16 - XY)\frac{48.8(X + Y) + 80.8XY + 24XY(X + Y)}{(4 + 3X)(4 + 3Y)(X + 12)(Y + 12)}$$

and this is non-negative. It follows that the required inequality

$$A_1' + A_2' + A_3' \geqslant A_4' + A_5' + A_6'$$

is true in this case also.

Thus the assumption that two vertices of Z lie on the negative side of z_0z_1 leads in every case to the construction of a member Z' of $Q(2n)$ with

$$\tau_A^*(C, Z') < \tau_A^*(C, Z).$$

Since this is impossible there cannot be two such vertices, and Lemma 14 is proved.

LEMMA 15. *The member Z of $Q(2n)$ for which $\tau_A^*(C, Z)$ attains its least value is either an n-sided convex polygon described twice, or two n-sided convex polygons.*

Suppose that this is not so. Let p be a point of $L(Z) \cap X$ which is not collinear with any two vertices of Z. Every segment (without its end-points) of Z subtends at p an open single sector which is either empty of vertices of Z or contains exactly one such. For if $z_0 z_1$ is such a segment, by Lemma 14 at most one vertex of Z lies on the negative side of $z_0 z_1$. Further the triangle $z_0 z_1 p$ is contained in $X \cup A(z_0) \cup A(z_1)$ and by Lemmas 7 and 12. There are no vertices interior to this triangle. By Lemma 13 there is no vertex of Z on $z_0 z_1$ apart from z_0 and z_1.

Now if there is no vertex inside this sector then there is a segment of Z say $z_i^* z_{i+1}^*$ meeting the half-rays $p z_0$ and $p z_1$ produced if necessary, in say l_0 and l_1 respectively.

If $z_0 \in l_0 p$ then $z_0 \in A(z_i^*)$ in contradiction with Lemma 12. Similarly $z_1 \notin l_1 p$ and $z_0 z_1$ both lie on the negative side of $z_i^* z_{i+1}^*$ in contradiction with Lemma 14. It follows that this case cannot occur. Hence there is exactly one vertex in each such sector.

Suppose Z is a single polygonal line: let its vertices in order be $z_1 z_2, \ldots, z_k, \ldots, z_{2n}$ and suppose that $p z_1$ intersects $z_k z_{k+1}$ in t. The sectors subtended by $z_i z_{i+1}$ at p, $i = 1, 2, \ldots, k-1$ each contain one vertex of Z. The sector subtended by $z_k z_{k+1}$ contains z_1. Thus that subtended by $z_k t$ contains no vertex of Z. The total number of vertices of Z is the sum of the number of vertices in $z_1 \ldots z_k$ and the number of vertices in the sectors subtended by $z_i z_{i+1}$ at p, $i = 1, 2, \ldots, k-1$, i.e. it is $2k - 1$. This is an odd number and cannot equal $2n$. Thus Z cannot be a single polygon.

Suppose that Z is two convex polygons of which one has $r < n$ vertices. The $n - r$ vertices of the other polygon lie in the r negative half planes defined by the sides of the first polygon. Since $n - r > r$ there must be at least 2 in one of these negative half planes. This is in contradiction with Lemma 14 and thus this case cannot occur.

Hence Lemma 15 is proved.

We can now prove the

Theorem

$$T_A(X; n) \text{ is a convex function of } n$$

There are two convex polygons P_1 and P_2 of $n - 1$ and $n + 1$ sides respectively such that

$$\tau_A(X, P_1) = T_A(X; n - 1)$$
$$\tau_A(X, P_2) = T_A(X; n + 1).$$

The interiors of P_1 and P_2 have a point in common. For if this were not so we should have

$$\tau_A(X, P_1) + \tau_A(X, P_2) > \text{Area } X.$$

But this cannot hold since X contains a triangle whose area is greater than or equal to $\dfrac{3\sqrt{3}}{4\pi}$ area X and a pentagon whose area is greater than or equal to $\dfrac{5 \sin 72°}{2\pi}$ area X and $\dfrac{3 \cdot \sqrt{3}}{4\pi} + \dfrac{5 \cdot \sin 72°}{2\pi} > 1$. Thus the union of P_1 and P_2 described in a clockwise manner is a member of $Q(2n)$. Further if C is the frontier of X,

$$\tau_A^*(C; P_1 \cup P_2) = \tau_A(X, P_1) + \tau_A(X, P_2)$$

By Lemma 14 there is a pair of n sided convex polygons P' and P'', possibly coincident, such that regarded as a member of $Q(2n)$

$$\tau_A^*(C; P' \cup P'') \leqslant \tau_A^*(C, P_1 \cup P_2)$$

i.e.

$$\tau_A(C, P') + \tau_A(C, P'') \leqslant \tau_A(X, P_1) + \tau_A(X, P_2).$$

Since

$$T_A(X; n) \leqslant \min(\tau_A(C, P'), \tau_A(C, P''))$$

it follows that

$$2T_A(X; n) \leqslant T_A(X; n-1) + T_A(X; n+1).$$

i.e.

$$T_A(X; n) \text{ is a convex function of } n.$$

References

1. DOWKER, C. H.; "On minimum circumscribed polygons" *Bull. American Math. Soc.* **50** (1944) 120–2.
2. FEJES TÓTH, L.; *Lagerungen in der Ebene auf der Sphere und in Raum* (Berlin, 1953).

6TH PROBLEM. GEOMETRICAL PROPERTIES FOR WHICH TRIANGLES ARE THE EXTREMAL CONVEX CURVES

One technique used in establishing geometrical properties of plane convex curves is that of finding the class of convex curves that is extremal with respect to the property concerned and then comparing other convex curves with members of this extremal class. Here we give some properties of plane convex curves for each of which the class of triangles is extremal. Of these properties those in §1 provide answers, for the two-dimensional case, to two questions raised by P. C. Hammer [5].† In §2 we establish a property of sixpartite points (i.e. points through which 3 lines can be drawn to divide the convex set into six parts of equal area; see [3]) which connects these points with the problem of finding that central

† For references see p. 129.

subset of a convex set with the largest area. From it we deduce that a triangle has only one sixpartite point. The results stated as Theorems 6.1, 6.2 and Corollary 1 to Theorem 6.3 characterise triangles amongst plane bounded convex curves.

Strictly speaking we consider a number of allied problems but they may be conveniently regarded as one problem.

§1.

A diameter of a convex curve is a line joining two points of the curve at which the support lines are parallel and distinct. If both these support lines meet the curve in segments, say ab and cd, let m be that diagonal point of the trapezium $abcd$ which is interior to the curve. Then of the diameters which cut both the segment ab and cd, those which pass through m are called essential diameters. If one of the support lines meets the curve in a single point the diameter is again said to be essential. There is a unique essential diameter in each direction and the position of the essential diameter depends continuously upon its direction.

THEOREM 6.1. *The area swept out by the segment of the essential diameter of a convex curve C, as the diameter rotates through $180°$, is less than or equal to three times the area bounded by C. Equality occurs if and only if C is a triangle.*

Proof. Let $H(u)$ be the support function of C with respect to the centroid of the area bounded by C as origin. If L denotes arc length along C, then

area swept out by the essential diameter

$$\leqslant \int_C \tfrac{1}{2}(H(u) + H(-u))dL$$

$$\leqslant \tfrac{3}{2} \int_C H(u)dL = 3 \text{ . area bounded by } C.$$

We have used the fact that $H(-u) \leqslant 2H(u)$.† It is obvious that there is equality when C is a triangle. Also if C is not a triangle then

$$H(-u) < 2H(u)$$

for all u, so that equality can occur only when C is a triangle.

THEOREM 6.2. *The triangle is the only plane convex curve with the property that through every point of the interior domain bounded by the curve there pass exactly three diameters of the curve.*

† See P. C. Hammer [4]. We could also have taken as origin the centroid of the largest triangle inscribed in C, see R. Rado [8], or the critical point, see B. H. Neumann [6]. The inequality used is simply that for the upper bound of the ratio of the area of the vector domain to the area of the set bounded by C, see [2], p. 105.

Proof. Let C be a convex curve with the property stated in the enunciation. C cannot contain two parallel line segments. Thus every diameter of C is an essential diameter. In addition to the properties mentioned above, the essential diameters have the property that if the direction varies monotonically, then the end-points of the diameter on C move round C in one and the same sense, except that one or other of the end-points may be fixed for certain changes of direction. (These properties are easily proved directly or may be found in [4].)

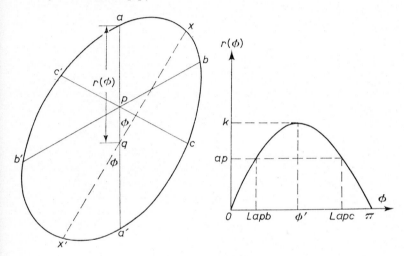

FIG. 24.

Let p be a point interior to C and apa', bpb', cpc' be the three diameters through p so that the points $abca'b'c'$ are in clockwise order round C. Consider the intersection of a variable diameter xx' with apa' as x varies from a to a' through the arc $abca'$. Let q be the point of intersection of xx' with aa', ϕ be the angle $\angle xqa$ and $r(\phi)$ be the length of the segment aq. If a' is x, define ϕ to be the angle supplementary to $\angle axx'$. If x is a, define ϕ to be $\angle a'xx'$. (See Fig. 24.)

$r(\phi)$ is a continuous function of ϕ in $0 < \phi < \pi$, and given t, a positive number less than the length of aa', there are exactly two values of ϕ for which $r(\phi) = t$. It follows that of the two values 0 and $k =$ length of aa', one is attained by $r(\phi)$ at an interior point ϕ' of $0 < \phi < \pi$. If $r(\phi) = k$ then

$$\angle apb < \phi' < \angle apc,$$

and if the diameter making angle ϕ' with aa' is yy', y lies between b and c; y' lies between b' and c'. But a' lies on yy'. Hence a' lies on cb'. If $r(\phi') = 0$ we similarly prove that a lies on bc'.

Suppose that a' lies on cb'. By a repetition of the argument either c' lies on ab' or c lies on ba'. But if c lies on ba', then $b'a'cb$ are collinear and the segment bb' lies in the curve C. This is impossible as p is a point of bb' and lies in the domain interior to C. Thus c' lies on ab'. Similarly b lies on ac and C is the triangle $ab'c$.

If a lies on bc', then by a similar argument the curve C is just the triangle $a'bc'$.

§2.

It has been shown by Ellen F. Buck and R. C. Buck [3] that for each bounded plane convex set P there exists at least one point p, such that there are three straight lines through p dividing the plane into six regions each of which contains a subset of P of area equal to one-sixth that of P. Such a point is called a sixpartite point and the three lines are called the division lines. We shall use $A(P)$ to denote the area of P.

A. S. Besicovith [1] has proved that every bounded plane convex set P contains a central subset of area at least $\frac{2}{3}A(P)$. His method is to construct a semi-regular hexagon (i.e. affine transform of a regular hexagon) whose vertices belong to the frontier of P. Any semi-regular hexagon has a centre, and the fact that its vertices lie on the frontier of P implies that

   (i) it is contained in P,
   (ii) its area is at least $\frac{2}{3}A(P)$.

We show here that every sixpartite point is the centre of a semi-regular hexagon contained in P and of area $\frac{2}{3}A(P)$. This semi-regular hexagon need not have its vertices on the frontier of P and its area is exactly $\frac{2}{3}A(P)$.

THEOREM 6.3. *Every sixpartite point of a bounded plane closed set P is the centre of a semi-regular hexagon contained in P whose area is $\frac{2}{3}A(P)$ and whose sides are bisected by the division lines.*

Proof. By an appropriate affine transformation we may reduce the general case to the particular case in which the division lines make angles of 60° with one another. In what follows we consider only this case.

Let the division lines be apa', bpb', cpc', meeting the boundary of P in aa', bb', cc', and suppose that the points $abca'b'c'$ are in anti-clockwise order round the boundary of P. On pa, pb, produced if necessary, let x, y, x', y' be four points such that x, x' lie on pa, with x' between p and x, y, y' lie on pb; $x'y'$ is perpendicular to pa, xy is perpendicular to pb; the area of the triangle pxy equals that of

$px'y'$ and both are $\frac{1}{6}A(P)$. Let z be the point of intersection of xy and $x'y'$. (See Fig. 25.)

We show next that the point z is contained in P. Any line through z cuts pa in s, say, and pb in t. The area of the triangle pst is less than that of pxy unless either s lies in segment px' or t in segment py. Suppose now that z were exterior to P and the line szt did not meet P anywhere. The part of P in the sector bounded by pa and pb is contained in the triangle stp and has area less than that of this

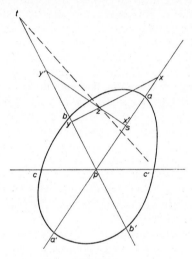

FIG. 25.

triangle. By the remark made above, st must meet an interior point either of the segment px' or of the segment py. Suppose st meets px' in s and pc' in r. Then the area of the triangle psr is less than the area of the triangle $px'y' = \frac{1}{6}A(P)$. But this is impossible because the triangle psr contains that part of P in the sector apc' and this is of area $\frac{1}{6}A(P)$. Similarly st cannot meet an interior point of the segment py. Thus every line through z meets P; therefore z belongs to P.

By an exactly similar argument the five points obtained from z by reflection in the lines apa', bpb', cpc' also belong to P. These five points with z form the vertices of a regular hexagon of area $\frac{2}{3}A(P)$. This hexagon has the required properties. If we now apply an affine transformation to get back to the original figure, the properties stated in the enunciation are not altered.

COROLLARY 1. *Every line through a sixpartite point of a plane bounded convex set P, divides P into two parts P', P'' such that the area* *of each lies between $\frac{4}{9}A(P)$ and $\frac{5}{9}A(P)$. If there is at least one such line such that*

$$A(P') = \tfrac{4}{9}A(P)$$

then P is the boundary and interior of a triangle.†

For, with the same notation as above, if dpd' is a line interior to the two sectors apb and $a'pb'$, then the part of P in the sectors apb, $a'pb'$ lying on one side of dpd', has area at least equal to the part of the semi-regular hexagon in the sectors apb and $a'pb'$ and lying on the same side of dpd'. This is exactly $\frac{5}{9}A(P)$. Thus the area of P on one side of dpd' is at least $\frac{1}{6}A(P) + \frac{1}{6}A(P) + \frac{1}{9}A(P)$, i.e. $\frac{4}{9}A(P)$.

Equality can hold if the part of P in the sector apb is bounded by either xy or $x'y'$ and the part in the sector $a'pb'$ by the reflection of $x'y'$ or xy respectively, in p. From the restrictions on the areas of the parts of P in the other sectors, it then follows that P is a triangle.

COROLLARY 2. *Every triangle has only one sixpartite point, namely its median point.*

Let the triangle be abc, with the median point m and the sixpartite point p. The line through m parallel to bc divides abc into a triangle of area $\frac{4}{9}$.area abc, and a trapezium of area $\frac{5}{9}$.area abc. By Corollary 1, p must belong to the interior or boundary of the trapezium. Similarly p belongs to the two other trapezia by drawing lines through m parallel to ca and to ab. But m is the only point common to these three trapezia, and so p is m.

Remark—The simple continuity argument that proves the existence of a sixpartite point for any convex set can be used to show the following. Let there be a finite positive mass distribution in the plane such that the total mass in any half plane varies continuously with the position of the line bounding the half-plane. Then there is a point and three lines through this point dividing the plane into six regions each of which contains an equal mass. It is clear that any line through this point has on each side of it a mass of at least one third of the total mass. This is the principal result given by B. H. Neumann in [7].

There may of course be more than one sixpartite point for a given convex set. In fact the set of sixpartite points is always of finite or enumerably finite linear measure and there are convex sets for which it is actually of positive linear measure.

§3. The division of a convex set by three non-concurrent lines

Consider a convex set X which is divided by three non-concurrent straight lines into six regions of equal area and one other triangular

† See also [7].

region. We shall show that the area of this triangle is at most one-eighth that of the other six regions. This result has been conjectured by Ellen F. and R. C. Buck [3].

It is assumed that the triangular region is an equilateral triangle. This does not involve any real loss of generality, for, if it were not true there would be an affine transformation of the plane which transforms the triangle into an equilateral triangle. We could then argue using the transform of X instead of X itself.

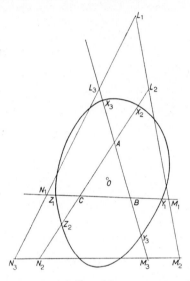

Fig. 26.

Denote the triangular region by ABC where the order A, B, C is in the clockwise sense round the triangle. Let α denote the area of the triangle ABC and let O be the centre of gravity of the triangle ABC. Let AB, BC, CA produced in both directions meet $\mathrm{Fr}\,X$ in X_3Y_3, Y_1Z_1, X_2Z_2 respectively, where the order of these points in the counterclockwise direction round $\mathrm{Fr}\,X$ is $X_3Z_1Z_2Y_3Y_1X_2$ and X_3ABY_3 is the order of the points on AB.

Draw a line L_2M_1 parallel to X_2Y_1 meeting AX_2 in L_2 and BY_1 in M_1 so that the area of the quadrilateral L_2ABM_1 is equal to the area bounded by X_2A, AB, BY_1 and the arc Y_1X_2 of $\mathrm{Fr}\,X$ that is in the counterclockwise sense from Y_1 to X_2. Denote the value of this area by λ. Similarly draw L_3N_1 parallel to X_3Z_1 and M_3N_2 parallel to Z_2Y_3 (we have thus L_3 on AB, N_1 on BC, N_2 on AC, and M_3 on AB, see Fig. 26). The areas of the quadrilaterals L_3N_1CA and M_3N_2CB are both equal to λ.

Let L_1, M_2, N_3 be the points of intersection of L_2M_1 and L_3N_1; M_3N_2 and M_1L_2; M_3N_2 and L_3N_1 respectively.

The part of the domain inside X contained between BY_1 and BY_3 is of area λ by hypothesis and is contained in the quadrilateral $BM_1M_2M_3$. From this and similar considerations it follows that

$$\lambda \leqslant \text{minimum (Area } BM_1M_2M_3, \text{ Area } AL_2L_1L_3, \text{ Area } CN_1N_3N_2) \text{ (1)}$$

Denote the minimum on the right hand side of (1) by $f(L_1M_2N_3)$. Now consider the triangle $L_1M_2N_3$ as a member of that class of triangles which are such that the areas ABM_1L_2, ACN_1L_3, BCN_2M_3 are all equal to λ. We consider the points $L_1M_2N_3$ as being variable whilst the points A, B, C are fixed. The maximum of $f(L_1M_2N_3)$ as $L_1M_2N_3$ varies in this class occurs when the areas $BM_1M_2M_3$, $AL_2L_3L_1$ and $CN_1N_3N_2$ are equal.

Write x, y, z for the lengths respectively of AL_2, BM_3, CN_1. x, y, z are three independent variables which determine the triangle $L_1M_2N_3$ uniquely in the class defined above. Also we may write

$$\text{Area } BM_1M_2M_3 = F(x, y);$$
$$\text{Area } CN_2N_3N_1 = F(y, z);$$
$$\text{Area } AL_3L_1L_2 = F(z, x).$$

The following LEMMA is required.

Let $F(x, y)$ be a function of two variables which is strictly decreasing in x for every fixed y and strictly increasing in y for every fixed x, then if

$$F(x, y) = F(y, z) = F(z, x)$$

it follows that $x = y = z$.

The proof is obvious.

It follows that the maximum of $f(L_1M_2N_3)$ occurs when $x = y = z$. In this case the triangle $L_1M_2N_3$ is equilateral with 0 as its centroid and $3 . f(L_1M_2N_3) = \text{Area } L_1M_2N_3 - 3\lambda - \alpha$. Thus $f(L_1M_2N_3)$ is largest when Area $L_1M_2N_3$ is largest, i.e. when the perpendicular distance from 0 to (say) L_1M_2 is largest. Now by construction L_1M_2 is tangent to a hyperbola of which CA and CB are asymptotes. Thus the area of $L_1M_2N_3$ is largest when L_1M_2 is parallel to AB. Direct calculation now shows that (1) implies that $\alpha \leqslant \frac{1}{8}\lambda$.

§4. Remarks

There are analogous problems in three dimensional space. But whereas the analogues of §1 are immediately clear those of §§2 and 3 are far from obvious. Three non-concurrent lines in a plane divide a convex set into at most 7 parts. Four non-concurrent planes divide a three dimensional set into possibly 15 parts, and the question of the possible relations of the values of the volumes of these parts is a much more difficult question than that solved here.

The problem of finding the most asymmetrical convex set in three dimensions is still unsolved.

References

1. A. S. BESICOVITCH; "Measure of asymmetry of convex curves," *J. London Math. Soc.*, **23** (1948) 237–240.

2. T. BONNESEN und W. FENCHEL; *Theorie der konvexen Körper* (1934).

3. ELLEN F. BUCK and R. C. BUCK; "Equipartition of convex sets," *Math. Magazine*, **22** (1949) 195–198.

4. P. C. HAMMER; "The centroid of a convex body," *Proc. American Math. Soc.*, **2** (1951) 522–525.

5. P. C. HAMMER; "Convex bodies associated with a convex body," *Proc. American Math. Soc.*, **2** (1951) 781–793.

6. B. H. NEUMANN; "On some affine invariants of closed convex regions," *J. London Math. Soc.*, **14** (1939) 262–272.

7. B. H. NEUMANN; "On an invariant of plane regions and mass distributions," *J. London Math. Soc.*, **20** (1945) 226–237.

8. R. RADO; "Some covering theorems (I)," *Proc. London Math. Soc.* (2), **51** (1949) 232–263.

CHAPTER IV

PROBLEMS CONCERNED WITH THE STRUCTURE OF SUBCLASSES OF THE CLASS OF CONVEX SETS

THE number of problems that could be considered under this heading is very large. Since all circles and triangles are convex sets it follows that much of Euclidean geometry could be considered in this chapter. We shall confine our attention to problems concerning sets of constant width and to problems concerning triangles. We have already used some properties of sets of constant width in Chapter II and some properties of triangles in Chapter III. In these chapters we were interested in more general classes of sets and used the properties of the particular subclasses of convex sets simply because they gave information about these more general classes. In the present chapter the interest lies in the properties of the sets themselves.

7TH PROBLEM. THE ASYMMETRY OF CURVES OF CONSTANT WIDTH

§1. Introduction

The area of a plane point-set Δ is denoted by $A(\Delta)$. The largest subset of Δ symmetric with respect to a point P is written $\Delta(P)$. The following definitions are used.†

(a) The coefficient of asymmetry of Δ with respect to P is

$$f(\Delta; P) = 1 - \frac{A(\Delta(P))}{A(\Delta)}$$

(b) The coefficient of asymmetry of Δ is

$$g(\Delta) = \min_P f(\Delta; P).$$

It has been shown by A. S. Besicovitch in the two papers cited above that

(i) if Δ is any convex set, then $0 \leqslant g(\Delta) \leqslant \frac{1}{3}$, and these inequalities are best possible; for the case $g(\Delta) = 0$ holds when Δ is a central set and $g(\Delta) = \frac{1}{3}$ when Δ is a triangle;

† See [1], [2] in the references on p. 140.

(ii) if Δ is any convex set of constant width, then $0 \leqslant g(\Delta)$ $\leqslant g(\Phi)$ where Φ is a Reuleaux triangle and $g(\Phi)$ is approximately 0.16.

We shall use Ω to denote the set of those points whose distances from a fixed Reuleaux triangle of side-length $2d - 1$ are equal to or less than $1 - d$, where $\frac{1}{2} \leqslant d < 1$. The object of this paper is to show that, if Δ is a set of constant width 1 and such that the radius of curvature at every point of δ, the frontier of Δ, exists and lies between d and $1 - d$, then $g(\Delta) \leqslant g(\Omega)$.

This result was conjectured by Professor A. S. Besicovitch and the methods of proof of Lemmas 1 and 2 are due to him.

§2. Notation

Greek capital letters are used for sets of points. The frontier of such a set is denoted by the corresponding small Greek letter for example δ is the frontier of Δ. Other curves are denoted by other small Greek letters, and points by Roman capitals.

Let Γ_1 and Γ_2 be, respectively, the circumcircle and incircle of Δ, where by "circumcircle" is meant the set of points on or interior to the smallest circle containing Δ, and there is an analogous meaning of "incircle." It is assumed that Γ_1 and Γ_2 are distinct since otherwise Δ is a circle, $g(\Delta) = 0$, and the required inequality is true. This assumption implies that $d \neq \frac{1}{2}$. Let the common centre of γ_1 and γ_2 be O and their radii be r_1, r_2 where $r_1 > r_2, r_1 + r_2 = 1$, and r_2 is greater than the radius of the incircle of Ω.†

The reflection of a set of points in O will be denoted by adding a dash to the symbol for the set of points concerned.

The ζ-curves.

By the "contact"‡ of two circular arcs or two circles is meant contact such that the convexity of both arcs or circles is from the same side of the common normal at the point of contact. §

At a point P on γ_1 there is a circle touching γ_1 of radius $1 - d$. Call this circle μ. There are two circles of radius d touching both μ and γ_2. Call these circles λ_1 and λ_2. Let λ_1 touch μ at P_1 and γ_2 at P_2. By "arc PP_1" we mean the smaller of the two arcs PP_1 of μ and by "arc P_1P_2" the smaller of the two arcs P_1P_2 of λ_1. Then the curve made up of arc PP_1 and arc P_1P_2 is a ζ-curve. Similarly another ζ-curve can be defined from λ_2. (See Fig. 27.)

The ζ-curves have the following properties.

(i) There are exactly two of them through each point inside the annulus between γ_1 and γ_2.

† See [6].   ‡ Or "touching."

§ This convention is also used for the contact of a circle with a convex curve.

(ii) The distance of O from a variable point Q of a fixed ζ-curve varies monotonically, as the line OQ rotates in a given sense, from the value r_1 at one end-point to the value r_2 at the other. If, as OQ rotates clockwise, the distance OQ increases, we call the ζ-curve a "clockwise ζ-curve." In the opposite case it is called an "anti-clockwise ζ-curve." There is one ζ-curve of each type through every point of the annulus.

(iii) Let $r_0 = \{\frac{1}{4} + (d - r_2)^2 - (d - \frac{1}{2})^2\}^{\frac{1}{2}}$. Then, for a point Q of the annulus on a ζ-curve ζ_1, Q lies on the part of ζ_1 which is an

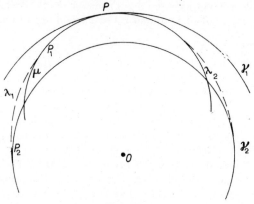

Fig. 27.

arc of radius d or Q lies on the part of ζ_1 which is an arc of radius $1 - d$ according as the distance OQ is less than r_0 or greater than r_0. If $OQ \leqslant r_0$ and λ is a circle through Q of radius d containing Γ_2, then the non-obtuse angle between OQ and the tangent to λ at Q is greater than or equal to the non-obtuse angle between OQ and the tangent at Q to ζ_1. If $OQ \geqslant r_0$ and μ is a circle of radius $1 - d$ through Q and contained in Γ_1, then the non-obtuse angle between OQ and the tangent to μ at Q is greater than or equal to the non-obtuse angle between OQ and the tangent at Q to ζ_1.

§3. Proof of the relation $g(\Delta) \leqslant g(\Phi)$

On γ_1 there are at least three points of δ that do not lie on a closed semicircle of γ_1.† Let three such points be A, B, C, where ABC is in the clockwise sense round γ_1 as in Fig. 28. Let AO, BO, CO meet γ_2 in the points X, Y, Z, such that $AX = BY = CZ = 1$. The points X, Y, Z lie on δ.

If δ has contact with an arc ρ of radius d, then the whole of δ is on ρ or on the concave side of ρ. If δ has contact with an arc ρ

† See [5].

of radius $1 - d$, then the whole of d is on ρ or on the convex side of ρ.†

LEMMA 1. *If a ζ-curve meets δ in a point Q, then the points of the ζ-curve nearer to O than Q lie on δ or inside Δ, and those farther than Q from O lie on δ or outside Δ.*

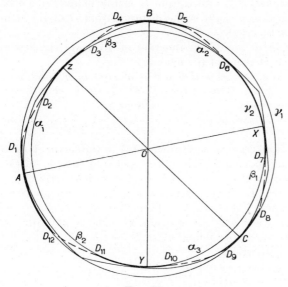

FIG. 28.

I shall show that the lemma is true for ζ-curves which are anti-clockwise. The proof for the clockwise ζ-curves is similar and is omitted. Let OK be a fixed line, angles be measured in the anti-clockwise sense from OK, and P on δ be the point such that $OP = r$, $\angle POK = \theta$. Denote the anticlockwise ζ-curve through P by ζ_P.

At P there are two circles which touch δ: one is of radius d and contains Δ and hence also Γ_2; the other is of radius $1 - d$, is contained in Δ and hence also in Γ_1. By property (iii) of the ζ-curves

$$\left(\frac{dr}{d\theta}\right)_{\zeta_P} \geqslant \left(\frac{dr}{d\theta}\right)_{\delta}$$

But for any fixed r, $dr/d\theta$ is constant on all ζ-curves ζ_P. Hence

$$\left(\frac{dr}{d\theta}\right)_{\zeta_Q} \geqslant \left(\frac{dr}{d\theta}\right)_{\delta}$$

† The first of these two statements has been proved by E. Blanc [3] p. 224. The second is an easy deduction from the first.

for any equal values of r, from which it follows that, if $Q = (r_0, \phi_0)$, then

$$r_\delta(\theta) \leqslant r_{\zeta_Q}(\theta) \ (\theta > \phi_0),$$
$$r_\delta(\theta) \geqslant r_{\zeta_Q}(\theta) \ (\theta < \phi_0),$$

where $r_\delta(\theta)$ is the distance from O of the point P on δ such that $\angle POK = \theta$, and $r_{\zeta_Q}(\theta)$ is the distance from O of the point R on ζ_Q such that $\angle ROK = \theta$.

Since r is an increasing function of θ on ζ_Q, these inequalities imply the statement of the lemma.

COROLLARY. *Suppose that δ and δ' meet in a point P, and that ζ_1, ζ_2 are the two ζ-curves through P. Then the curvilinear triangle bounded by arcs of ζ_1, ζ_2, γ_1 is exterior to both Δ and Δ', whilst the curvilinear triangle bounded by arcs of ζ_1, ζ_2, γ_2 is interior to both Δ and Δ'.*

Now denote the area of the part of Δ in the sector AOC' by a and the area of the part of Δ in the sector $A'OC$ by b. Consider a variable point P on that arc AZ of δ which is contained in the sector AOC'. Let the anticlockwise ζ-curve through P have endpoints E on γ_2 and H on γ_1. Then the arc AH of γ_1, the ζ-curve HPE, the arc EZ of γ_2, the linear segment ZO, and the linear segment OA together bound a convex set whose area $h(P)$ has the following properties:

(i) $h(P)$ varies continuously with P;

(ii) $h(Z) \geqslant a, h(A) \leqslant a$.

The property (ii) is a consequence of Lemma 1. It follows that there exists a point P on AZ such that $h(P) = a$. For this P, the curve consisting successively of the arc AH of γ_1, the ζ-curve HPE, and the arc EZ of γ_2 is called α_1.

Similarly, in sector $A'OC$ construct a curve β_1 using a clockwise ζ-curve so that β_1, XO, OC enclose an area b. Repeat the process in sectors BOA', COB' to obtain curves α_2, α_3 and in sectors $B'OA$, $C'OB$ to obtain curves β_2, β_3 respectively.

The closed convex curve made up successively of α_1, β_3, α_2, β_1, α_3, β_2 is called δ_1, and the set which it bounds is called Δ_1; δ_1 may be denoted by

$$AD_1D_2ZD_3D_4BD_5D_6XD_7D_8CD_9D_{10}YD_{11}D_{12}A,$$

where

$$D_{12}AD_1, \ D_4BD_5, \ D_8CD_9 \text{ are arcs or points of } \gamma_1,$$

$$D_2ZD_3, \ D_6XD_7, \ D_{10}YD_{11} \text{ are arcs or points of } \gamma_2,$$

$$D_1D_2, \ D_5D_6, \ D_9D_{10} \text{ are anticlockwise } \zeta\text{-curves},$$

$$D_3D_4, \ D_7D_8, \ D_{11}D_{12} \text{ are clockwise } \zeta\text{-curves}.$$

LEMMA 2. $f(\Delta; O) \leqslant f(\Delta_1; O)$.

By the definition of Δ_1, $A(\Delta_1) = A(\Delta)$ and thus, in order to prove the lemma, it is sufficient to show that $A(\Delta(P)) \geqslant A(\Delta_1(P))$ when P is O.

Consider the intersection of the parts of Δ and Δ_1 in the sector AOC' with the reflections in O of the parts of Δ and Δ_1 respectively in $A'OC$. It is impossible for α_1 and β_1' to intersect in an arc or point of γ_1, for, if they did, we should have

$$a + b > \tfrac{1}{2}(r_1^2 + r_2^2) \, (\angle AOC'),$$

whereas in fact

$$a + b = \tfrac{1}{2} \int_0^{\angle AOC'} \{(r(\theta))^2 + (r(\theta + \pi))^2\} \, d\theta$$

$$\leqslant \tfrac{1}{2} \int_0^{\angle AOC'} \{(r(\theta))^2 + (1 - r(\theta))^2\} \, d\theta$$

$$\leqslant \tfrac{1}{2}(r_1^2 + r_2^2) \, (\angle AOC'),$$

where $r(\theta)$ is the distance from O of a point P on δ such that $\angle POC' = \theta$.

Thus there are two cases to consider.

(i) α_1 intersects β_1' in an arc or point of γ_2. In this case the common part of Δ_1 and Δ_1' inside the sector AOC' lies inside Γ_2 and is therefore not more than the common part of Δ and Δ' in this sector.

(ii) α_1 and β_1' meet in a point interior to the annulus. Let this point be K and L be any point of intersection of δ and δ' that lies in the sector AOC'. It is clear that there is at least one such point L.

For every point P in the annulus between γ_1 and γ_2 the two arcs of ζ-curves through P and the smaller of the two arcs of γ_1 which join two of the end-points of the ζ-curves, bound a set of points whose area is written $k_1(P)$. Similarly the two arcs of ζ-curves through P and the smaller of the two arcs of γ_2 which join two of their end-points bound an area $k_2(P)$. Both $k_1(P)$ and $k_2(P)$ are functions of OP only, $k_1(P)$ a decreasing function and $k_2(P)$ an increasing function.

By the corollary to Lemma 1, the area common to both Δ and Δ' in the sector AOC' is greater than or equal to both $k_2(L) + \tfrac{1}{2}r_2^2(\angle AOC')$ and $a + b + k_1(L) - \tfrac{1}{2}r_1^2(\angle AOC')$. Similarly the area common to both Δ_1 and Δ_1' in AOC' is equal to both $k_2(K) + \tfrac{1}{2}r_2^2(\angle AOC')$ and

$$a + b + k_1(K) - \tfrac{1}{2}r_1^2(\angle AOC').$$

Either $k_1(K) \leqslant k_2(L)$ or $k_1(K) \leqslant k_1(L)$. Thus in all cases the area of $\Delta \cap \Delta'$ in AOC' is greater than or equal to the area of

$\Delta_1 \cap \Delta_1'$ in the sector AOC'. Similar relations hold for all the other sectors. Thus

$$A(\Delta(O)) \geqslant A(\Delta_1(O)).$$

This proves the lemma.

Denote the sum of the lengths of the arcs of γ_1, $D_{12}AD_1$, D_4BD_5, D_8CD_9 by l and the sum of the lengths of the arcs of γ_2, D_2ZD_3, D_6XD_7, $D_{10}YD_{11}$ by m. Construct a set Δ_2 whose boundary δ_2 is made up of a similar succession of arcs to that which forms δ_1. Here

$$\delta_2 \text{ is } E_1E_2E_3E_4E_5E_6E_7E_8E_9E_{10}E_{11}E_{12}E_1,$$

where

$E_{12}E_1$, E_4E_5, E_8E_9 are arcs of γ_1 of length $\tfrac{1}{3}l$,

E_2E_3, E_6E_7, $E_{10}E_{11}$ are arcs of γ_2 of length $\tfrac{1}{3}m$,

E_1E_2, E_5E_6, E_9E_{10} are anticlockwise ζ-curves,

E_3E_4, E_7E_8, $E_{11}E_{12}$ are clockwise ζ-curves.

Δ_2 is symmetric with respect to each of three axes through O making angles of $60°$ with one another. We have

LEMMA 3. (i) $A(\Delta_2) = A(\Delta_1)$. (ii) $A(\Delta_2(O)) \leqslant A(\Delta_1(O))$.

(i) Suppose PQ is a ζ-curve with end-points P, Q. Together with linear segments OP, OQ it forms the boundary of a set whose area is (say) c. This area is the same for all positions of PQ. Hence

$$A(\Delta_1) = \tfrac{1}{2}r_1l + \tfrac{1}{2}r_2m + 6c = A(\Delta_2).$$

(ii) Consider a variable point X on a fixed ζ-curve PQ where P lies on γ_2 and Q on γ_1 and let $\angle XOP$ be χ measured positively so that when X is at Q, χ has a positive value. Denote the area contained in the contour XO, OP and arc PX of the ζ-curve by $j(\chi)$. For $\chi < 0$ define $j(\chi)$ to be $\tfrac{1}{2}r_2^2\chi$, for $\chi > \angle QOP$ define $j(\chi)$ to be $\tfrac{1}{2}r_1^2\chi$. Then

$$\frac{dj(\chi)}{d\chi} = \begin{cases} \tfrac{1}{2}r_2^2 \ (\chi < 0), \\ \tfrac{1}{2}OX^2 \ (0 \leqslant \chi \leqslant \angle QOP), \\ \tfrac{1}{2}r_1^2 \ (\chi > \angle QOP). \end{cases}$$

Since OX is an increasing function of χ, it follows that $dj(\chi)/d\chi$ is a non-decreasing function of χ, so that $j(\chi)$ is a convex function of χ.

Now the intersection of arcs AD_1D_2Z of δ_1 and $X'D_7'D_8'C'$ of δ_1' may occur in one of two different ways (see the proof of Lemma 2);

(i) in a point of ζ-curve D_1D_2, (ii) in an arc or point of γ_2. In case (i) the point is called X_1; in case (ii) the mid-point of arc D_2D_7' of γ_2 is called X_1. Similarly define X_2 on ZD_3D_4B and

$Y'D'_{10}D'_9C'$; X_3 on BD_5D_6X and $Y'D'_{11}D'_{12}A'$. Let $\angle X_1OD_2 = \chi_1$, $\angle X_2OD_3 = \chi_2$, $\angle X_3OD_6 = \chi_3$.

The part of $\Delta_1(0)$ in the sector $D_2OD'_7$ is symmetric about OX_1 and similarly for OX_2, OX_3, while the set $\Delta_1(0)$ is symmetric about O. Thus

$$A(\Delta_1(O)) = r_2m + 4\{j(\chi_1) + j(\chi_2) + j(\chi_3)\}.$$

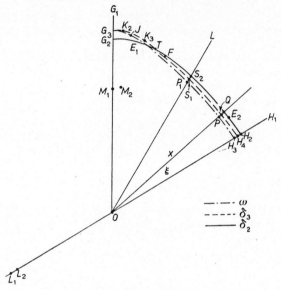

FIG. 29.

Since the function $j(\chi)$ is convex, it follows that

$$A(\Delta_1(O)) \geqslant r_2m + 12j\{\tfrac{1}{3}(\chi_1 + \chi_2 + \chi_3)\}$$

It is easy to see that this last expression is precisely $A(\Delta_2(0))$.

This completes the proof of Lemma 3.

It follows from Lemma 3 that $f(\Delta_2; 0) \geqslant f(\Delta_1; 0)$. We are now in a position to construct a set Δ_3 which can be compared both with Δ_2 and with Ω. Let Ω be considered to lie so that it is symmetric about the same three axes through O as is Δ_2, and so that the direction in which a half-line through O meets ω in points whose distance from O is the largest possible, has this same property with respect to δ_2.

Let two of the axes of symmetry through O be OG_1 and OH_1 so that $\angle G_1OH_1$ is 60°. Let δ_2 in this sector be $G_2E_1E_2H_2$, where G_2 lies on OG_1 and H_2 lies on OH_1. Let ω in this sector be G_3H_3. See Fig. 29. On the ζ-curve E_1E_2 let F be the point at which the

10

radius of curvature changes from d to $1 - d$. Let J be a similar point on G_3H_3.

Now, denote the circumcircle and incircle of Ω by σ_1 and σ_2 respectively, and construct the curve $G_3K_2K_3H_4$ where G_3 is the point of σ_1 on the half-line OG_1, G_3K_2 is an arc of σ_1 which may reduce to a point, K_2K_3 is a circular arc of radius $1 - d$ touching σ_1 internally at K_2, K_3H_4 is a circular arc of radius d touching K_2K_3 at K_3 and intersecting OH orthogonally at H_4, and where also the area enclosed by $G_3K_2K_3H_4OG_3$ is equal to the area enclosed by $G_2E_1FE_2H_2OG_2$.

Let Δ_3 be the set bounded by $G_3K_2K_3H_4$ and by the five other curves that can be obtained from this one by symmetry in the three axes of symmetry through 0.

LEMMA 4.   (i) $A(\Delta_3) = A(\Delta_2) \geqslant A(\Omega)$

$$\text{(ii) } f(\Delta_3; O) \geqslant f(\Delta_2; O).$$

(i) An immediate consequence of the definition of Δ_3 is that $A(\Delta_3) = A(\Delta_2)$. Now $A(\Delta_2) = A(\Delta_1) = A(\Delta)$ and it is known that of all curves of width 1 and with radii of curvature being between d and $1 - d$, the curve ω contains the least area.†

This proves (i).

(ii) To prove $f(\Delta_3; 0) \geqslant f(\Delta_2; 0)$: since $A(\Delta_3) = A(\Delta_2)$, it is sufficient to show that $A(\Delta_3 \cap \Delta_3') \leqslant A(\Delta_2 \cap \Delta_2')$.

The curves $G_3K_2K_3H_4$ and $G_2E_1FE_2H_2$ cut in exactly one point. It is clear that these two curves have at least one point of intersection. No point of intersection can lie on G_3K_2. K_2H_4 is a ζ-curve defined in the annulus formed by the circle σ_1 and the circle θ whose centre is O and whose radius is OH_4.

Although $G_2E_1E_2H_2$ is not part of the boundary of a set of constant width, it is made up of circular arcs of radii r_1, r_2, d, and $1 - d$, and the method of proof of Lemma 1 applies. There is one point or one arc $G_3K_2K_3H_4$ on $G_2E_1FE_2H_2$. The second possibility can only arise if the arcs FE_2 and K_3H_4 have some part in common. This can be so only if H_4 is at H_2, and this implies that γ_2 is σ_2 and γ_1 is σ_1. This case has been ruled out as it was assumed initially that γ_2 has radius greater than that of σ_2.

Let the point of intersection of $G_3K_2K_3H_4$ and $G_2E_1FE_2H_2$ be T. Let OL be the bisector of angle G_1OH_1, meeting G_3H_4 in S_1 and G_2H_2 in S_2. Now a variable point X on G_3H_4 is such that OX is monotonic non-decreasing as X moves from H_4 to G_3. Hence

$$A(\Delta_3 \cap \Delta_3') = 12 \times \text{area bounded by } S_1OH_4S_1.$$

Similarly, $A(\Delta_2 \cap \Delta_2') = 12 \times \text{area bounded by } S_2OH_2S_2$.

† See [4] p. 132.

If T lies in or on the boundary of the sector LOG_1, area bounded by $S_1OH_4S_1 \leqslant$ area bounded by $S_2OH_2S_2$.

If T lies in the sector LOH_1, area bounded by $G_3OS_1K_2G_3 \geqslant$ area bounded by $G_2OS_2G_2$, and this in turn implies that area bounded by $S_1OH_4S_1 \leqslant$ area bounded by $S_2OH_2S_2$.

Thus in any case $A(\Delta_3 \cap \Delta_3') \leqslant A(\Delta_2 \cap \Delta_2')$ and this proves the lemma.

LEMMA 5. $f(\Delta_3; O) \leqslant f(\Omega; O)$.

Because of LEMMA 4(i) the curve G_3JH_3 lies inside the area $OG_3K_2K_3H_4O$. Let a variable half-line through O meet G_3JH_3 in P and $G_3K_2K_3H_4$ in Q. We show first that OQ/OP decreases as P moves along H_3JG_3 from H_3 to G_3.

Let $OP = x$, and angle $\hat{POH_1}$ be ξ. Then, if $\varepsilon(P)$ is the angle subtended at P by O and the centre of the circular arc on which P lies,

$$\frac{dx}{d\xi} = x \tan \varepsilon(P).$$

Thus, to prove the required result we only have to show that $\varepsilon(Q) \leqslant \varepsilon(P)$.

Divide the range of ξ, $0 \leqslant \xi \leqslant \frac{1}{3}\pi$, into three or four parts, as follows. If $\angle K_2OH_1 \geqslant \angle JOH_1$, then take the division—

   (i) $0 \leqslant \xi \leqslant \angle K_3OH_1$,

   (ii) $\angle K_3OH_1 \leqslant \xi \leqslant \angle JOH_1$,

   (iii) $\angle JOH_1 \leqslant \xi \leqslant \angle K_2OH_1$,

   (iv) $\angle K_2OH_1 \leqslant \xi \leqslant \angle G_1OH_1$.

If $\angle K_2OH_1 < \angle JOH_1$, replace (ii), (iii), (iv) by (ii′) $\angle K_3OH_1 \leqslant \xi \leqslant \angle K_2OH_1$ and (iii′) $\angle K_2OH_1 \leqslant \xi \leqslant \angle G_1OH_1$. We consider the first case only, since the second is similar but simpler.

(i) Let L_1, L_2 be the centres of the circles of which the circular arcs JH_3 and K_3H_4 are respectively parts. L_1 and L_2 lie on the same side of OPQ or on OPQ. $OL_1 \geqslant OL_2$, $OP \leqslant OQ$, and so either L_1P meets L_2Q in the obtuse sector L_1OQ or L_1P coincides with L_2Q. In either case,

$$\varepsilon(P) = \angle L_1PO \geqslant \angle L_2QO = \varepsilon(Q).$$

(ii) Let M_2 be the centre of the arc K_2K_3. QM_2 meets OL_1 in L_2 when Q is at K_3, and QM_2 meets OL_1 in O when Q is at K_2. Thus for Q on K_2K_3, QM_2 meets OL_1 in a point of the line segment OL_2. Also M_2 and L_1 lie on the same side of OPQ and $OQ \geqslant OP$. Thus, for

$$\angle K_3OH_1 \leqslant \xi \leqslant \angle JOH_1,$$
$$\varepsilon(P) = \angle L_1PO \geqslant \angle M_2QO = \varepsilon(Q).$$

(iii) Let M_1 be the centre of the circle containing arc G_3J. Then M_2 is inside the triangle OM_1P and Q is a point outside this triangle on OP. Hence $\varepsilon(P) \geqslant \varepsilon(Q)$.

(iv) On G_3K_2, OQ is constant, OP increases as ξ increases. Hence OQ/OP is decreasing.

This proves the required result. OL meets $G_3K_2K_3H_4$ in S_1 and let it meet G_3JH_3 in P_1. Let $OP_1/OS_1 = e$, and denote by Δ_4 the set obtained from Δ_3 by a similitude with O as centre of similarity and linear dimensions reduced in the ratio $e:1$. Then Δ_4 is bounded by a curve that lies outside Ω in the sector LOH_1 and inside Ω in the sector LOG_1. Also the distance of a point of this curve from O is non decreasing as the point moves on the curve inside the sector from a point of OH_1 to a point of OG_1.

Thus $f(\Delta_3; O) = f(\Delta_4; O) \leqslant f(\Omega; O).$

This completes the proof of Lemma 5.

From Lemmas 2, 3, 4, 5, $f(\Delta; O) \leqslant f(\Omega; O)$. And thus $g(\Delta) \leqslant f(\Omega; O)$. The theorem will be proved if it can be shown that $f(\Omega; O) g(\Omega)$. This, however, follows trivially from the two facts:

(i) for each convex set, say Π, there is a point P for which

$$f(\Pi; P) = g(\Pi);$$

(ii) if Π is symmetrical about a line, then the point P of (i) may be taken to lie on that line.

This concludes the proof of the statement given in the introduction.

References

1. A. S. Besicovitch; "Measure of asymmetry of convex curves." *J. London Math. Soc.* **23** (1948) 237–40.
2. A. S. Besicovitch; "Measure of asymmetry of convex curves II." *ibid.* **26** (1951) 81–93.
3. E. Blane; *Annales de L'École Normale* (3), **60** (1943) 224.
4. T. Bonnesen and W. Fenchel; "Theorie der konvexen Körper." *Ergebnisse der Math.* (Berlin, 1934).
5. A. E. Mayer; "Der Inhalt der Gleichdicke. Alschätzungen für ebene Gleichdicke." *Math. Annalen*, **110** (1934–5) 97–127.
6. A. E. Mayer; "Über Gleichdicke." *Z. Ver. Deutsch Ing.* **76** (1932) 884–6 and **77** (1933) 152.

8th Problem. Sets of Constant Width Contained in a Set of Given Minimal Width

Introduction

We shall show

(i) there is a plane convex set of minimal width† λ which does

† All convex sets are assumed to be closed.

not contain any convex set whose width is constant and greater than $\lambda/(3 - 3^{1/2})$,

(ii) every plane convex set of minimal width λ contains a convex set whose width is constant and is equal to $\lambda/(3 - 3^{1/2})$.

§1. Proof of (i)

It is sufficient to show that an equilateral triangle whose minimal width is λ does not contain a convex set of constant width μ if $\mu > \lambda/(3 - 3^{1/2})$. This is equivalent to showing that the smallest equilateral triangle that circumscribes a set of constant width μ has itself minimal width not less than $\mu(3 - 3^{1/2})$.

Let $a_1a_2a_3$ be an equilateral triangle T, circumscribing a set K which is convex and of constant width μ. The triangle $a_1a_2a_3$ is transformed into itself by a rotation about its centroid through an angle of $2\pi/3$ and also by a reflection in one of its medians. The group of transformations generated by these two operations has six members $\tau_1, \tau_2, \ldots, \tau_6$. Each of the sets $\tau_i(K)$ is of constant width μ and is inscribed in the triangle $a_1a_2a_3$.

Define the set L by vector addition as follows:

$$L = \frac{1}{6}\left(\sum_{i=1}^{6} \tau_i(K)\right) \tag{1}$$

L has constant width μ, is contained in T and touches each side of T in a single point. The set L is invariant under each of the operations τ_i and thus meets each side of $a_1a_2a_3$ in a mid-point. Through each mid-point of a side of $a_1a_2a_3$ construct the circle of radius μ that touches the side at its mid-point. The centres of these circles are points of L and L is contained in each circle. Thus L lies in the region bounded by three circular arcs each of radius μ, whose centres form an equilateral triangle of side at most μ. This region contains a Reuleaux triangle $b_1b_2b_3$ of width μ such that the equilateral triangle $b_1b_2b_3$ is similar and similarly orientated to $a_1a_2a_3$ with the centroid of $a_1a_2a_3$ as the centre of similitude.

Hence the minimal width of $a_1a_2a_3$ is at least $\mu(3 - 3^{1/2})$ and (i) is proved.

§2. Proof of (ii)

Denote the class of convex polygons of minimal width λ and with not more than N sides by $\mathscr{X}(N, \lambda)$. We shall suppose that each of these polygons contains a certain fixed point of the plane. It is only necessary to prove the result when the given convex set is a member of $\mathscr{X}(N, \lambda)$ for $N = 3, 4, \ldots$, since the general case then follows by a standard approximation argument combined with the fact that the property with which we are concerned is congruence invariant.

Let X be a member of $\mathscr{X}(N, \lambda)$ and denote by $\mathscr{B}(X)$ the class of all sets which are of constant width and which are contained in X. Let $\mu(X)$ be the upper bound of the diameters (i.e. widths) of the members of $\mathscr{B}(X)$. This upper bound is attained for at least one member of $\mathscr{B}(X)$ and we denote the subclass of all such members of $\mathscr{B}(X)$ by $\mathscr{M}(X)$. We write $M(X)$ for a typical member of $\mathscr{M}(X)$.

Let $\delta(N, \lambda)$ be the lower bound of $\mu(X)$ as X varies in the class $\mathscr{X}(N, \lambda)$ and let $\mathscr{Y}(N, \lambda)$ be the subclass of those members of $\mathscr{X}(N, \lambda)$ for which $\mu(X) = \delta(N, \lambda)$. We have to show that the class $\mathscr{Y}(N, \lambda)$ is not void. Now a convex set X of minimal width λ and diameter v contains a segment of length λ in the direction in which X is of width λ and a point which lies on a perpendicular to this segment at a distance $\frac{1}{2}(v^2 - \lambda^2)^{1/2}$ from the segment. Thus X contains a triangle of area $\frac{1}{4}\lambda\sqrt{(v^2 - \lambda^2)}$ and of perimeter not more than $\lambda + \frac{1}{2}(v^2 - \lambda^2)^{1/2} + \frac{1}{2}(v^2 + 3\lambda^2)^{1/2}$. Hence X contains a circle of radius

$$\tfrac{1}{2}\lambda\sqrt{(v^2 - \lambda^2)}/(\lambda + \tfrac{1}{2}(v^2 - \lambda^2)^{1/2} + \tfrac{1}{2}(v^2 + 3\lambda^2)^{1/2}),$$

and this expression tends to $\frac{1}{2}\lambda$ as v tends to infinity. Thus $\mu(X) \to \lambda$ as $v \to \infty$. Now if we select a sequence of members of $\mathscr{X}(N, \lambda)$ say $\{X_i\}$ such that

$$\lim_{i \to \infty} \mu(X_i) = \delta(N, \lambda),$$

then, since by (i) $\delta(N, \lambda) \leqslant \lambda/(3 - 3^{1/2}) < \lambda$, the sequence $\{X_i\}$ lies in a bounded part of the plane and Blaschke's selection theorem can be applied. Any set which is the limit of a convergent subsequence of the $\{X_i\}$ belongs to $\mathscr{Y}(N, \lambda)$.

Let $n(N, \lambda)$ be the least integer which is such that some member of $\mathscr{Y}(N, \lambda)$ has exactly $n(N, \lambda)$ sides and denote by $\mathscr{Z}(N, \lambda)$ those members of $\mathscr{Y}(N, \lambda)$ which have $n(N, \lambda)$ sides. Finally let $\mathscr{W}(N, \lambda)$ be the subclass of those members of $\mathscr{Z}(N, \lambda)$ which do not contain some other member of $\mathscr{Z}(N, \lambda)$ as a proper subset. The class $\mathscr{W}(N, \lambda)$ is not void because the intersection of a decreasing sequence of members of $\mathscr{Z}(N, \lambda)$ is again a member of $\mathscr{Z}(N, \lambda)$.

We next show that for any member X of $\mathscr{W}(N, \lambda)$ the following six statements hold.

(A) Any set of constant width that is contained in X has width less than or equal to $\mu(X)$.

(B) If $Y \in \mathscr{X}(N, \lambda)$ there is a set of constant width contained in Y whose width is greater than or equal to $\mu(X)$.

(C) Every $M(X)$ meets every side of X.

(D) Through every vertex of X there passes one of a pair of parallel support lines of X whose distance apart is λ.

(E) No two sides of X are parallel.

(F) There is a set $M(X)$ of the class $\mathscr{M}(X)$ that does not contain any vertex of X.

(A) is simply a restatement of the definition of $\mu(X)$, whilst (B) follows from the fact that $X \in \mathscr{W}(N, \lambda) \subset \mathscr{Y}(N, \lambda)$. Suppose next that (C) is false. Select an $M(X)$ that does not meet every side of X, and produce the remaining sides (those that meet $M(X)$) to form a polygon Y containing X. Now Y has fewer sides than X, hence $Y \notin \mathscr{Y}(N, \lambda)$, and since $Y \supset X$ we must have $\mu(Y) > \mu(X)$. Consider the set formed by the vector sum

$$S(\theta) = (1 - \theta)M(X) + \theta M(Y), 0 < \theta < 1,$$

where $M(Y)$ is of constant width $\mu(Y)$. $S(\theta)$ is of constant width $(1 - \theta)\mu(X) + \theta\mu(Y) > \mu(X)$ and as $\theta \to 0$, $S(\theta)$ tends to $M(X)$. It follows that for θ sufficiently small $S(\theta)$ is contained in X. But this is in contradiction with (A). Thus (C) is true.

If (D) were not true there would be a vertex of X, say p, such that every support line of X through p (and in particular the two sides of X, pq_1 and pq_2, on which p lies) is at a distance greater than $\lambda + \varepsilon$ from the parallel support line, for some $\varepsilon > 0$. Let p' be an interior point of the segment pq_2 such that the distance pp' is less than ε. Denote by X' the closure of the set of points of X that do not belong to the triangle $pp'q_1$. Then $X' \in \mathscr{X}(N, \lambda)\dagger$ and as $X' \subset X$, $\mu(X') \leqslant \mu(X)$. Thus $\mu(X') = \mu(X)$ and $X' \in \mathscr{Y}(N, \lambda)$. But X' has the same number of sides of X and thus $X' \in \mathscr{Z}(N, \lambda)$. This is in contradiction with the fact that $X \in \mathscr{W}(N, \lambda)$. Thus (D) is true.

If (E) were false then by (C) we should have

$$\lambda = \mu(X).$$

But by (i) and (B), with an equilateral triangle for Y, $\mu(X) \leqslant \lambda/(3 - 3^{1/2})$. This contradiction shows that (E) is true.

To prove (F) suppose firstly that however the set $M(X)$ is chosen in the class $\mathscr{M}(X)$ it always contains a certain vertex, say p, of X. Denote the two sides of X that end in p by q_1p and q_2p. Since the sets $M(X)$ are each of constant width, p is the only point of the two segments q_1p, q_2p that belongs to any of the sets $M(X)$. By (D), p lies on a support line L of X such that the parallel support line L' is at a distance λ from L.

† It may happen that the fixed point used in defining the class $\mathscr{X}(N, \lambda)$ belongs to the triangle $pp'q_1$. In that case there is a member of $\mathscr{X}(N, \lambda)$ congruent to X' and we use this set instead of X'.

Either L or L' meets X in a side, for if they both met X in a vertex then a slight rotation of direction would lead to two support lines whose distance apart (if the rotation were in the appropriate sense) would be less than λ.† If L' met X in a side then, by (C), L' would meet $M(X)$ and we should have $\mu(X) = \lambda$. This is impossible and thus L' meets X in a vertex, say p', and L meets X in a side, say q_1p. The perpendicular from p' to L meets q_1p in a point r. The point r is not an end-point of the segment q_1p or again X would be of minimal width less than λ. Let s be an interior point of the segment rp and let $L(\phi)$ be a line that meets L in s and makes an angle ϕ with L, $\phi > 0$, where these angles are measured so that $L(\phi)$ cuts the segment pq_2 when ϕ is small. Let $X(\phi)$ be the polygon bounded by the lines which bound X except that L is replaced by $L(\phi)$. There is a positive number ϕ_0 such that for $0 < \phi < \phi_0$, $X(\phi)$ is of minimal width not less than λ. For if this is not the case let ϕ_i be a sequence of positive numbers decreasing to zero such that $X(\phi_i)$ is of minimal width less than λ. If $L(\phi)$ meets pq_2 in the point $t(\phi)$ there is a support line of $X(\phi_i)$ through the point $t(\phi_i)$ such that the opposite support line meets $X(\phi_i)$ in a side and their distance apart is less than λ. Since these lines take on at most a finite number of orientations we may suppose them all parallel. But then the existence of the sequence of support lines implies that there are two parallel support lines to X at a distance λ apart and that the one through p does not meet X in any other point. We have already seen that this situation is impossible. Thus the number ϕ_0 exists.

Next, there is a number ϕ_1, $0 < \phi_1$, such that for $0 < \phi < \phi_1$ no set $M(X(\phi))$ of the class $\mathscr{M}(X(\phi))$ meets the segment q_1s. For again if ϕ_i is a sequence of positive numbers decreasing to zero such that each $X(\phi_i)$ contains a set $M(X(\phi_i))$ meeting q_1s then there is a subsequence for which $M(X(\phi_i))$ converges (to say) K. It is clear that K is an $M(X)$ meeting q_1s and thus not containing p. This is impossible by hypothesis and hence ϕ exists.

For ϕ satisfying $0 < \phi < \min (\phi_0, \phi_1)$, any $M(X(\phi))$ is contained in the common part of X and $X(\phi)$ and thus does not contain p. Hence $\mu(X(\phi)) < \mu(X)$ and this is in contradiction with (B). Thus (F) is proved provided we can show that the statement "to each vertex of X corresponds a set $M(X)$ not containing that vertex" implies the existence of a set $M(X)$ not containing any vertex of X. But this is easily seen to be the case. For if the vertices of X are $p_1, p_2, \ldots, p_m$ and if $M_i(X)$ is a set of the class $\mathscr{M}(X)$ that does not contain P_i then the set

$$M = (M_1(X) + M_2(X) + \ldots + M_m(X))/m$$

† See 3rd Problem p. 43.

also belongs to the class $\mathscr{M}(X)$ and does not contain any vertex of X. Thus (F) is proved.

Consider next a set $M(X)$ that satisfies (F). Denote the vertices of X by $p_1, p_2, \ldots, p_m$. (See Fig. 30.) Let t_i be the point of $p_i p_{i+1}$ on $M(X)$ for $i = 1, 2, \ldots, m-1$, and t_m be the point of $p_m p_1$ on $M(X)$. Denote the length of the segment $t_i t_{i+1}$ by κ_i for $i = 1, 2, \ldots, m-1$ and of $t_m t_1$ by κ_m. Define the angle α_i by

$$\kappa_i = 2\mu(X) \sin \alpha_i \qquad i = 1, 2, \ldots, m.$$

The arc of the frontier of $M(X)$ that is contained in the triangle†

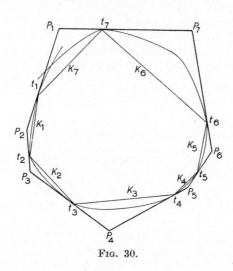

FIG. 30.

$t_i t_{i+1} p_{i+1}$ is of length not less than $2\mu(X) \, \alpha_i$. For if the small arc $t_i t_{i+1}$ of the circle of radius $\mu(X)$ that passes through t_i and t_{i+1} and whose centre is on the side of $t_i t_{i+1}$ opposite to p_{i+1} were cut by a support line of $M(X)$, then, since $M(X)$ is contained in the circles of radii $\mu(X)$ and centres t_i, t_{i+1}, $M(X)$ would have width less than $\mu(X)$. Since the total frontier length of $M(X)$ is $\pi\mu(X)$ we have

$$\sum_{i=1}^{m} \alpha_i \leqslant \tfrac{1}{2}\pi.$$

We consider next those vertices of X which have a property which we call property (P). A vertex of X has property (P) if one of the support lines through it is parallel to a side of X which is distinct

† Here and in what follows to avoid the unnecessary repetition involved in writing down the end cases it is supposed that if a suffix is greater than m it is reduced mod m.

from the two sides of X which contain the vertex. We shall show that there are exactly three vertices with property (P).

To see that there are at least three such vertices, select a side of X, say $p_1 p_2$. Let L be the support line parallel to and distinct from $p_1 p_2$. By (E), L meets X in a vertex, say p_i. There are two sides of X that end in p_i; let L_1, L_2 be the support lines parallel to and distinct from these sides meeting X in say p_j and p_k. The three vertices p_i, p_j and p_k are distinct and each has property (P).

Next, consider a vertex which has property (P), say p_2. Then there is a pair of parallel support lines of X one of which, L, meets X in the single point p_2 whilst the other, L', meets X in a side. The two support lines of $M(X)$ parallel to L are a line L'' and the line L'. Also L'' meets $M(X)$ in a point q which lies in the triangle $t_1 p_2 t_2$. The distance between L and L'' is at least $\lambda - \mu(X)$. Since t_1 and t_2 lie at a distance κ_1 apart the side of L'' remote from p_2 it follows that

$$\angle t_1 p_2 t_2 < 2\tan^{-1}\left\{\frac{\kappa_1}{2(\lambda - \mu)}\right\} = 2\tan^{-1}\left\{\frac{\mu}{(\lambda - \mu)}\sin\alpha_1\right\}.$$

Now suppose that s of the m vertices of X, say p_{i_1}, p_{i_2}, . . . ,p_{i_s} have property (P). The sum of the interior angles of X is $(m - 2)\pi$. By the above inequality and the convexity of X this sum is less than

$$(m - s)\pi + \sum_{j=1}^{s} 2\tan^{-1}\left\{\frac{\mu}{\lambda - \mu}\sin\alpha_{i_j}\right\}.$$

Now $\sum_{j=1}^{s}\alpha_{i_j} \leqslant \frac{1}{2}\pi$ and the function $\tan^{-1}\left\{(\mu/(\lambda - \mu))\sin x\right\}$ is a concave increasing function of x. It follows that we have the inequality

$$(m - 2)\pi < (m - s)\pi + 2s\tan^{-1}\left\{\frac{\mu}{\lambda - \mu}\sin\frac{\pi}{2s}\right\}.$$

Calculation shows that this implies that $s < 5$.

Thus X has either three or four vertices with property (P). If p_i is a particular vertex of X with property (P) then the set of sides of X which are parallel to support lines of X through p_i, and which do not themselves pass through p_i, form an arc $\gamma(p_i)$ on the frontier of X. Those interior points of the arc $\gamma(p_i)$ that are also vertices of X do not have property (P), but the end points of $\gamma(p_i)$ (which are necessarily vertices of X) do have property (P). Moreover if p_j is an end-point of $\gamma(p_i)$ then p_i is an end-point of $\gamma(p_j)$. It follows that the number of vertices with property (P) is three, for the conditions described above cannot be satisfied with four such vertices. (There must in fact be an odd number of vertices with property (P), just as a Reuleaux polygon must have an odd number of vertices.) The three vertices of X with property (P) are denoted by q_1, q_2, q_3.

Let T be the triangle whose vertices are q_1, q_2, q_3 and let C_j, $j = 1, 2, 3$, be the circle whose centre is q, and whose radius is λ.

Each side of the triangle T is of length greater than or equal to λ and each angle is less than or equal to 2θ where cosec θ is equal to $5 - 2\sqrt{3}$. The first of these statements is true because through each pair of vertices of T there pass one each of a pair of parallel support lines to X, and the minimal width of X is λ. The second statement is true because X contains that sector of C_j bounded by the sides q_iq_j and q_kq_j of T for which i, j, k is a permutation of 1, 2, 3. This sector contains a circle of diameter

$$\frac{2\lambda}{1 + \text{cosec } \frac{1}{2}\angle q_iq_jq_k},$$

which is greater than $\lambda/(3 - 3^{1/2})$ unless $\angle q_iq_jq_k$ is less than or equal to 2θ. Thus T is an acute angled triangle.

We next construct from T a set $E(T)$ as follows. Join each pair of vertices, say q_iq_k, by an arc $\alpha(i, k)$ which has the shortest possible length subject to not meeting the interior of C_j $(i, j, k$ being a permutation of 1, 2, 3). The three arcs $\alpha(1, 2)$, $\alpha(2, 3)$, $\alpha(3, 1)$ bound a convex set which we denote by $E(T)$. Clearly

$$T \subset E(T) \subset X.$$

Let $\mu(E(T))$ be the maximum of the widths of sets of constant width contained in $E(T)$. The result (ii) will be proved if we can show that $\mu(E(T)) \geqslant \lambda/(3 - 3^{1/2})$.

Let T vary in the class $\mathscr{I}$ of triangles whose sides are of length at least λ and whose angles are at most $\frac{1}{2}(\frac{1}{2}\pi + 2\theta)$. Denote by $\mathscr{E}$ the class of sets $E(T)$, $T \in \mathscr{I}$. From $\mathscr{I}$ select a set T_0 such that $\mu(E(T_0))$ attains its lower bound and $E(T_0)$ does not contain any other set of $\mathscr{E}$ is a proper subset. The proof that T_0 exists is omitted. Write E_0 for $E(T_0)$. We know that $\mu(E(T_0)) \leqslant \lambda/(3 - 3^{1/2})$ and thus that every angle of T_0 is less than $\frac{1}{2}(\frac{1}{2}\pi + 2\theta)$. Thus small variations from T_0 will lead to triangles of class $\mathscr{I}$ provided the sides are all of length greater than or equal to λ.

Let the vertices of T_0 be r_1, r_2, r_3 and let K_j be the circle with centre r_j and radius λ for $j = 1, 2, 3$. (See Fig. 31.) Each K_j meets the side of T_0 opposite to its centre. For suppose that K_1 did not meet r_2r_3. Then a small displacement of r_1 towards r_2r_3 and a corresponding displacement of K_1, could be made to give rise to a set T_1 for which $E(T_1)$ would be a proper subset of E_0. This is impossible.

The arc $\alpha(1, 2)$ of the frontier of E_0 is composed of a segment r_1u_1, an arc u_1v_1 of K_3, and a segment v_1r_2. These may degenerate in that r_1 may be u_1; or u_1 be v_1; or v_1 be r_2. If the segments exist they are parts of tangents to the circle K_3. We show next that both the segments exist. If, for example, r_1 is u_1, then r_1 and r_3 are at a distance λ apart and E_0 contains the segment r_1r_3, the arc

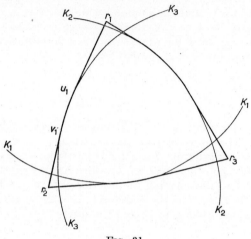

FIG. 31.

r_3w of K_1 and the arc wr_1 of K_3 (where w is a point of intersection of K_1 with K_3). This curve bounds a set which can easily be seen to contain a Reuleaux triangle of width $3^{1/2}\lambda/2$. But this is impossible because

$$\mu(E_0) \leqslant \mu(E(T)) \leqslant \mu(X) \leqslant \lambda/(3 - 3^{1/2}) < 3^{1/2}\lambda/2.$$

Thus the segments r_1u_1 and v_1r_2 are non-degenerate.

Next, any set M contained in E_0 and of constant width equal to $\mu(E_0)$ meets each of the three arcs $\alpha(1, 2)$, $\alpha(2, 3)$, $\alpha(1, 3)$. For suppose that it did not meet $\alpha(1, 2)$. There is a direction ζ such that the two support lines to E_0 in the direction ζ pass one through r_1 and one through r_2. A translation of M in the direction ζ away from r_3 would give rise to a set M' of constant width $\mu(E_0)$ and contained in the interior of E_0. This is impossible.

Also, corresponding to any segment of the frontier of E_0 such as r_1u_1 there is a set M contained in E of constant width $\mu(E_0)$ and which meets the segment. If this were false for, say, r_1u_1, then a small movement of r_1 along that tangent to K_2 on which r_1 lies, away from r_3 would give rise to a set E'. Each set M has points exterior to E', for M meets $\alpha(2, 3)$ which, apart from the points r_2, r_3, is exterior to E'. M cannot meet r_2 or r_3 for if it did we should have $\mu(E_0) = \lambda$. This by an argument similar to one used previously (see proof of (F)) implies that $\mu(E') < \mu(E_0)$ provided the displacement is sufficiently small.

Thus one set, M_1, meets r_1u_1 and another, M_2, meets r_2v_1. Suppose that $u_1 \neq v_1$ and that M_1 meets r_1u_1 in t_1, M_2 meets r_2v_1 in t_2. The circle of radius $\mu(E_0)$ through t_i tangential to $\alpha(1, 2)$ contains M_i and, because the curvature of $\alpha(1, 2)$ is less than that of the circle, the circle meets $\alpha(1, 2)$ only in the point t_i. Denote this circle by G_i. Then

$$\tfrac{1}{2}(M_1 + M_2) \subset \tfrac{1}{2}(G_1 + G_2).$$

The set $\tfrac{1}{2}(M_1 + M_2)$ is of constant width $\mu(E_0)$; is contained in E_0, and does not meet $\alpha(1, 2)$. This is impossible and u_1 is v_1.

Thus E_0 is a triangle with three altitudes each equal to λ, i.e. E_0 is an equilateral triangle of width λ. But then we know that $\mu(E_0) = \lambda/(3 - 3^{1/2})$. Hence the proof of (ii) is complete.

9TH PROBLEM. EXTREMAL PROPERTIES OF TRIANGLES CIRCUMSCRIBING PLANE CONVEX SETS

Introduction

We here establish extremal properties of triangles circumscribed about plane convex sets. The results obtained are inequalities between the geometric elements of the circumscribing triangle and those of the plane convex set. For each inequality we give the extremal cases in which equality can occur. All the results are best possible in that there are always cases in which equality occurs.

Of the properties which are proved, those in the first paragraph are true for all circumscribing triangles whilst those in the second and third paragraphs are true for at least one circumscribing triangle. It will be convenient to regard as a circumscribing triangle that convex figure which contains the given convex set Γ and is bounded by three support lines of Γ, even if two of these support lines are parallel.

In the first paragraph we show that if the convex set has a boundary of length l then the minimal width of any circumscribing triangle is less than or equal to $l/\sqrt{3}$, and that if it is also given that the convex set is central, then the minimal width of any circumscribing triangle is less than or equal to $\tfrac{1}{2}l$. A number of applications of this result are given, and in particular it is shown to be related to the Tarski plank problem in two dimensions.†

In the second paragraph we show that every convex set of Area A can be circumscribed by a triangle of area less than or equal to $2A$, and that this result remains true if the direction of one of the sides of the triangle is prescribed. The first of these results may be compared with those due to Fejes [4]. The second is the dual of a result of J. L. Hodges [5].

In the third paragraph we obtain similar results connecting the length of perimeter of a circumscribing triangle with the length of boundary of the convex set by using methods due to Hurwitz [6] and Meissner [7]. It is shown that if the convex set has a boundary of length l then there is a circumscribing triangle which is equilateral and whose length of perimeter is less than or equal to $(3\sqrt{3}l)/\pi$, and that if one of the sides of the triangle is in a prescribed direction then the perimeter is of length less than or equal to $\sqrt{3}l$.

In what follows "convex set" will always mean "plane bounded closed convex set with interior points". The definitions of the other terms used are given in Bonnesen and Fenchel [3], except that a triangle, as remarked above, may have two parallel sides.

§1.

THEOREM 9.1. *If Γ is a convex set with boundary of length l and ABC is a triangle which circumscribes Γ, then the minimal width of ABC is less than or equal to $l/\sqrt{3}$. Equality occurs for some triangle ABC if and only if Γ is an equilateral triangle, and then only if ABC is an equilateral triangle with sides parallel to those of Γ but oriented in the opposite sense.*

Amongst all the convex sets Γ and all the triangles which circumscribe Γ, there is one convex set Γ and one triangle circumscribing Γ for which the ratio

$$R = \frac{\text{minimal width of circumscribing triangle}}{\text{length of boundary of } \Gamma}$$

attains its largest value. This is an immediate consequence of the Blaschke selection theorem with minor qualifications.‡ The only point that is not clear is that the extremal figure has interior points. However when Γ is a segment (whose length of boundary is twice the length of the segment) the above ratio is at most $\frac{1}{2}$, and when Γ is an equilateral triangle and ABC an equilateral

---

† See Thøger Bang [1]. The references are on p. 160.
‡ See [2], 62, or [3], 34.

triangle as described in the enunciation of the theorem, the value of the ratio is $1/\sqrt{3}$. Thus the extremal figure has interior points,

$$\left(\text{since}\frac{1}{\sqrt{3}} > \frac{1}{2}\right).$$

Denote one such convex set by Γ and one such triangle by ABC. We may suppose that ABC either has two sides parallel or is an isosceles triangle with its two equal sides at least as long as its third side. (In the first case it is convenient to use the notation ABC with one of the vertices A, B or C at infinity.) For if ABC satisfied neither of these possibilities then we could choose the notation so that $AB > BC \geqslant CA$. Take C' on BC near to C and such that C lies between B and C'. Let $C'A'$ be the support line of Γ through C' other than BC', and let it meet BA in A'. If there is a point of Γ on CA other than C, then as C' tends to C so does A' tend to A. It follows that in this case we can find C' near C so that the minimal width of $BA'C'$ (i.e. the least of the three altitudes of $BA'C'$) is greater than that of BAC. This is impossible by the definition of ABC. Thus C is the only point of Γ on AC and we may replace AC by the line through C parallel to AB. The triangle thus obtained circumscribes Γ, has minimal width equal to that of ABC and is of the first type.

Consider these types separately.

(i) ABC has two parallel sides. The minimal width of ABC is less than or equal to the diameter of Γ and this is less than $\tfrac{1}{2}l$. This case cannot occur.

(ii) ABC is isosceles with $AB = AC \geqslant BC$. Let L, M, N be points of Γ on BC, CA, AB respectively. Each point L, M, N is an interior point of the segment on which it lies. For if, say, N were at A, then as L is on BC, the perimeter of LMN is greater than or equal to twice AL, and AL is greater than or equal to the minimal width of ABC. As Γ contains the triangle LMN it follows that the ratio R is less than or equal to $\tfrac{1}{2}$. As before, this is impossible.

It follows also that Γ is LMN, since otherwise we could increase the ratio R by replacing Γ by LMN. Now the broken line LN, NM is the shortest broken line that joins L and M to a point of AB. For if this were not the case we could replace LMN by another triangle inscribed in ABC with a perimeter of length less than that of LMN, and this is in contradiction with the extremal property of LMN (i.e. Γ) with ABC. Thus $\angle ANM = \angle BNL$. Similarly $\angle AMN = \angle CML$, $\angle BLN = \angle CLM$.

In the triangles BLN, CML,

$$\angle BLN = \angle CLM, \qquad \angle LBN = \angle LCM, \tag{1}$$

where the last equality holds because ABC is isosceles. Thus $\angle BNL = \angle CML$ and we have

$$\angle ANM = \angle BNL = \angle CML = \angle AMN = \angle ABC = \angle ACB. \quad (2)$$

Hence MN is parallel to BC and $MC = BN$. The triangles MLC and NLB are congruent and are isosceles. $ML = LC = BL$, and so BM is perpendicular to AC.

If the triangle ABC is not equilateral, then $AB = AC > BC$. We can give the point A a small displacement towards BC in the direction perpendicular to BC until it moves into the position A''. Let $A''N$, $A''M$ meet BC in B'', C'' respectively. The perpendicular from B'' to $A''C''$ has length equal to

$$BM \cos \angle AMA'' + BB'' \sin \angle A''C''B''. \quad (3)$$

Since $\cos \angle AMA'' = 1 + O(AA'')^2$ and $AA'' = O(BB'')$, it follows that if AA'' is sufficiently small the triangle $A''B''C''$ has minimal width greater than that of ABC.

This is impossible and so the triangle ABC is equilateral, and minimal width of ABC equals AL, which is $(LM + MN + NL)/\sqrt{3}$. As $LM + MN + NL$ is the length of boundary of Γ, the theorem is complete except for the cases of equality.

That equality does occur in the case stated is clear, and an examination of the above argument shows that equality can occur only in this case.

THEOREM 9.2. *If Γ is a central convex set whose boundary is of length l and ABC is a circumscribing triangle to Γ, then the minimal width of ABC is less than or equal to $\frac{1}{2}l$. Equality can occur for some triangle ABC if and only if Γ is a central six-sided polygon whose interior angles are all $\frac{2}{3}\pi$.*

We shall suppose that there is some convex set Γ and a circumscribing triangle for which the ratio

$$\frac{\text{minimal width of circumscribing triangle}}{\text{length of boundary of } \Gamma}$$

has the value R. For a given convex set Γ,† the largest value of R occurs when ABC either has two parallel sides or is isosceles with its equal sides larger than or equal to its third side. The proof of this is the same as that used in Theorem 1. In the first case R is less than $\frac{1}{2}$, (Γ has interior points and cannot therefore be a segment). In the second case denote the minimal width of ABC by δ. Let Γ meet BC, CA, AB in L, M, N respectively. Let O be the centre of Γ and L', M', N' be the points of Γ obtained from L, M, N

† With interior points.

by reflection in O. O is an interior point of the triangle ABC because otherwise Γ would be a linear segment.

The extremal problem is next reduced to a simpler one. Let MX be a line through M parallel to LN' and LX a line through L parallel to MN'. Then $MX = LN' = NL'$, $MN' = LX = NM'$, $NX = L'M = M'L$. Thus the length of the perimeter of $LN'ML'$ NM' is equal to twice $XM + XN + XL$. This sum is least for a fixed X when XL, XM, XN are perpendicular respectively to BC, CA, AB. Because of the form of ABC the sum of the three perpendiculars from X to BC, CA, AB is least when X is on BC, and its value is then precisely the minimal width of ABC. Hence R is less than or equal to $\frac{1}{2}$.

From the above argument it is clear that we have strict inequality unless ABC is equilateral and Γ is the central six-sided polygon $LN'ML'NM'$, and XL, XM, XN are perpendicular to BC, CA, AB respectively. Since LN' and NL' are parallel to XM etc. it follows that all the interior angles of $LN'ML'NM'$ are $\frac{2}{3}\pi$. Finally, if Γ is of this form we have equality for Γ and the appropriate triangle ABC.

As a consequence of Theorem 9.2 we are able to deduce the following:

THEOREM 9.3. *If Γ is a convex set of minimal width d and Θ is a central convex curve of length l and $l \leqslant 2d$, then Θ may be translated until it lies entirely contained in the set Γ.*

Consider the class of curves which are similar to Θ, similarly situated to Θ and contained in Γ. This class is non-empty and contains a member that is at least as large as any other member. Denote this curve by Θ_1. There are two possibilities.

(i) Θ_1 and Γ have in common two parallel support lines. These lines are at a distance apart that is at least d and so Θ_1 has length l_1, where $l_1 \geqslant 2d \geqslant l$. Thus Θ_1 is at least as large as Θ.

(ii) Θ_1 and Γ have a common circumscribing triangle. The minimal width of this triangle is greater than or equal to d and, by Theorem 2, this minimal width is less than or equal to $\frac{1}{4}l_1$, where l_1 again denotes the length of Θ_1. Thus $l_1 \geqslant 2d \geqslant l$ and again Θ_1 is at least as large as Θ.

Thus in any case Γ contains a curve obtained from Θ by a translation.

Relation to the Tarski plank problem in two dimensions

Let Γ be a convex set of minimal width d and $S_1S_2, \ldots S_p$ be a finite number of strips between pairs of parallel lines. Suppose that S_i is of width d_i. The problem is to show that if Γ is contained in the union of the S_i, $i = 1, 2, \ldots, p$, then $d_1 + d_2 + \ldots + d_p \geqslant d$.†

† See [1].

A solution of this problem in two dimensions may be obtained from Theorem 3 as follows. We suppose that a set of strips S_i, for which $d_1 + d_2 + \ldots + d_p < d$, is given and show that their union does not contain Γ. Let Θ be a central convex polygon with $2p$ sides, which is such that each pair of opposite sides is perpendicular to one of the S_i and of length equal to the width of the corresponding S_i. By Theorem 3 there is a curve similar and similarly situated to Θ, of length $2d$, contained in Γ. Call this curve Θ_1 and the set bounded by Θ_1, Γ_1. We shall show that however the S_i are arranged there is always a point of Γ_1 not contained in their union.

There is no loss of generality in supposing that no two of the lines bounding the strips S_i are coincident, and that no three are concurrent. For if this condition were not fulfilled we could expand the strips S_i slightly until we had a set of strips S_i', $i = 1, 2, \ldots, p$ with S_i' of width d_i', $S_i' \supset S_i$, $d_1' + \ldots + d_p' < d$ and the strips S_i' satisfying the required conditions. We therefore assume that they are satisfied by the S_i, and we call these conditions (C).

Let O be the centre of Θ_1, and also the origin of a rectangular system of coordinates. Let (α_i, β_i) be the components of the vector which is perpendicular to S_i and of magnitude $\tfrac{1}{2}d_i$, and let c_i be the perpendicular distance from O to the mid-line of S_i measured in the sense of (α_i, β_i).

If Q is the point (q_1, q_2) then Q will lie outside or on the bounding lines of the strip S_i if

$$q_1\alpha_i + q_2\beta_i \geqslant \tfrac{1}{2}d_i(c_i + \tfrac{1}{2}d_i) \text{ or } -q_1\alpha_i - q_2\beta_i \geqslant \tfrac{1}{2}d_i(-c_i + \tfrac{1}{2}d_i). \quad (4)$$

The next step is to show that (4) can be satisfied for $i = 1, 2, \ldots, p$ with $\quad (q_1, q_2) \equiv (\alpha_1\varepsilon_1 + \alpha_2\varepsilon_2 + \ldots + \alpha_p\varepsilon_p, \beta_1\varepsilon_1 + \ldots + \beta_p\varepsilon_p)$, where each ε_j is ± 1 and the choice of sign of ε_j is at our disposal.

Consider the 2^p numbers[†]

$$(\alpha_1\varepsilon_1 + \ldots + \alpha_p\varepsilon_p)^2 + (\beta_1\varepsilon_1 + \ldots + \beta_p\varepsilon_p)^2$$
$$- (c_1d_1\varepsilon_1 + \ldots + c_pd_p\varepsilon_p), \quad (5)$$

where each ε_j can be ± 1 independently. Of these numbers select the largest. Denote this particular set of $\varepsilon_1, \varepsilon_2, \ldots, \varepsilon_p$ by η_1, $\eta_2, \ldots, \eta_p$. The point $(\alpha_1\eta_1 + \alpha_2\eta_2 + \ldots + \alpha_p\eta_p, \beta_1\eta_1 + \beta_2\eta_2 + \ldots + \beta_p\eta_p)$ will do for Q. For example, to prove (4) for $i = 1$, form the difference of the two values of the expression (5) which arise firstly when $\varepsilon_i = \eta_i$, $i = 1, 2, \ldots, p$, and secondly when $\varepsilon_1 = -\eta_1$, $\varepsilon_i = \eta_i$, $i = 2, 3, \ldots p$. We have

$$4\alpha_1\eta_1(\alpha_2\eta_2 + \ldots + \alpha_p\eta_p) + 4\beta_1\eta_1(\beta_2\eta_2 + \ldots + \beta_p\eta_p)$$
$$- 2c_1d_1\eta_1 \geqslant 0,$$

† This is the argument of T. Bang, *loc. cit.*

i.e.

$$\alpha_1\eta_1(\alpha_1\eta_1 + \ldots + \alpha_p\eta_p) + \beta_1\eta_1(\beta_1\eta_1 + \ldots + \beta_p\eta_p)$$
$$\geqslant \tfrac{1}{2}c_1d_1\eta_1 + \alpha_1^2 + \beta_1^2 = (c_1\eta_1 + \tfrac{1}{2}d_1)\tfrac{1}{2}d_1,$$

i.e. one of the inequalities (4) with $i = 1$. It may be shown similarly that one of the two inequalities (4) holds for each i, $i = 1, 2, \ldots, p$.

Thus the point Q does not lie interior to any strip S_i. By the conditions (C) which the S_i satisfy, Q is therefore a limit point of points exterior to the union of the S_i. But Q is clearly an interior point of Γ_1. Thus Γ_1 is not contained in the union of the S_i, and this is the required result.

Further consequences of Theorems 9.1 and 9.2 are as follows:

(i) If Γ is a convex set of minimal width d and Δ is a triangle inscribed in Γ such that either

(a) each vertex of Δ is separated from the opposite side of Δ by a chord of Γ of maximal length and parallel to the side of Δ, or

(b) the support lines at the vertices of Δ form a triangle circumscribing Γ, then the length of the perimeter of Δ is greater than or equal to $d\sqrt{3}$.

(ii) If Γ is a convex set of minimal width d and Θ is a $2n$-sided convex polygon inscribed in Γ whose sides are equal and parallel in pairs, $n \geqslant 2$, then the length of Θ is greater than or equal to $d\sqrt{3}$. If also Θ is central then the length of Θ is greater than or equal to $2d$.

(ii) is a trivial deduction from (i) (a) except for the clause concerning the case when Θ is central. Conditions (i) (a) imply those of (i) (b). Consider then (i) (b) and let Δ_1 be the circumscribing triangle formed by the support lines to Γ at the vertices of Δ. Then $d \leqslant$ minimal width of $\Delta_1 \leqslant$ (length of perimeter of Δ)$/\sqrt{3}$, where the first inequality holds because Δ_1 contains Γ and the second because Δ_1 is circumscribed to Δ.

To prove (ii) we have only to establish the existence of a common circumscribing triangle to Γ and Θ. If Θ is coincident with the boundary of Γ, or if two support lines to Γ at two points of Θ are parallel and not coincident, there is nothing to prove. Otherwise there is a segment PQ of Θ which meets the boundary of Γ only in the points P, Q. The two support lines to Γ at P and Q are not coincident, and therefore we may suppose them to be not parallel. These two lines together with the support lines to Γ at the points of Θ opposite to P and Q with respect to the centre of Θ form a triangle or quadrilateral circumscribing Γ. Thus three of them form a circumscribing triangle.

§2.

In this section we consider the ratio of the area of a convex set to that of a circumscribing triangle.

THEOREM 9.4. *Suppose that θ is a fixed direction and that Γ is a given convex set; then there is a triangle circumscribing Γ with one side in the direction θ and such that the area of the triangle is less than or equal to twice the area of Γ. There is stirct inequality for one such triangle unless Γ is a particular type of at most six-sided convex polygon.*

Let the two support lines of Γ parallel to θ be l and l'. Let LMN be a triangle circumscribing Γ with LM a segment of l and of the least possible area. Similarly define $L'M'N'$ with $L'M'$ a segment of l', with the notation chosen so that $L'M'$ is in the same sense as LM. Denote by P, Q, P', Q', the mid-points of MN, LN, $M'N'$, $L'N'$ respectively. P, Q, P', Q' belong to Γ. Let the points R, R' of LM, $L'M'$ respectively also belong to Γ, and finally let the perpendicular distance from N to LM be h and that from N' to $L'M'$ be h'.

Then   area of $LMN = h \cdot PQ$,

area of $L'M'N' = h' \cdot P'Q'$,

area of $RP'PR'QQ' = \frac{1}{4}(h' \cdot PQ + h \cdot P'Q')$.

If a, b, c, d are any four positive numbers then

$$\text{minimum } (ab, cd) \leqslant \tfrac{1}{2}(ac + bd),$$

and equality occurs if and only if $a = d$, $b = c$.

Thus at least one of the triangles LMN, $L'M'N'$ has area less than or equal to twice the area of $RP'PR'QQ'$. As this last polygon is contained in Γ the result follows.

Also there is strict inequality unless $h = h'$, $PQ = P'Q'$ and Γ is the polygon $RP'PR'QQ$.

THEOREM 9.5. *Let Γ be a convex set. Then every triangle circumscribing Γ is of area greater than or equal to twice that of Γ if and only if Γ is a parallelogram.*

That every triangle circumscribing a parallelogram has at least twice the area of the parallelogram is trivial and the proof is omitted. Suppose then that Γ is a convex set for which every circumscribing triangle is of area at least twice that of Γ. In the notation of Theorem 9.4, Γ is a polygon $RP'PR'QQ'$. If Γ has 5 or 6 distinct sides we could apply Theorem 9.4 with the direction PP' or QQ' prescribed and we should obtain a triangle circumscribing Γ and of area twice that of a certain polygon contained in $RP'PR'QQ'$ which is either the parallelogram $PQQ'P'$ or has only one point on PP'. In either case it has strictly less area than $RP'PR'QQ'$. This is impossible and Γ is a quadrilateral. Apply Theorem 9.4 with the prescribed direction along one of the sides of Γ. It follows that there is another equal parallel side of Γ, thus Γ is a parallelogram.

§3.

In this section we consider the lengths of boundaries of a convex set and of its circumscribing triangles.

THEOREM 9.6. *If Γ is a convex set with boundary of length l then*

(i) *there is a circumscribing triangle with angles α, β, γ whose perimeter p satisfies*

$$p \leqslant \frac{1}{2\pi} \cdot \frac{(\sin \alpha + \sin \beta + \sin \gamma)^2}{\sin \alpha \cdot \sin \beta \cdot \sin \gamma}$$

Equality occurs for every such triangle when Γ is a circle. This is the only form of Γ for which this is true unless α, β, γ are rational multiples of π, when it is also true for the "irrevolvable" curves of such a triangle;

(ii) *there is an equilateral circumscribing triangle of perimeter p_1 where $p_1 \leqslant (3\sqrt{3}l)/\pi$, and every circumscribing equilateral triangle has perimeter less than or equal to $2l$;*

(iii) *if Γ is central then every circumscribing equilateral triangle has perimeter less than or equal to $\sqrt{3}l$.*

The first part of (ii) is the particular case $\alpha = \beta = \gamma = \frac{1}{3}\pi$ of (i). The second part of (ii) and (iii) are particular cases of Theorems 1 and 2. Thus we only have to prove (i).

Let O be a point inside the triangle ABC; OL, OM, ON the perpendiculars from O to BC, CA, AB of lengths q_1, q_2, q_3. If the angles of the triangle at A, B, C are α, β, γ then

$$\frac{q_1 \sin \alpha + q_2 \sin \beta + q_3 \sin \gamma}{\sin \alpha \sin \beta} = \frac{(q_1 \cdot BC + q_2 \cdot AC + q_3 \cdot AB) \sin \alpha}{\sin \alpha \sin \beta} \frac{}{BC}$$

$$= \frac{2 \cdot \text{Area } ABC}{BC \sin \beta} = AB.$$

Thus the perimeter of the triangle ABC is

$$\frac{(q_1 \sin \alpha + q_2 \sin \beta + q_3 \sin \gamma)(\sin \alpha + \sin \beta + \sin \gamma)}{\sin \alpha \sin \beta \sin \gamma} = I(q_1, q_2, q_3).$$

$$(6)$$

Let $H(\theta)$ be the support function of Γ with respect to the point O interior to Γ. Then with $q_1 = H(\theta)$, $q_2 = H(\theta + \alpha + \beta)$,

$q_3 = H(\theta + \alpha + 2\beta + \gamma)$ in (6), we have on integration with respect to θ from 0 to 2π.

$$\int_0^{2\pi} I(q_1, q_2, q_3)\, d\theta = \frac{(\sin \alpha + \sin \beta + \sin \gamma)^2}{\sin \alpha \sin \beta \sin \gamma} \int_0^{2\pi} H(\theta)\, d\theta$$

$$= l \frac{(\sin \alpha + \sin \beta + \sin \gamma)^2}{\sin \alpha \sin \beta \sin \gamma} \tag{7}$$

If p is the lower bound of I, then

$$p \leqslant \frac{1}{2\pi} \int_0^{2\pi} I(q_1, q_2, q_3)\, d\theta \tag{8}$$

(7) and (8) imply the inequality in (i).

It is trivial that there is equality for all such circumscribing triangles when Γ is a circle. That the circle is the only such convex curve except when α, β, γ are rational multiples of π, follows from the fact that the only triangle in which a convex curve (apart from a circle) can rotate so as to be always tangent to the three sides of the triangle, is such a triangle. See M. Fujiwara [8]. The class of curves about which the triangle can be rotated is the class of irrevolvable curves.

This completes the proof of the theorem.

Remark—The method of proof shows that there exist circumscribing triangles with perimeters p, p_1 satisfying the inequalities of (i) and (ii) reversed.

In the general case when Γ is any convex set then the lower bound of perimeters of circumscribing equilateral triangles is, trivially, the length of the boundary of Γ. If however Γ is restricted to be central we have

THEOREM 9.7. *If Γ is a central convex set whose boundary is of length l then a circumscribing triangle with angles α, β, γ where $\alpha \geqslant \beta \geqslant \gamma$, has perimeter greater than or equal to*

$$l\,(\sin \alpha + \sin \beta + \sin \gamma)/2 \sin \alpha.$$

There can be equality if and only if Γ is of the following forms: when $\alpha \geqslant \beta \geqslant \gamma$, a segment (a degenerate convex set); when $\alpha = \beta > \gamma$, a parallelogram; when $\alpha = \beta = \gamma$, a convex central polygon with at most six sides.

In particular a circumscribing equilateral triangle has perimeter greater than or equal to $\frac{3}{2}l$.

Let ABC be a triangle circumscribing Γ with angles α, β, γ. Let O be the centre of Γ and $A'B'C'$ the triangle obtained from ABC by reflection in O. Γ is contained in the common part of ABC and $A'B'C'$. This common part is a central polygon with at most six sides whose length of perimeter is a continuous and linear function of the position of O, if O is allowed to vary on a straight line and ABC is kept fixed. It follows that this perimeter has length not more than twice that of the longest side of ABC, i.e. BC. On the other hand this polygon contains Γ and so its length is greater than or equal to l.

Thus $l \leqslant 2 . BC$, and if ABC has perimeter p then

$$p = AB + BC + CA = (\sin \alpha + \sin \beta + \sin \gamma) \cdot \frac{BC}{\sin \alpha}$$

$$\geqslant \frac{l}{2 \sin \alpha}(\sin \alpha + \sin \beta + \sin \gamma).$$

This proves the theorem except for the cases of equality. For these suppose that $A'B', A'C'$ meet BC in L, L'; $B'C', B'A'$ meet CA in M, M'; $C'A', C'B'$ meet AB in N, N' respectively. The triangles $NBL', M'LC$ are similar to ABC. If $\alpha > \beta \geqslant \gamma$, then $BC > AC \geqslant AB$; thus $BL' > L'N$, $LC > LM'$ unless N is B and M' is C, i.e. equality can occur if and only if Γ is a segment. If $\alpha = \beta > \gamma$, then $BC = AC > AB$, $BL' = L'N$ and $LC > LM'$ unless M' is C, i.e. equality can occur if and only if Γ is a parallelogram. If $\alpha = \beta = \gamma$ then $BC = CA = AB$, $BL' = L'N$, $LC = LM'$ and equality can occur if and only if Γ is a convex central polygon with at most six sides (for it must coincide with the common part of ABC and $A'B'C'$).

From Theorems 9.7, 9.6 (ii) and 9.6. (iii) we see that the lengths of equilateral triangles circumscribing a convex set of length of boundary l, lie between

l and $2l$ for an arbitrary convex set,

$\frac{3}{2}l$ and $\sqrt{3}l$ for a central convex set.

These bounds are attained in the first case for an equilateral triangle and in the second case for a central convex six-sided polygon with all interior angles equal to $\frac{2}{3}\pi$. These are the only figures for which both bounds are attained.

Another result is as follows:

THEOREM 9.8. *Every convex set Γ with boundary of length l can be circumscribed by an equilateral triangle with some side in a prescribed direction and of length less than or equal to $\sqrt{3}l$.*

Let Γ_1 be the set obtained from Γ by a central symmetrisation. If ABC and $A'B'C'$ are two triangles that circumscribe Γ and have pairs of parallel sides (so that they are formed from three pairs of parallel support lines, both the triangles are genuine triangles), then the effect of the central symmetrisation is to enlarge the smaller of these two triangles. The result now follows from Theorem 9.2.

References

1. T. BANG; "A solution of the 'plank problem,'" *Proc. American Math. Soc.*, 2 (1951) 990–993.
2. W. BLASCHKE; *Kreis und Kugel* (New York, 1949).
3. T. BONNESEN und W. FENCHEL; *Theorie der konvexen Körper* (New York, 1948).
4. L. FEJES; "Eine Bemerkung zur Approximation durch n-Eckringe," *Compositio Math.*, 7 (1940) 474–476.
5. J. L. HODGES; "An extremal problem of geometry," *J. London Math. Soc.*, 26 (1951) 312–313.
6. A. HURWITZ; "Sur quelques applications geometriques des series de Fourier," *Annales de l'École Normale* (3), 19 (1902) 371–80.
7. E. MEISSNER; "Über die Anwendung von Fourier-Reihen auf einige Aufgaben der Geometrie und Kinematik," *Vierteljahrsschrift der Naturforsch. Gesellschaft in Zürich* (1909) 309–329.
8. H. FUJIWARA; *Sci. Rep. Tohôku Imp. Univ.* (1), 4 (1915) 43–55.

10TH PROBLEM. ON THE CLOSEST PACKING BY
EQUILATERAL TRIANGLES

Introduction

The problem with which we are concerned here is that of packing non-overlapping plane figures into a given plane figure. It is of a different type from the usual packing problem in which equal figures are used in the whole plane, and the aim is to calculate the limit of the ratio of covered area to the total area inside a large circle, as the radius of the circle tends to infinity. A closest packing in this problem is an arrangement of the figures in such a way that this limit attains its largest value.

In our problem the figures need not be of the same size, but they are all similar and oriented in a similar manner. By Vitali's theorem there exists a packing of this type in which the uncovered part of the given plane figure is of zero plane measure. This uncovered part will, however, have a certain fractional dimension, and the problem is to find the minimum of this dimension. An arrangement of the non-overlapping plane figures inside the given plane figure for which the set of uncovered points has this least fractional dimension is said to be a closest packing.

Two problems of this type have been suggested by Prof. A. S. Besicovitch. In the first a square† is covered by circles, and in the second an equilateral triangle is covered by equilateral triangles oriented in the opposite sense. Of these two problems the first is,

† The words square, circle, etc., are used to mean either the bounding curve or the bounded domain according to the context.

of course, the more interesting, but it appears to be a difficult problem, and we give here the solution to the second problem only.

ABC is a given equilateral triangle of unit side-length. Let Γ be the closed domain bounded by ABC. Inside this triangle are placed a number of equilateral triangles $A_1B_1C_1$, $A_2B_2C_2, \ldots,$ bounding open domains Γ_1, $\Gamma_2, \ldots$ For these triangles $\Gamma_i \cup \Gamma_j$ is empty for any i or $j(i \neq j)$, and the orientation of $A_iB_iC_i$ is opposite to that of ABC, i.e. B_iC_i is parallel to BC and A_i lies inside the strip bounded by the lines BC, B_iC_i produced.

Let $$\Theta_0 = \Gamma, \quad \Theta_n = \Gamma \cap \mathscr{C}(\bigcup_{i=1}^{n} \Gamma_i) \qquad n \geqslant 1$$

where $\mathscr{C}$ denotes complement, and let $\Theta = \bigcap_{n=1}^{\infty} \Theta_n$. Then

THEOREM 10.1. Θ *has dimension at least* $(\log 3)/(\log 2)$ *and measure at least* $\frac{1}{3}$ *in that dimension.*

THEOREM 10.2. *The* Γ_i *can be arranged so that* Θ *has dimension* $(\log 3)/(\log 2)$ *and measure not more than unity in that dimension.*

§1. Proof of Theorem 10.1

We shall suppose that the points ABC, $A_iB_iC_i$ are in counter-clockwise order round Γ and Γ_i respectively.

Any line parallel to BC lying between A and BC intersects Θ_n in a number of closed segments, a point being regarded as a segment of zero length. Let (ξ, η) be oblique Cartesian coordinates with A as origin, AB as the positive ξ-axis, and the line through A parallel to BC as positive η-axis. Then the line $\xi = x(0 \leqslant x \leqslant 1)$, meets Θ_n in (say) k segments of lengths $t_{n,i}(x)$ $(i = 1, 2, \ldots, k)$ where k depends on both n and on x. Write

$$f_n(x) = \sum_{i=1}^{k}(t_{n,i}(x))^{p-1} \quad \text{where} \quad p = \frac{\log 3}{\log 2}.$$

We need the following lemmas:

LEMMA 1. $g(y) = (y + k)^{p-1}y^{p-1}$ *is a decreasing function of* y *when* $1 < p < 2$, $k > 0$, $y > 0$.

For $$\frac{dg}{dy} = (p - 1)\left((y + k)^{p-2} - y^{p-2}\right) < 0$$

LEMMA 2.

$$\int_0^1 f_n(x)\,dx \geqslant \int_0^1 f_0(x)\,dx = \frac{1}{p}$$

Of the triangles $A_1B_1C_1$, $A_2B_2C_2, \ldots, A_nB_nC_n$, one has its side B_iC_i nearest to BC. There may be more than one such triangle, but in any case we can choose one, and it is merely a matter of notation to arrange that it is $A_nB_nC_n$.

Let the line through C_n parallel to AB meet BC in L and the line through B_n parallel to AC meet BC in M. No point of any $\Gamma_i(i \leqslant n-1)$ lies interior to the trapezium LC_nB_nM, for as B_iC_i is at least as far from BC as is B_nC_n, such a triangle would intersect Γ_n.

Next, consider the two functions $f_n(x)$, $f_{n-1}(x)$. Let the ξ coordinate of A_n be u and that of B_n be v. Then $f_n(x) = f_{n-1}(x)$ if $x \leqslant v$ or $x \geqslant u$. For $u > x > v$ one of the segments that makes a contribution to $f_{n-1}(x)$ is divided by $A_nB_nC_n$ into two segments, each contributing to $f_n(x)$. Let the lengths of these two segments be y_1, y_2, and then the length of the corresponding segment which contributes to $f_{n-1}(x)$ is $y_1 + y_2 + u - x$. Thus

$$f_{n-1}(x) - f_n(x)$$
$$= (y_1 + y_2 + u - x)^{p-1} - y_1^{p-1} - y_2^{p-1} \ (v < x < u).$$

By choice of the position of $A_nB_nC_n$ we have $y_1 \geqslant x - v$ and $y_2 \geqslant x - v$. Thus by Lemma 1, for $v < x < u$, we see that

$$f_{n-1}(x) - f_n(x) \leqslant (x + u - 2v)^{p-1} - 2(x-v)^{p-1} .$$

Thus

$$\int_0^1 (f_{n-1}(x) - f_n(x)) \, dx \leqslant (u-v)^p(2^p - 3)/p = 0,$$

i.e.

$$\int_0^1 f_{n-1}(x) \, dx \leqslant \int_0^1 f_n(x) \, dx.$$

By induction it follows that $\displaystyle\int_0^1 f_n(x) \, dx \geqslant \int_0^1 f_0(x) \, dx = \frac{1}{p}$.

LEMMA 3. *A set X of diameter d is contained in an equilateral triangle PQR oriented similarly to ABC and of diameter $2d$.*

For X is contained in a circle of diameter $2d/(3^{\frac{1}{2}})$, and any equilateral triangle which circumscribes this circle has diameter $2d$.

We can now prove the result.

The set Θ is closed. Thus in calculating its dimension we need only consider coverings by classes of sets with a finite number of members. Let $U_1, U_2, \ldots, U_s$ be the members of such a covering and let d_i be the diameter of U_i. Further, let $P_iQ_iR_i$ be an equilateral triangle containing U_i, of diameter $2d_i$ and with an orientation similar to that of ABC. Let $L_iM_iN_i$ be the triangle obtained from $P_iQ_iR_i$ by a magnification in the ratio $1 + \varepsilon : 1$ about the centroid of $P_iQ_iR_i(\varepsilon > 0)$. Denote the closed domain bounded by $L_iM_iN_i$ by Δ_i. Write $d(X)$ for the diameter of the set X.

Since Θ is closed, and $\bigcup\limits_{i=1}^{s} \Delta_i$ contains every point whose distance from Θ is less than η for some positive number η, it follows that there is an integer n such that Θ_n is contained in $\bigcup\limits_{i=1}^{s} \Delta_i$.

Next we modify the two sets of triangles $L_iM_iN_i$ and $A_jB_jC_j$ as follows:

(i) From the set of triangles $\Delta_1, \Delta_2, \ldots, \Delta_s$ omit those that are included in one or other of the Γ_j, and rename the remaining ones $\Omega_1, \ldots, \Omega_k$.

(ii) Similarly, from the set $\Gamma_1, \ldots, \Gamma_2$ omit each triangle that is included in one of the Ω_i and rename the remaining ones $\Phi_1, \Phi_2, \ldots, \Phi_m$.

(iii) Consider Φ_j, let Λ_j be the union of all the Ω_j which have no vertex interior to Φ_j. Remove from Φ all those points that lie interior to Λ_j. In place of Φ_j, we are left with a number of equilateral triangles or the void set. This process is carried out for each integer j and the triangles with which we are left are called $\Phi_1^{(1)}, \Phi_2^{(1)}, \ldots$

(iv) Repeat the process of (iii) with the new set $\Phi_j^{(1)}$ in place of Φ_j, and keep on repeating the process in this fashion until we arrive at a set of equilateral triangles $\Xi_1, \Xi_2, \ldots \Xi_1$ such that if Ξ_j^0 meets Ω_i^0 then Ξ_j contains either one or two vertices of Ω_i. This position must be reached after a finite number of steps because the bounding lines of the various triangles Δ_i and Γ_j divide Γ into a finite number of regions and the process consists in the removal of certain of these regions from the Φ_j.

Then the Ω_i and Ξ_j have the following properties:

(a) $$\sum_{i=1}^{s} d_i^p \geqslant \sum_{i=1}^{k} (d(\Omega_i)/2(1 + \varepsilon))^p \qquad (1)$$

(b) The triangles $\Xi_1, \Xi_2, \ldots$ are open, equilateral, oriented in the sense opposite to ABC, contained in ABC and non-overlapping.

(c) The triangle ABC is covered by the combined class of triangles Ω_i, Ξ_j.

(d) Any triangle Ω_i is such that there are at most three triangles Ξ_j for which $\Omega_i^0 \cap \Xi_j^0 \neq \emptyset$, and any such triangle Ξ_j contains one or two vertices of Ω_i.

Now define $f_n(x)$ with respect to the triangles Ξ_j. The line $\xi = x(0 \leqslant x \leqslant 1)$, meets $\mathscr{C}(\bigcup\limits_{j=1}^{n} \Xi_j)$ in segments of length $t_{n,1}(x)$, $t_{n,2}(x), \ldots, t_{n,k}(x)$. The segment of length $t_{n,i}(x)$ has a subsegment in Ω_r of length $m_{n,i,r}(x)$. This is of course zero when the segment of length $t_{n,i}(x)$ does not meet Ω_r. Then, since $0 < p - 1 < 1$,

$$\sum_r (m_{n,i,r}(x))^{p-1} \geqslant (t_{n,i}(x))^{p-1}.$$

Thus by Lemma 2,

$$\sum_i \sum_r \int_0^1 (m_{n,i,r}(x))^{p-1}\, dx \geqslant \frac{1}{p},$$

i.e.

$$\sum_r \int_0^1 \sum_i (m_{n,i,r}(x))^{p-1}\, dx \geqslant \frac{1}{p}. \tag{2}$$

But if n is equal to l the number of the triangles Ξ_j then

$$\int_0^1 \sum_i (m_{n,i,r}(x))^{p-1}\, dx \leqslant \frac{(d(\Omega_r))^p}{p} \tag{3}$$

For consider the effect, on the integral of the left-hand side, of removing from the set of all the triangles Ξ_j those that meet Ω_r. The final value of the integral is $(d(\Omega_r))^p/p$, and it is increased at each stage of the removal process (since each segment $m_{n,i,r}(x)$ is either left unchanged or increased in length), except possibly when Ξ_j contains that vertex of Ω_r which is in the same position relative to Ω_r as is A to ABC, and does not contain either of the other vertices. When there is such a triangle denote it by $E_jF_jG_j$ and let Ω_r be $X_rY_rZ_r$, where the order of these two sets of vertices is counter-clockwise round the triangles.† Then $E_jF_jG_j$ contains X_r and not Y_r or Z_r. We remove this triangle last. Let E_jF_j meet X_rZ_r in H and E_jG_j meet X_rY_r in K. Suppose that $KX_r \leqslant HX_r$. (The argument in the other case is similar.) Let the line through K parallel to Y_rZ_r meet X_rZ_r in K_1, and the line through E_j parallel to Y_rZ_r meet X_rY_r in I and X_rZ_r in I_1. Let the ξ-coordinate of X_r be v and that of E_j be e. Let $m'_{n,i,r}(x)$ be the length of segment before removing $E_jF_jG_j$ and $m'_{n,i,r}(x)$ be the length after. Let $X_rK = k$. Then before removing $E_jF_jG_j$:

for $\quad v \leqslant x \leqslant v + k \qquad$ no segment

$\quad\quad v + k \leqslant x < e - k, \quad$ 1 segment length $x - v - k$,

$\quad\quad e - k \leqslant x < e \qquad$ 2 segments of lengths $x - v - k$ and $\qquad\qquad\qquad\qquad\qquad\qquad x - e + k$.

After removing $E_jF_jG_j$:

for $\quad v \leqslant x \leqslant e \qquad\qquad$ 1 segment of length $x - v$.

Thus

$$\int_0^1 \left\{ -\sum_i (m_{n,i,r}(x))^{p-1} + \sum_i (m'_{n,i,r}(x))^{p-1} \right\} dx$$

$$= p^{-1}((e - v)^p - (e - v - k)^p - k^p) > 0$$

† X_rY_r and E_jF_j are both to be parallel to AB.

From (1), (2) and (3)

$$\sum_i d_i^p \geqslant \frac{1}{(2(1 + \varepsilon))^p} \sum (d(\Omega +))^p \geqslant (2(1 + \varepsilon))^{-p}$$

Since ε is arbitrarily small it follows that Θ is of measure at least $\frac{1}{3}$ in the dimension p, where $p = (\log 3)/(\log 2)$.

§2. Proof of Theorem 10.2

The result in the other direction is trivial. Take A_1, B_1, C_1, to be the mid-points of BC, CA, AB respectively, i.e. $A_1B_1C_1$ is the mid-point triangle of ABC. Similarly, let $A_2B_2C_2$, $A_3B_3C_3$, $A_4B_4C_4$ be the mid-point triangles of AC_1B_1, C_1BA_1, B_1A_1C, etc. Consider an integer N and the integer n defined by $n = 1 + 3 + 3^2 + \ldots + 3^{N-1}$. In this case Θ_n consists of 3^N equilateral triangles of side-length 2^{-N}. Θ_n is a covering of Θ and

$$\sum_{\Theta_n} d^p = 3^N 2^{-Np} = 1$$

Thus the p-dimensional measure of Θ is less than or equal to 1.

It is also clear that any plane convex figure can contain a non-overlapping family of equilateral triangles with a fixed orientation in such a way that the uncovered part has dimension at most $(\log 3)/(\log 2)$. For we can cover the whole of the convex figure except its frontier and an enumerable infinity of line segments, by non-overlapping equilateral triangles which either have the given fixed orientation or are reflexions of such triangles.

Printed in Northern Ireland at The Universities Press, Belfast